DESIGN THIS DAY

DESIGN THIS DAY

THE TECHNIQUE OF ORDER
IN THE MACHINE AGE

WALTER DORWIN TEAGUE

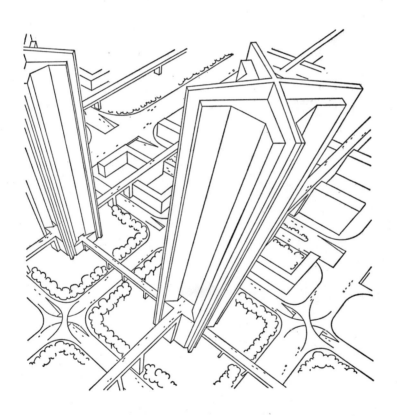

HARCOURT, BRACE AND COMPANY, NEW YORK

Typography by Robert Josephy

PRINTED IN THE UNITED STATES OF AMERICA
BY QUINN & BODEN COMPANY, INC., RAHWAY, N. J.

To R. M. T.

I do not mean by beauty of form such beauty as that of animals or pictures, which the many would suppose to be my meaning; but, says the argument, understand me to mean straight lines and circles, and the plane or solid figures which are formed out of them by turning-lathes and rulers and measurers of angles; for these I affirm to be not only relatively beautiful, like other things, but they are eternally and absolutely beautiful.

—SOCRATES

—From Plato's Philebus
  Jowett's Translation

CONTENTS

TO BEGIN   1

I.   RIGHTNESS RESURGENT   5

II.   MASTERY IN THE MACHINE AGE   21

III.   SOURCES OF FORM   35

IV.   FITNESS TO FUNCTION   50

V.   FITNESS TO MATERIALS   67

VI.   FITNESS TO TECHNIQUES   84

VII.   UNITY   98

VIII. SIMPLICITY   112

IX.   RHYTHMIC RELATIONSHIPS   125

X.   RHYTHM OF PROPORTION   141

XI.   RHYTHM OF LINE AND FORM   162

XII.   DOMINANCE, ACCENT AND SCALE   175

XIII. BALANCE AND SYMMETRY   191

XIV.   STYLE   206

XV.   BEYOND THE RULES   219

XVI.   PROSPECT   232

XVII. PROGRAM   246

Appendix A. THE PROPORTIONAL SCHEME OF THE PARTHENON   263

Appendix B. AMERICA'S CAPACITY TO PRODUCE AND TO CONSUME   274

Appendix C. COLLATERAL READING   278

Index   285

ILLUSTRATIONS

THE OLD AND THE NEW CRAFTSMANSHIP   28

    1 *Neolithic work in flint*
    2 *Wall of Carcassonne, France, Thirteenth Century*
    3 *Italian helmets, Fifteenth Century*
    4 *Kitchen of house built by Thomas Haskell, West Gloucester, Mass., before 1650*
    5 *Covered bridge, Athol, Mass., early Nineteenth Century*
    6 *Corliss Steam Engine, Centennial Exposition, 1876*
    7 *Generator Hall, Pickwick Dam, TVA*
    8 *Boulder Dam*
    9 *Transformer Station, Boulder Dam*
  10 *Oil tanks, The Texas Company*
  11 *Gantry Crane, Wheeler Dam, TVA*
  12 *Research chemist*
  13 *Copper stripping machine, Edison Storage Battery Plant*
  14 *Conveyor belt, Rouge Plant, Ford Motor Company*
  15 *Drafting Room and Laboratory*
  16 *Dodge Half-Ton Truck Plant, Chrysler Corporation, Detroit*

ADAPTATION OF FORM TO FUNCTION   60

  17 *Beauty through functional adaptation in:*
      Feminine legs
  18   *Male torso*
  19   *Female torso*
  20 *Bridge of the steamship "Queen Mary"*
  21 *Detail, Westinghouse Portable X-Ray Unit*

22 Water tower and powerhouse, Chevrolet Motor and Axle Division, Tonawanda, N. Y.

23 Stairs to loading platform, Ford Exposition, New York World's Fair

24 Detail of Spillway, Boulder Dam

25 Nose of Douglas Transport Plane

26 Evolution of airplane form:
   Wright brothers' first flight, Kitty Hawk, 1903
   DH-4B, Speed Plane, 1921

27 Ford Air Mail Plane, 1926
   Douglas Transport Plane, loading, 1939

28 Evolution of automobile form:
   Henry Ford in first car built by him, 1896
   Record-breaking "999," 1904

29 Lord Northcliffe's touring caravan, 1903
   Thomas car, "fully equipped," 1909

30 Cadillac 16, January, 1931
   Marmon 16, January, 1931

31 Special Marmon body, 1932
   Design for rear-engined car, 1939

32 Adaptation of form to speed:
   John R. Cobb's record-holding car, 1939
   Sir Malcolm Campbell's record-holding boat, 1939

ADAPTATION OF FORM TO MATERIALS
AND TECHNIQUES 92

33 Evolution of steel frame construction:
   Park Avenue Hotel, New York, 1869
   Sullivan's Guaranty Building, Buffalo, 1895

34 Raymond Hood's Tribune Tower, Chicago, 1922
   Eliel Saarinen's design for Tribune Tower, 1922

35 Hood's Daily News Building, New York, 1930
   Hood's McGraw-Hill Building, New York, 1931

36   Rockefeller Center Buildings, New York, 1930-1939

37 United States Steel Building, New York World's Fair

38 The beauty of steel:
Steel frame of the Perisphere, New York World's Fair
Steel frame of entrance court, du Pont Building, New York World's Fair

39 Pier of the Golden Gate Bridge, San Francisco

40 Masonry buttresses of Chartres Cathedral

41 Detail of steel pier, Triborough Bridge, New York

42 Harlem River Crossing, Triborough System

43 Kill Van Kull Bridge, Staten Island, New York

44 Exterior of Spiral Ramp, Ford Exposition, New York World's Fair

45 Interior of Ford Spiral Ramp

46 Light as a factor in design:
Ford Exhibit, San Diego, 1935

47 Glass as a factor determining form:
Wall of "Hall of Light," Eastman Kodak Exhibit
Wall of Entrance Hall, Ford Exposition, both at New York World's Fair

48 Materials influencing furniture forms:
Chair of aluminum and Lucite
Glass coffee table and wall

UNITY AND SIMPLICITY EMERGING IN MODERN FORMS

124

49 Dresser 600-H.P. Radial Motor, before and after redesign

50 Mimeograph Duplicator, Model 92, with a previous model of comparable rating

51 Sales slip register, before and after redesign

52 Transformation of the domestic kitchen through consistent design

53 Floyd-Wells coal and gas range, before and after redesign

54 The Super Kodak, open and closed

55 New Haven de Luxe Day Coach, two views

56 Westinghouse Portable X-Ray Unit

57 Controls of the X-Ray Unit

58 Spillway of Norris Dam, TVA

59 Gantry Crane, Pickwick Landing Dam, TVA

60 Bronx-Whitestone Bridge, New York, 1939

61 Plant of the Burroughs Adding Machine Company, Plymouth, Mich.

62 Detail of Road of Tomorrow, Ford Exposition, New York World's Fair

63 Entrance to United States Steel Exhibit, New York World's Fair

64 Elbow of cable anchorage, Triborough Bridge, New York

RHYTHM OF PROPORTION, LINE AND FORM   156

65 Post and lintel construction of the Parthenon

66 Corner of the Parthenon

67 Column bases of the Parthenon

68 Façade, Temple of Ceres, Paestum, B.C. 550
Façade, Parthenon, B.C. 454-438

69 Proportional scheme of the Parthenon façade

70 Circle-and-square scheme of rhythmic proportions

71 Architectural designs determined by the circle-and-square scheme:
Arch of Titus, Rome, A.D. 81
Loggia dei Lanzi, Florence, 1376

72 Two proportional schemes frequently used:
Five-pointed star, golden-section divisions
Six-pointed star, root-three divisions

73 West front of Notre Dame de Chartres

74 Nave and crossing, Notre Dame de Chartres

75 George Washington Bridge, New York
76 Rhythmic repetition of characteristic forms in architectural design:
    Brunelleschi's Dome, Florence, 1437
    Taj Mahal, Agra, 1630
77 Douglas Transport Plane
78 Tail of Douglas Transport Plane
79 Administration Bridge, New York World's Fair
80 Oil tanks, "Hortonspheroids"

ACCENT, SCALE AND EMPATHIC BALANCE   188

81 Façade of Rheims Cathedral
82 Petit Trianon, Versailles, 1768
    Present façade of St. Peter's, Rome
83 Dome and apse of St. Peter's, as built by Michelangelo
84 Notre Dame d'Amiens
85 Sculpture of the West Portals, Chartres
86 RCA Building, Rockefeller Center, New York
87 Doors of the Generator Hall, Norris Dam, TVA
88 Steel tower of transmission line, TVA
89 George Washington Bridge, New York
90 General office, S. C. Johnson and Son, Racine, Wisconsin, by Frank Lloyd Wright
91 Erechtheion, Athens
92 Louis XII Portal, Château de Blois
93 Louis XII Façade, Château de Blois
    H. H. Richardson's Glessner house, Chicago, 1886
94 House at Miquon, Pa., by Kenneth Day
    Wasserman house, Whitemarsh, Pa., by George Howe
95 Court in apartment building, Palm Springs, Cal., by A. Lawrence Kocher and Albert Frey
96 Philadelphia Savings Fund Society Building

ILLUSTRATIONS

OUR CRYSTALLIZING STYLE   220

97 Victorian mansion
98 Sarah Bernhardt's drawing room, about 1900
99 Room in apartment at River House, New York, 1939
100 Robie house, Chicago, by Frank Lloyd Wright, 1908
101 Kaufmann house, Bear Run, Pa., by Frank Lloyd Wright, 1937
102 Stairway to Executive Lounge, Ford Exposition, New York World's Fair
103 Furniture group in Ford Executive Lounge
104 Interior, Ford Salesroom, 1710 Broadway, New York, 1937
105 Stairway, Ford Salesroom
106 Furniture group, State Reception Room, U. S. Government Building, New York World's Fair
107 Detail, residence of H. V. Manor, Monte Vista, Cal., by Clarence W. W. Mayhew, 1939
108 Texaco Exhibit, Dallas, 1936
109 Model of Ford Exposition, New York World's Fair
110 Plant of the American Can Company, Jersey City Sewage Disposal Plant, Hightstown, N. J.
111 Two standard service stations for The Texas Company, 1936
112 Detail, Ford Exhibit, Dallas, 1936

PROSPECT AND PROGRAM   252

113 Walls of Rothenburg, Germany
114 Street in Rothenburg
115 Typical slum in an eastern American city
116 Typical unplanned suburban developments, aerial view and detail

xvi

117 Cedar-Central Apartments, Cleveland, general view and detail

118 Childhood under slum conditions

119 Planned environment for childhood, Jane Addams Houses, Chicago

120 Project for a replanned San Francisco

121 Model of a possible future metropolis

122 Manhattan Approach, Triborough Bridge, New York

123 Traffic distribution system, Triborough Bridge, Randall's Island, New York
79th Street Entrance, Hendrick Hudson Parkway, New York

124 Hutchinson River Parkway, Westchester County, New York

125 Hendrick Hudson Parkway in the Bronx, New York

126 Jacob Riis Park, Long Island

127 Municipal Swimming Pool, Astoria Park, Long Island

128 Spectators at Municipal Swimming Pool, Astoria Park

DESIGN THIS DAY

TO BEGIN

This book has not been ghost-written: its faults are my own. And it has not been written for lack of anything more pressing to do. In fact it has been done in odd hours fitted into a program of the most intense professional activity: on trains and planes and in automobiles, during rainy week-ends in the country and during occasional sunbaths beside a swimming pool or on the beach—Jones or Palm. It has been written in all sorts of places and times except at a desk or during regular working hours.

There are obvious disadvantages in this kind of scrappy production, and they will appear in the book conspicuously enough without my pointing them out. But there is some compensation in the fact that every idea or principle I have expressed has been tested against actual, practical problems of design, before and after and while it was being formulated. This is a healthy process: it makes fluent theorizing more difficult, and it holds one fairly true to a line of common sense. What is lost in imaginative freedom may be partly replaced by truth and practicality.

It may seem that I have given design too great an importance in the scheme of things today, that I have exaggerated the implications of my subject and should have stuck to the problem of better electric ranges and business machines without spreading my interest over environmental reconstruction. But I submit that better household equipment and better mechanical devices are of no real value unless they are easy first essays in the fundamental redesign of our world: harbingers of a wholesale reorganization of our chaotic scene. The world is in too dire need of redesign, in its broad aspects as a place where human life can flourish and develop, for us to be satisfied to stop at better gadgets. We can cut our teeth on them, but we have stronger meat to chew and digest.

God help me if I had tried to solve the world's problems. Too many people are attempting that with words, as well as with guns, already. What I have tried to do is to outline with reasonable clarity the technique that must be applied to the solution of any problem of design, whether it is a new motor car or a new city or a new environment. If this technique is basically sound for one it will be sound for the others. It is a method of approach, a listing of the factors that must be dealt with if satisfactory order is to be created on a small or a large scale. Like any technique, it doesn't guarantee results: the results depend on the skill of the men who use it. But years of struggle with practical design problems of many kinds have convinced me that these are the basic principles which must guide all constructive work. I present them in the hope that they may help to clarify thinking and accelerate progress in dealing with the innumerable urgencies, large and small, that confront us in this changing world of ours.

I want to express my gratitude to the many who have helped me to accomplish this book. First of all are my clients among the industrial corporations, the great producers of America, who have given me the opportunity to develop and test and prove my own principles of design—not always, I hope, without adequate returns to them. My intimate contact with these great producing organizations and the men in them—I distinguish them from the purely financial powers of which I know little—has given me great confidence in the machinery and the spirit now available for the building of a proper world. I do not mean that our industrial system is as good as it should be, either on the labor side, the scientific side, or the management side. But if I am looking for intelligent and unselfish understanding of our problems, and a generous approach to their solution, I shall seek it among the makers and builders with far more confidence than among the talkers, the manipulators and the vote seekers.

Also I want to thank my staff of co-workers for their constant, loyal aid and support in this and all my work. John Brophy, Martin Dodge, my son, Walter Dorwin Teague, Jr., Charles Colby, Robert Harper, Stowe Myers—these men and others have stood by my side for years, contributing to my undertakings, enduring my temperament, relieving me of a vast amount of effort and guarding my time and strength. I am indebted to them beyond expression. I am especially grateful to Edward Mabley, another of my associates, for his patient reading of my manuscript and his many helpful suggestions; and to Carl Conrad, who has performed so well the difficult task of tracking down and obtaining the illustrative material I wished to use. I want to express my thanks to the many institutions and individuals who have supplied this material, and whom I have tried to credit in each instance; and to Mr. Robert Josephy, who on behalf of the publishers has prepared the volume for the press, and done it so admirably.

But more than all others, I feel that an author's debt is to those who voluntarily undertake to read his book; for these my feeling of gratitude is tinged with wonder.

CHAPTER ONE: RIGHTNESS RESURGENT

"Beauty has come to be associated with all our notions of order, of goodness, of health, and of more complete life; and ugliness, on the contrary, with everything by which the life of body and soul is diminished and jeopardized."
— VERNON LEE

Here, while we have peace, beauty is becoming a familiar thing in our world once more. Beauty, for a long time truant, is returning to the common rounds of daily life: we encounter a new and thrilling, man-made beauty on our highways and parked by our curbstones; it flies in the air above us and spans in graceful webs our rivers and our bays; occasionally it rises high and serene in our cities, and in long winding ribbons of parkway it penetrates the country. Some fortunate men work in the midst of beauty in our factories and workshops, pioneers in a new concept of labor, and beauty is bought again in shops that sell only useful things. It enters our homes and takes up its abode in our kitchens, our bathrooms and our cellars, the first essays toward a frame of beauty for our routine hours. It is still sparse and too hard to come by, but it is like the first green reappearing in a devastated land: give it time and care, and it will make the whole countryside fruitful and a proper home for men once more.

Time and care? We live in a sardonic anachronism. Madness is epidemic in the world, threatening to seize us here and shove us back into havoc and distress; and at the same moment all around us in these un-mistakable signs of emerging order and peace we see the promise of well-being such as our race has never known.

While war rises like a flood, we find ourselves at the end of a long term that has been very much like war: a century and a half of turmoil and confusion, suffering and bleak unloveliness, a turbulent period filled with the unhappiness that is inevitable when basic readjustments of human living are being effected. It has been an age busy with gigantic problems absorbing all its powers, ruthless in its reconstruction, having little time or thought for the amenities of life. In war all interests are subordinated to the State: in the Industrial Revolution all interests were sacrificed to the accomplishment of a technological advance which has in it great po-tentialities for the ultimate betterment of human living. Because we ac-commodate ourselves to change only painfully, and have never been very intelligent in ordering our affairs even under the best conditions, the Industrial Revolution throughout its duration has been a time of wide distress.

Now that a season of fruition has arrived, after all our labors, we are confronted with a conflict of destinies: unprecedented well-being within our power of achievement, immanent disaster threatening to lose for us all the advances we have made. It would be completely disheartening except for one thing—the strange unreality, the bizarre, nightmarish aspect of the impending danger. It is so obviously a reversal of all logical trends, so epileptic a seizure, so stark a manifestation of frantic hysteria and manic psychosis; it has an aspect of visionary impermanence, the kind of lapse from which one wakes up suddenly to recovered sanity, and astonishment that anything so utterly fantastic could be so violent. The race has not gone mad—only a handful of men generate the great insanity; and we

6

cannot believe that as a source of virus even they are strong enough to poison the whole human race and reverse all its vital movements.

By contrast, in our growing clarity of vision and the power we hold in our hands for the building of a more humane world, we feel a deep-rooted, earthy vitality: these are in accord with the invincible trend of our destiny, the stream of our racial life flows this way. The emergent beauty and order we find around us, in the common ways of life, are the fruition of instinctive effort as old as our race itself. The roots of the new age ripening go down to the springs of our racial life, and cannot be destroyed by sudden blazes of dementia. The sanity of the race as a whole is not touched: it is not even subjugated for long. We have a deep confidence that we will not be diverted from our course by madmen.

The period from which we find ourselves emerging has been like war in its upheavals and privations, but it does not end in the complete futility of war. The logic of its progress strengthens our faith in its outcome. It has been difficult, but it has not been basically evil. We cannot blame an exuberant child unreservedly for the destruction it wreaks while it learns how to deal with an unfamiliar world. And while the Industrial Revolution had none of the grace and charm of childhood, it had the clumsiness, the ineptness, the unintentional cruelty and the pains of a gigantic, lumbering, grimy immaturity. It had, too, the eagerness and vitality of youth.

So it was not illogical that in its awkward age it should fill the land with sprawling, planless cities devoid of any trace of urbanity; that it formed these cities, largely, of shoals of jerry-built slums and near-slums which were uncomfortable and ungracious at their best and positively lethal at their worst. It accepted as a matter of course that the new industrial system, on which the whole new scheme of life was based, should proliferate in sinister black factories that blighted the lives of their workers and the coun-

7

trysides they invaded. It received with uncritical acceptance the floods of crudely embryonic wares that poured from these factories to supply our needs ineptly, while they swamped our lives in ugliness. And it did not know what to do about the violent dislocations of lives and habits, the unsettlements of traditional markets and national economies caused by its new methods of production. Even while it gained mastery of its tools it allowed these maladjustments to generate the disastrous reactions that threaten us now.

All this ineptitude was accepted by the people with an effect of indifference. But the people were not so much indifferent, really, as calloused with a protective armor against what otherwise would have been an unendurable irritation. We have this gift of growing a shell of imperception against an environment we could not stand if we saw it clearly and constantly, and we are apt to become blind to evil circumstances around us even while they are deforming our lives and wrecking our health and happiness. And so there was a patient submission to ugliness and disorder as the normal setting of our lives.

But submission is not our natural attitude, and is never permanent. What we see around us today, giving us confidence, are signs of the resurgence of an ancient, primitive human instinct, vastly older than the Industrial Revolution and submerged by it for only an instant of racial time. It is not natural for us human beings to be satisfied to live in ugliness and disorder, to be content with crude workmanship and inadequate solutions of urgent practical problems of living. The whole history of man has been a struggle to create a humanized order in an unfriendly environment, and our strongest and oldest racial traditions have been the traditions of skill and mastery. On them all our comfort, all our safety, our well-being, our life itself, have depended. They are bred deep in our blood,

8

they are the background of our subconscious minds, and they cannot be suppressed for long. It is their renaissance we are witnessing in our land today.

The traditions of skillful making are as old as our race. We began our racial career with notable handicaps—almost any other animal would have seemed better adapted to make its way in an inimical world. We had no fangs or claws to speak of, no hooves or horns, not much strength or speed, only verbal poison, and spotty and inadequate fur. We did very well so long as we were satisfied to live in tropical tree-tops and eat the fruit we could find there. But the more adventurous of us did not stay in the tree-tops: we came down to earth and acquired a taste for meat, and it takes a great deal more cunning and skill to catch a rabbit than to pick a banana. With all our handicaps, we brought to the struggle one unique and incomparable asset: it so happened that one of our five fingers neatly and accurately opposed each of the other four. In our cunning hands lay our destiny.

It was a supreme stroke of fortune that this hand, as Spengler says, "requires a weapon to become itself a weapon. As the implement took form from the hand, so also the hand from the shape of the tool." They advanced together, this hand-and-tool combination, the one in skill and the other in effectiveness and variety. And between them they developed in cleverness and power the brain that used them.

With brains, hands, tools, we little men undertook to make over the unfriendly world we had invaded. We undertook to change and subjugate and humanize it, reduce it to an orderliness in which we could live with safety and happiness; and our means were the things we made with our hands and brains. So much depended on these things we made—comfort, safety, life itself, it was so necessary that these things be good. And thus

9

skill became a racial preoccupation, and delight in skill, and in things skillfully made, became a universal human trait.

Skill and mastery were soon acquired, and greatly cherished. There is supreme virtuosity in some of those incredible Neolithic stone knives, as gracefully shaped as pinnate leaves and almost as thin; and some of the arrow heads and spear points and axes of our own Indians are amazing feats of delicate and sensitive workmanship. Much of this work on flint, according to Sophus Müller, was sheer display of artistry, on which the maker lavished all the care, taste and skill at his command "with the sole intent of producing a masterpiece of handiwork." Slovenly workmanship is unknown among savage tribes, on the testimony of Franz Boas, at least before they become corrupted by an alien civilization. Every long-established peasantry has produced a characteristic art of great beauty and subtlety, not only in such easily decorative crafts as weaving and pottery but in the making of purely utilitarian tools and furnishings. In our museums today we are accumulating vast stores of the arts of primitive peoples, treasured beyond the possibility of any practical utility, simply because some craftsman lavished on each piece far more loving care than the bare utilitarian needs of the moment demanded.

All this patient seeking for perfection, all this spending of infinite care on exquisite workmanship, has been guided by a sure instinct: these craftsmen have had an intuitive awareness that high worth in the things they make, as in nature, reveals itself to the eye; and on this rightness their security depended. Not only the superior craftsmen: every worker of any degree of competence knows that no work is really done unless it is done skillfully and rightly. It is not enough that our handiwork should serve indifferently well: it must go further and by the perfect adaptation of its form to its purpose, by its proportions and balance and grace of line, it must convince us of its superiority and give us confidence in its service-ability. These things we make and these things we use become part of ourselves, extensions of our ego, and our pride and confidence are nourished by their superiority. They are responsible for whatever dominance over natural circumstances we have won. We have supplemented nature's organisms with others of our own devising, better suited to our purpose; and a very primitive arrogance demands that these creations of ours should rival nature's own in their orderliness and perfected organization. We are not satisfied unless the things we make have that look of inevitability, of perfect adaptation to a designated end, to be found in living things.

In this way the world's craftsmen have been driven to seek patiently a perfect harmony of form and function, and they have arrived, many times, at results that must have filled them with the calm assurance of ultimate mastery. Many simple tools and utensils have this look of finality. Generation after generation has contributed to their refinement, perfecting their forms until no further improvement is possible and they take their places beside the forms of nature. An ax helve, so gracefully curved in its strange shape, a plowshare, an ox yoke, a hay wain, swords and helmets, bells and pots, a thousand simple objects that have been in use over long periods of time, have arrived at this satisfying perfection of form. By trial and error—the endless trials and eliminated errors of countless painstaking craftsmen—beauty has been achieved. This beauty, like the beauty of a panther or an oak tree, is our eye's recognition of the fact that within their own class and metier these things are just about the best that can be made. In this way beauty appeared in the arts long before men had any concept of beauty, and was sought patiently for ages before it had a name. It was the guarantee of serviceability, and the assurance of power in a world where power in the face of nature is essential to life.

Many times these craftsmen of the past, by means of their perfected skill, succeeded in creating a satisfying frame for life itself. Within their limitations, they enforced a satisfactory order on their environment. They did it only in spots, for brief times, but they did it in the face of social and economic problems as acute and as immediate as those that trouble us, and with only a tiny fraction of our resources. We see the shell of their work at Carcassonne and Rothenburg, in countless hamlets of England and the Continent, on New England village greens and in the ghost of Williamsburg. The men who built these farms and towns, in the face of appalling menaces and limitations, were driven by the force of circumstances to work toward a common end, a clearly envisioned ideal shared at the moment by all concerned. They succeeded in creating settings in which life could be lived with dignity and a measure of serenity, without unbearable irritations and with peace at least in their surrounding circumstances. Their means may have been limited, their politics precarious, their creeds narrow and perverted, but they saw no reason to tolerate disorder and disharmony in the world as they built it. They had a concept of a well-built world in which art is an immediate and friendly servant of man.

Art for them was not a few esoteric activities practised on a plane remote from everyday life: for them, intuitively and without conscious definition, everything made by the hand of man was art, and had in it the potentiality of beauty. If a thing was made well enough, it was good, and satisfying. If it was made badly, crudely, clumsily, it was poor, ugly, unacceptable. Their concern was with the great mass of workshop and fireside and curbstone art with which they were surrounded every hour of their waking and sleeping lives. All this they strove to unite into a harmonious and satisfying ensemble—the city walls, the streets, the houses that line the streets, all the furnishings and equipment within the houses, the shops where these things were made and the markets where they were sold. Their achievements were imperfect, but in the disorderly world of today the remains of their work fill us with nostalgia.

These men were artists who did not call themselves by that name. They may not have used the word "beauty," even, or known the concept. But they were driven by the urge to skill and mastery; they knew that they were good workmen, and that their work was good: good in a soul-satisfying sense that was balm to their spirits. In spite of all their handicaps, they made a world that, for their time and needs and conditions, was good to live in. Better than we have made, as yet.

But now we can see around us, in our streets and shops and houses, the evidences of this ancient ideal of order resurgent. The period of transformation nears its end, the old crafts are gone, the new tools grow familiar in our hands. We find ourselves facing a chaotic world, but with incredible powers for constructive action in our hands and vast knowledge in our minds. With tools and resources beyond anything the world has ever known before, beyond anything the ancient builders of civilizations ever dreamed of, we have the means to create an order in which life can expand to unimagined well-being. We have the means, and in spite of all distractions a vision is growing clear in our minds: a vision of the world as a fair and friendly place, a setting of serenity, peace and beauty, in which men may live a life of equanimity and creative effort. It will be a world subjugated to humanized order and organized for human welfare.

And actually the advances are being made—not broad, conclusive advances, but the taking of an outpost here and there. The stones are being laid. Amid the welter of chaotic towns, we can discover oases of gracious order appearing, very small as yet but significant, and focusing on themselves a wholly disproportionate amount of enthusiastic interest. A few housing developments, rationally and generously planned, a few miles of beautiful parkways, a few splendid bridges and dams and power plants, are the material evidences of a great wave of eager thinking about the problems of living that press us for solution. They are the first essays at an entire environment reconstructed for human welfare. Factories of steel and glass are building in forms that are triumphs of rational planning and of a sense of the true objectives of industry. Industry itself, in fact, having done so much to blight the world with dirt and disorder, has rightly been the first to acquire a wide and deep conviction of the uneconomic waste of those evil products of its own awkward age; and industry is effecting, as a matter of intelligent self-interest, a great practical reordering of its own house.

The products of industry, those things made by science working with our modern tools and techniques, have led the advance of our new order. Because they are more manageable units than our towns and transportation and farming systems, they are the first to be brought under critical controls. They bring into our homes, in ranges and refrigerators, heating and sanitary equipment and a long list of minor appliances, a Utopian perfection of organization that arouses our delighted enthusiasm. Outside our homes, and in addition to the fantastically efficient cars we drive, we see the same high order appearing at many widely scattered points: in our incredible internal combustion engines, so uncannily mighty and dependable, our Boulder Dams and other great hydroelectric plants and irrigation controls, some portions of our highway system, our bridges and planes, some of those immaculate, air-conditioned factories and the machinery that fills them.

These may be the minor equipment of Utopia, but they are the things that arouse the great popular enthusiasms of today. Here is the most heartening sign of all the times—the revival of the ancient pride in skill and joy in things skillfully made, the old arrogant demand that the things we make shall not only serve us well but shall give us pleasure and augment our racial pride. Men welcome the achievements of modern technologies with a fervor that betrays the tenor of their thoughts. There is in their response an element of confidence and competence: here we are on sure ground, we know what we see and we have the equipment to appraise it accurately and adequately. We are seeing around us a rebirth of the intuitive, unself-conscious spirit of craftsmanship. We have made a start, at least, at the rational reorganization of our world.

Again we are beginning to seek beauty without giving it a name, and we respond to it with sincere and unforced emotion without realizing that it is beauty that stirs us. What we seek, and what we recognize and respond to, are values of which beauty is only a sign, a visible evidence, important to us because it is the outward revelation of inward soundness and rightness, the aspect of a perfectly functioning order. We see it as the index of quality, of skill successfully applied and problems rightly solved. It becomes for us a *visible rightness*, the evidence of human power augmented. And we do not need to know that this is or should be called "beauty."

Santayana said that beauty is "pleasure regarded as the quality of a thing." In certain things we recognize a rightness that is the constant object of our search, the existence of a perfectly functioning order adapted to our needs. These things satisfy our desire, give us pleasure; we are grateful to them, and it is not necessary for us to know that the quality we delight in is called beauty.

There is no scarcity of this keen sense of beauty, authentic beauty.

A man may be constrained and uncomfortable in the presence of, let us say, Picasso's or Brancusi's work: he has been conditioned to a different kind of pictorial art, he feels himself on unfamiliar ground, and all his defense mechanisms are aroused. But show him works of art in the categories with which he is familiar—a fine tool of his trade, or a superlative example of any of the many mechanical products which are intimate factors in his daily life—and his response is immediate and spontaneous. These things have a quality he recognizes, a degree of rightness which is the object of his intuitive desire. From the satisfaction of this age-old instinct springs his pleasure, the immediacy and sincerity of his response. He feels himself in the presence of admirable order and he gives it his acclaim. He has had a genuine esthetic experience without knowing it, because he has responded emotionally to an increase in the humane values of the world he shares.

Delight in skill and mastery grow with feeding. As we encounter rightness reappearing in our world more frequently, find it surprising us in unexpected and unrelated places, the esthetic gratification we experience grows into an appetite. We find around us, in innumerable men, a restless dissatisfaction with the imperfections of our chaotic scene, resentment at the normal irritations and frustrations that hem us in. We find growing clearer, in more minds, that concept of a fair and orderly world which has always flickered before men's eyes; but never so clear, so well defined, as now, and never with so great and wondering a realization that we have in our hands the means to make the vision real. The building of a humanized world waits only on the crystallization of our wills: and we begin to think that all these sporadic appearances of fine achievement around us are the beginnings of a great reconstruction. A realization dawns on us that the stones are being laid, quietly, effectively, obscurely, in a thousand places, by an army of men who do not yet realize that they are an army.

There is a hardy optimism in this, of course, with dictators driving millions of men to destruction, whole nations devastated, bombs falling on school children and peoples subjected to torture and terror. Even where there is supposed to be peace, there are millions of ill-housed, underfed people, many overworked and more with no work at all to do. To hordes of people life is suffering, frustration, futility; the face of the earth is defiled unforgiveably by those very powers we have devised to make it habitable. Certainly the world has not presented a less attractive picture for a very long time, and the Nineteenth Century, which prepared both our strength and our weaknesses, seems a peaceful backwater of history by comparison.

But it is the spread of a vision, and the very strength of our desire, that gave power to these forces of destruction that threaten us. Because the desire is so strong, vociferous messiahs with diseased egos arise on all sides and tell their gullible peoples, "I will lead you to Utopia; it is thus and so, and I know a short cut to it." And the people give their lives and liberty to the service of their dream and are led to disillusionment.

But all the time the vision persists, and will outlast this manic seizure. Meanwhile, it is firmly lodged in the minds of many who do not believe in violence, and are not misled into short cuts. There are imaginative and practical men who are aware that a decent world will not be built by fiat, or made of theories and creeds and symbols. It will be built by common agreement, and of tangible materials: it must be an actual world in which men can live and work, live a day-by-day life of the body as well as of the mind and the emotions, and until the vision is realized in physical reality it will not translate itself into terms of human happiness.

There is no doubt, of course, that the order and benignity of a new world must be a reflection of a new serenity in men's minds, an expression of an ideal on which men have agreed. But it is obvious, too, that the building of the new world, as it progresses, will stimulate the clarity of thought from which it derives its sanction, and that the ideal will grow clearer, more acceptable, as it takes on visible form. The two processes are inseparable and must proceed together: the creation of order in a disorderly world, the clarifying of thought in confused minds.

Even now these proceed, and if the storm does not overcome us they will gather momentum steadily. Give us peace, and we shall find it progressively easier to solve the broad problems of human relations, social and economic, that perplex us. Instead of devising theories and ideologies, for which even the cleverest minds are so poorly adapted, and which demand such appalling sacrificial loyalty, we shall be dealing with concrete problems of environmental adjustment. These we have all the means at hand to solve, and in solving them we shall create an enormous expansion of human effort and of means of production, involving all our resources of materials, labor and creative enterprise. And instead of seeking blanket panaceas in the foggy realm of words, we shall have definite requirements to which our economic and social structures must be adapted as we proceed; adapted to the new frame in which they must serve our needs, as rapidly as that frame becomes clear to us; adapted tentatively, a step at a time, without violence; without the destructive waste and futility of revolution, without loss of individual liberty and individual initiative.

A remote and difficult ambition? Perhaps, but then there is the great army of men who are already working for its realization. These men are not over-hurried, they have patience to outlast irrational storms. They hate violence and they are skeptical of dogmas and ideologies. For them a theory must be based on evidence, and it must be tested in practice before it has any validity. They work that way, on the immediate task. They pick their way carefully, one move after another, as they sort out the debris with which the world is littered. The building of our entire environment may be the ultimate goal, but they know that stones are laid up one by one. Even while the world is shrieking and fighting, they are busy with the way the stones are laid.

Chemists, physicists, biologists, metallurgists, engineers, designers, builders and makers—they are exploring, testing, forging new tools, perfecting their controls, extending order a little further into chaos. Their laboratories and workshops are expanding, the vast machinery of industrial production is coming more and more under their control, being directed to serve human welfare more effectively and in new ways. The problems of human living are being treated by them, not in the realm of theory, but as matters of immediate concern on which one works painstakingly day by day. The race is to be housed more than decently, cities are to be built in a way to foster health and happiness. Goods are to be produced in abundance, better goods and cheaper, and they are to be distributed equably. Bodies are to be made healthy, strong, well-nourished, minds are to be serene, amiable. Men are to move freely, without bars and handicaps. A standard of sound workmanship is to control all our making of things, and beauty, the beauty of rightness, is to make this present ramshackle world a place where life can be lived with dignity.

These are vast undertakings, not to be accomplished by any tour-de-force: but they are one's job, to be worked at patiently and with all the intelligence one can bring to them. Threats have no power to distract these workers: they will go on with their tasks, at least until some sort of doom overtakes them.

These builders of a new world are not a class apart; they are not united in any hierarchy and they do not always realize the full implications of what they are doing. And they would be completely ineffective if they did not have the support and the stimulus of an enormous popular movement of which they are only the most creative elements. They are serving a popular will, ministering to those profound desires once more become insistent after an interval of numb indifference. The conception of an orderly world is present not only in the minds of those who are building it: it has been recovered with fresh clarity and force by great numbers of those whose only part in it will be to live in it. This popular sanction gives strength to the builders, and immediate and enthusiastic approval to every fresh advance they make.

They draw their strength from this popular sanction, and from their own sense of mastery. For them the world is emerging from turmoil and confusion of the Industrial Revolution into a new maturity. The violent dislocations of this Revolution may still threaten us, a last and terrific crisis of readjustment: but at the very same moment we approach the peace of achievement. Give us time now, time and care, and our mistakes can be made good, our vast new powers put to work. All our abortive fumbling, our catastrophic clumsiness, as we changed over from ancient tools and crafts to new and more powerful agents of order, can be written off to the account of education, now that we feel competence flooding back. Even in the face of the gravest dangers our modern world has ever faced, there is a stiffening of conscience, a clearing of vision, a return to the standards of well-building that were responsible for whatever order we had previously achieved.

CHAPTER TWO: MASTERY IN THE MACHINE AGE

"Science is the captain, practice the soldiers."—LEONARDO DA VINCI

We human beings have only twice rearranged our affairs on a grand scale. We have indulged in only two major revolutions; and we have just been going through the more violent of these two upheavals. The first was the Agricultural Revolution and it began when men grew dissatisfied with what food they could find or capture and settled down to raise their rations in one spot. This beginning was made many thousands of years ago, the change-over from hunting to farming has been going on ever since, and it has not been accomplished everywhere even yet. But the second, the Industrial Revolution, when handicrafts were abandoned for machine and mass production, began only a scant hundred and fifty years ago and has been more complete in our western world than the first: with overwhelming speed and explosive power it has penetrated every nook and cranny of our lives and of our minds and left nothing as it was before.

The order that was uprooted by the Industrial Revolution was ancient, and fixed in quite definite patterns. For thousands of years the work of the world had been done in ways that underwent comparatively little change. Smiths were smiths and tailors were tailors throughout recorded history, working in changing fashions but with almost unchanging techniques. Carpenters, cobblers and carters pursued their crafts in the France of Louis XV in very much the same way as they had done in Egypt of the Hyksos kings. A weaver from Alexandria could have operated a loom in the Lancaster of George II, after a few minutes' private investigation. Masons of Chartres might have learned their trade in the Rome of Augustus, and practised it again in the Washington of General Grant—with some shock to their sensibilities, perhaps. The persistence of handicraft techniques may be seen in the hand-blowing of glass, which still exists today in a vestigial though delightful form at Corning and a few other places, although almost all glass made in America is now blown by machinery: the tools used in hand-blowing today are identical with those shown in Antonio Neri's *The Art of Glass*, published in London in 1662, except that the calipers used for measuring diameters are now made of steel instead of wood. There has been no change of technique or tools for at least 277 years.[1]

But in the last quarter of the Eighteenth Century new forces began to appear in the world. They had been preparing for a long time, ever since speculative thinkers began to use the methods of the crafts to check their theories and took to weighing, measuring, testing and trying. Experimentation made science practical, and as soon as science had gotten together enough exact knowledge to be usable it turned to the crafts that had assisted it and handed them a set of novel and potentially gigantic tools. The tools proliferated and expanded, became difficult to control and impossible to curtail. The association between science and industry became a partnership that has existed ever since, with science rising steadily toward a position of major influence.

---

[1] Lewis Mumford, in his *Technics and Civilization*, has assembled a formidable mass of data to prove that machines were in use before the Industrial Revolution. We might have been convinced by a tenth of his citations, but the fact remains that crafts persisted for centuries with little change until toward the end of the Eighteenth, and that since that time they have been superseded by wholly new ways of producing goods, entailing wholly different ways of working and living.

It may not have begun with the classic date of Watt's invention of the steam engine. But a train had been laid, and events from that time on touched off one another like a string of giant firecrackers. In swift succession the marvels came. Mechanical looms, machines for carding and spinning, for working wood, metal, clay, glass—anything. Machines that carry us over the water, over the land, through the air, each one faster than the last. Railroads superseded highways for travel and freight carrying, and stimulated the growth of towns along their rigid and limited courses. Then automobiles returned traffic to the highways and rendered meaningless the arbitrary pattern of population fostered by the railways. At the same time the automobile required first the resurfacing of our highways and then the complete redesign and reorganization of the whole highway system, while they made impractical the traditional type of city thoroughfare and hence the city plan that had served very well for centuries.

Industry has coagulated in dense masses along the railroad lines, but now it realizes that it may spread into more desirable surroundings and its eyes are turning toward the open country. The working population, too, was first collected in unprecedented congestion around its centers of employment, but now it too is beginning a movement of dispersal over the land. While this flux has been going on, we have been acquiring steadily more fantastic extensions of our senses and powers. We have found means to spy on electrons going about their business, and on far-off solar systems being born. Men are able to fling their voices across continents and oceans to a single specified listener or to millions; we can record what we see or hear—and things we cannot see or hear—and have the sounds repeated and the scenes re-enacted at will. We have devised machines that operate with an accuracy measured by ten-thousandths of an inch—invisible dimensions—but with the strength of thousands of horses. We have learned how to make deserts bear rich crops and how to generate enormous power at one point to be used hundreds of miles away. We have found means of doing a multitude of things that human strength or manual dexterity could not compass, or any human sense detect. These machines of ours have given us what in medieval times would have passed for divine omnipotence.

As enterprises based on machine production expanded, and the flows and ebbs of population were accompanied by revolutionary changes in our systems of transportation and communication, new formulas for economic and social relationships had to be found. New systems of finance and credit, new methods of distributing and marketing, new ways of living, new systems of education, even new social hierarchies, were not planned but allowed to come into existence without forethought, in the most deadly disorder. Philosophies, religions, governments—nothing was left unchanged, not even men's pastimes nor morals, nor habits of thought. The Revolution has been complete.

Revolutions are ugly and bloody affairs, and this was no exception. The early days of factory production, with their long hours, infant labor and starvation wages, and all the horrors of a wholly unplanned and uncontrolled disturbance of settled ways of living, make a history too terrible to read. There was a generation or two that suffered from Watt's steam engine more frightfully than any people suffered from the first World War. And the purely physical hideousness the factories spread around them was worse than anything the world has ever seen before—the devastation of invasion and battle was a passing storm compared with the chronic blight spread over much of Europe and America by the advancing machines.

24

Not only were pleasant countrysides and ancient handicrafts withered by the spreading factories; so were countless white-faced workers, and with them all their heritage of skill and pride in skill. The machines came between a man and the thing he made, and how could a man take pride in a thing he never touched? The craftsman had shaped his work with his own sensitive hands, molding it with loving care, and he might alter, improve, enjoy it as his skill advanced. Thoughtful variation was the law of his progress, the source of his pride. His standards were high and his efforts were rewarded, for success came to the man of great skill. He accomplished no more than he did, and he was superseded in the end, because his achievements were limited by his own human powers; and unaided human powers are not adequate for the building of a Utopia in this unpropitious world. The craftsman was forced to give up his own way of working for the more productive, but for a long time far less pleasant, way of the machine operator.

To improve by trial and error is not in the nature of machines, limited as they are to exact, unvarying repetition: their operator has no chance to sense that feeling of advancing quality born of advancing skill. Such skill as he acquires, and it may be great, is exerted on the machine itself and not upon its product. In fact, he may never see the ultimate result toward which his own, to him, self-sufficient operation contributes. He has little or no creative influence on the form of the thing he is making.

Nor were the directors of the machines, who set their patterns, in better case. Many keen intelligences were busy in the early stages of the Industrial Revolution, but they were busy with the technologies of the machines themselves, or with the economic structure in which they functioned— not with insuring the rightness of machine output or with eliminating the evil by-products of machine production. It seemed to be enough for the time being that the new tools could be made to work at all—it was in fact a gigantic task to create the mere equipment of this machine age in so short a time. With old crafts being abandoned day by day, and new ones to replace them being invented in crudely tentative forms, these immediate problems absorbed all the creative energy available. There were new tools, new techniques, new materials to be mastered every season, and this left no time to do more than keep abreast of the advancing tide of technical knowledge. If a shoe or a glass bottle could be made by machines instead of by hand, or a steel building be made to stand thirty stories high, or a motor car be made to start and stop without demur, it was triumph enough—never mind how otherwise imperfect these things might be or what they might do to the face of the earth or the people on it. There was pride and to spare for all who had a share in the parade of mechanical marvels. These were magnificent tools, and what was to be done with them in the interest of the race as a whole might be left for more mature consideration.

So it is not surprising that the machines let loose on the world a flood of imperfect and hence ugly wares as shocking as the black devastation they spread over so many fair countrysides and growing towns. Ugliness was the inevitable product of undeveloped and unmastered techniques, so quickly emerging and so imperfectly understood. The vigor and speed of the Industrial Revolution, its admirable vitality in fact, served to augment the rising turmoil of disorder; and perfection, charm, serenity became rare survivals in a sea of confusion.

The creation of visual beauty, as a conscious aim, persisted only in a few lonely backwaters, and in those arts of expression in which certain sensitive people are driven to make their comments on life and the world we live in. The need of expression is so strong in some men that not even the Industrial Revolution could thwart it, but those who were possessed by it were forced to seek refuge in a world wholly apart from their fellow men. Hence the invisible quarantine that seemed to isolate such men as Cézanne and Van Gogh and their confreres.

In well-developed, well-integrated ages it has been difficult to distinguish between the "fine" arts and the "applied" arts—the arts of expression and the arts of utility—and to say definitely where one left off and the other began. In such times, painting and sculpture as well as architecture have served decidedly utilitarian ends, and pots and pans gave esthetic pleasure by their perfection of form while they boiled our beans or held our soap and water; the arts, both of expression and utility, were deeply and inextricably rooted in the daily lives of men, from whose common understanding and intimate appreciation they derived their vitality. But during the Industrial Revolution, with the arts of expression cut off from their roots in the soil and the arts of utility lacking any esthetic control, the whole concept of art became more and more tenuous to the average man, and more and more remote from his own concerns. It was thus that he came to accept patiently the absence of beauty, the beauty of rightness, from his own shops and homes and streets.

Amid the vast unhappiness of the Industrial Revolution, one of the most fundamental sources of tragedy has been this retreat of beauty from the ordinary circumstances of daily life and work. With the handicrafts passed not only the excellent workmanship they strove for but the happiness of daily exercise of skill in the creation of beautiful things. There have been many laments over the dying crafts, and quite justifiably for anything so ancient and fine. And of course there have been revolts against the advancing machines, and efforts to preserve or revive the passing order. But these efforts have been doomed to futility, for the very basic reason that the machines, for all their crude beginnings, held within themselves the promise of such freedom and fullness of life as men had never known before; just as they held within themselves the potentiality of rightness as sound as the handicrafts ever achieved, and far more abundant. We need to bear in mind the fact that a good tool cannot be blamed if poor use is made of it, especially in hands that have not yet acquired skill in its use.

But pride in work is essential to our self-respect and we could not live for long without it. Our innate love of skillful making and our ambition to enforce serviceable order on our environment might be submerged for a time by the flood of new technologies, but they were certain to revive. The ugliness of the Industrial Revolution being simply the evidence of waste and inefficiency, the proof of techniques not yet mastered and skills not yet acquired, it could last only as long as this state of awkward apprenticeship lasted. As soon as the marvel of the new wonders began to pall, and a genuine control of the new tools began to be achieved, the old demand again asserted itself: again we felt the restless desire that what we made should not only serve us effectively but that it should give us the satisfaction of a thing well and rightly made; and we looked with new resentment at the unattractive scene around us, with its offenses against nature and its frustrations of human happiness.

Signs of maturity began to show themselves in the Machine Age early in this Twentieth Century. The past thirty-five years have seen the development of an amazing system of controls over mechanical production, controls of accuracy and controls of quality, which had to be effected before our great complex of modern industrial equipment could be made to serve purely human ends. Our controls represent our mastery over our tools, enabling us to use them with precision and direct them to exactly

28

The traditions of skill and mastery are older than history. Feats of delicate and sensitive workmanship in flint. Pre-dynastic Egyptian blade, 4,000 B.C., and Amerindian blades.

METROPOLITAN MUSEUM OF ART
MUSEUM OF THE AMERICAN INDIAN

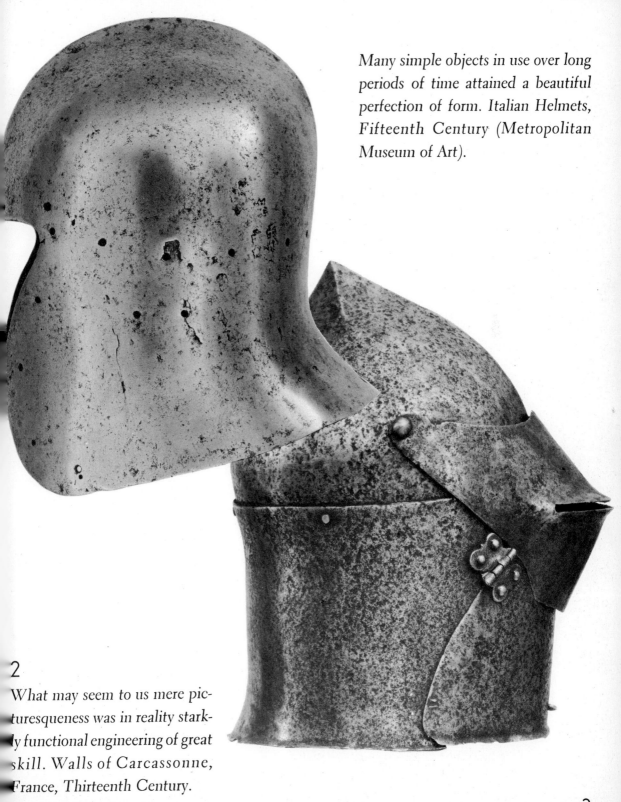

Many simple objects in use over long periods of time attained a beautiful perfection of form. Italian Helmets, Fifteenth Century (Metropolitan Museum of Art).

2

What may seem to us mere picturesqueness was in reality starkly functional engineering of great skill. Walls of Carcassonne, France, Thirteenth Century.

The old craftsmanship was beautifully skillful, but its scope was largely limited by human accuracy and strength. Hand-hewn and fitted timbers of covered bridge near Athol, Mass. Early Nineteenth Century.

5

These craftsmen of the past often succeeded in creating a satisfactory setting for the life of their times. Haskell House, West Gloucester, Mass., before 1650.

4

Great power under control brought an end to the old craftsmanship. President Grant starting the huge Corliss Engine, Centennial Exposition, 1876.

Great power, cheaply and efficiently generated, is the basis of the new crafts-manship. Generator Hall at Pickwick Dam, Tennessee Valley Authority.

BOURKE-WHITE ⟫⟫⟫→

We have learned how to collect enormous power at one source to be used where it may be needed. Boulder Dam, with Transformer Station opposite.

8

Coal, water and oil—our chief power sources—each requires an elaborate system of production and distribution. Oil storage tanks of The Texas Company.

Controlled power makes it possible to supplement our own human strength with machines of super-human might. Gantry Crane at Wheeler Dam, lifting 540,000 pounds.

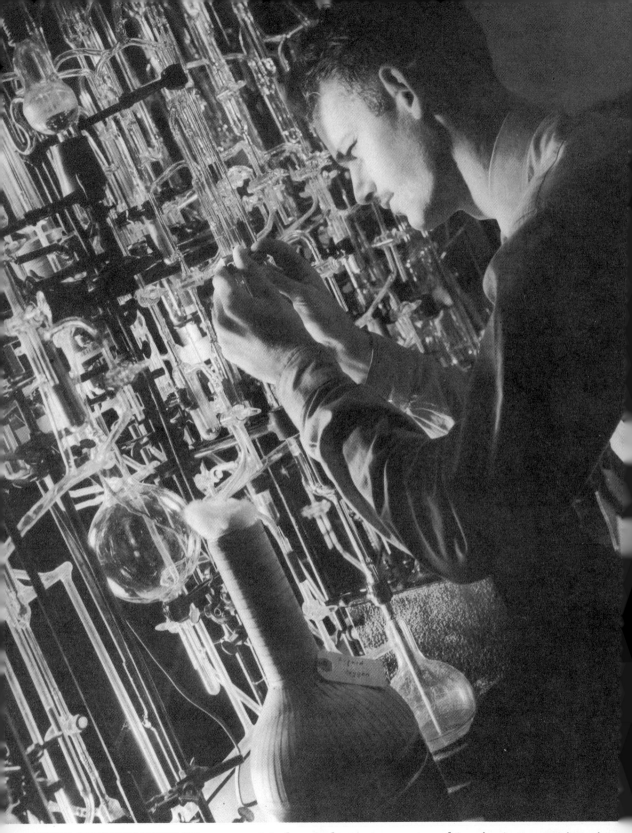

Modern industry is a partnership of science, engineering and design, with science rapidly rising in influence.

Our new craftsmanship depends on the most exact and
constant controls of precision and quality.

13

Industry today steadily
reduces the amount of
mere weight-lifting and
burden-bearing required
of its workers. Camshaft
conveyor chain, Rouge
Plant, Ford Motor Co.

|◄

At the same time, industry enlarges the field of knowledge, training, and skill. Above, a modern drafting room, and below, Laboratory of Henry Ford Trade School, Dearborn.

15

16

Light, cleanliness, order, characterize the modern industrial plant. Dodge Truck Plant, Chrysler Corp. Albert Kahn, Architect. See also Plate 61.

defined results. They are the skill of a new craftsmanship. It was essential that we should attain this technical mastery before we could give our whole attention to the kind of work we are to do with it.

There are men not yet aged who recall that, in the early days of the automobile industry, mechanics worked to dimensions of a sixty-fourth of an inch, standards of visible accuracy that had been adequate for the approximations of the handicrafts, and had persisted into a scheme of which precision is the basic essential. Today it is not uncommon for our machines to work automatically within dimensional variations—known as "tolerances"—of two ten-thousandths of an inch. One small part of the Ford car has three dimensions that are held to this unbelievable accuracy. By means of Johansson Gauges it is possible to measure the expansion of a block of steel caused by the warmth of a hand laid on it. There are many machine shops and tool rooms today which must be held at an unvarying temperature throughout the year, so that the precision instruments used in them will give uniform results. By means of scientific tests used in inspecting certain finished parts, variations of a millionth of an inch can be detected and the parts automatically sorted accordingly.

At the same time that we have been attaining precision, we have been developing means to insure uniform and adequate quality. By means of microscopy, X-rays and polarized light it is possible to study the crystalline structure of metals and other materials, and observe their reaction to specific stresses and strains. These invisible attributes on which serviceability depends cannot only be seen but they can be photographed and thus recorded for subsequent study. While a complicated machine is completing its cycle of movement thousands of times a minute, the stroboscope will "slow down" its action for us so that we can watch it as if the cycle lasted whatever time we choose. High speed motion picture cameras, making thousands of exposures a second, enable us to record and study such swift actions as the movement of air currents around a revolving propeller blade, or the explosion of gases in a cylinder. The vibrations of moving parts, or of sound waves, can be translated into quivering beams of light and their nature analyzed at leisure. The photronic cell, in which a feeble electric current is generated by the impact of a beam of light, is used in many automatic controls, and coupled with the X-ray it reports the presence of foreign matter or defects inside closed or solid bodies.

These are merely typical of innumerable methods now in use to insure that we get exactly the results we want to get from our machines. In addition there is a long list of devices for testing the tensile or the torsional strength of metals, the strength of many kinds of fibers, the sizes or the perfection of finished parts. These are not laboratory apparatus: they are the common resources of industry moving toward greater and greater success in mechanical production. But they were created or discovered in laboratories and they are evidence of the way laboratories in industry have expanded their scope of activity and their influence during the past generation. The research staff is the heart, the nuclear center, of most great industries today. The scientists are no longer negligible employees from whom an occasional useful idea can be obtained: they are rapidly assuming control and direction, as the lists of executives of many major corporations today prove in a quite literal sense. Industry is beginning to be understood as not merely an affair of buying and selling, but as being basically a process of production.

Science not only improves the technique of production by advancing its controls, but it expands the variety of materials and the range of processes. Invention is no longer left to chance inspiration or unaided genius.

Inventions are planned as the result of known needs and accomplished with the deliberate strategy of a military campaign. Synthetic materials made from cotton and wood do not have the strength or elasticity of natural silk. It would be vastly desirable to produce an artificial fiber having "long-chain polymer" cells which was not made from a cellulose base and would equal the virtues of natural silk. The du Pont Company commissions Dr. Wallace Hume Carothers to undertake its creation, and places adequate facilities at his disposal. Since Dr. Carothers was searching for a "long-chain polymer" which was not cellulose, he began not with the cellular structures such as spruce and cotton, but with, of all things, coal. From this unlikely material, plus air and water, he succeeds after years of amazingly skillful work in producing a synthetic fiber which approximates the cellular structure of natural silk, has all its valuable properties and a number besides. Two young musicians, Leopold Mannes and Leopold Godowsky, Jr., begin as schoolboys to experiment with color photography and decide that color films can be made by suspending dyes in layers of gelatine solution. Years later, they take their crude experiments to Dr. Mees of the Eastman Kodak Company, who tells them that with ten years' work and the resources of the research laboratories at Kodak Park, their idea may be brought to fruition. In seven years a method of color photography, simpler and more accurate than any known before, is ready for use. As one unforeseen by-product, surgical operations are photographed in full color at close range without any inconvenience, so that surgical students learn much more from the projected pictures than they could observe under the difficult conditions of an operating theater.

Along countless lines such as these, the alliance between science and industry is widening the scope of mechanical production in the interest of human welfare. And this has accompanied a steady subjection of machines to the most precise direction, and an astounding increase in their dependability and their subtlety of performance. Machine technique has so far surpassed the possibilities of hand production that it has acquired an almost awesome, superhuman capacity. As a result, the proportion of intelligent planning—"brain work"—in industry has increased as the proportion of mere muscular labor has declined. A steadily increasing number of trained, skilled and creative workers are required to direct and serve the machines while the unthinking, routine tasks are eliminated in equal numbers.

We have been waiting for this access of power, when we could feel that our task of devising an adequate machine technique had been fairly well advanced, and the Industrial Revolution had arrived not at completion but at a plane of orderly progress. With so much to our credit, so much ability at our command, we at last could give our attention to what we should do with our unprecedented resources. We looked up from the machines themselves to see what they were making and what they were doing to the world we must live in. Like all strong movements of thought, this shifting of interest was evident and influential before it was put into words. It made itself felt as a stirring of dissatisfaction with crude and ugly results, a revival of critical appraisal on the part of innumerable men within industry itself, directors and workers, and on the part of still more people who went to market to buy the wares offered to them. There was of course an outburst of chatter from the professional messiahs whose part in the social and economic scheme is purely vocal: but as always the constructive work was being quietly and effectively done by men who looked askance at their own jobs and decided they could be done better. There was a tendency, everywhere in evidence, to let that "sovereign judge," the eye, have more and more influence over the shaping of the wares we made and over our choice of those we bought. We began to give our patronage as a reward to those things which struck us as being better organized, more orderly, more seemly than their rivals. Henry Ford decided it was time to abandon his Model T Ford, of which many millions had been gladly accepted by the public; and, influenced by this dramatic example, many less brilliant manufacturers in other lines began to wonder if they too were making wares that needed revision. They went on from considerations of efficiency and cost to consider the quality of planning and workmanship revealed in the appearance of their products. A new profession of industrial design came into sudden success, taking the organization of all products as its broad field without specialization in anything but design. Manufacturers came to realize that a dirty and unkempt factory in which labor is a disagreeable experience, a factory that afflicts the country around it or the workers it employs, is a poorly run and uneconomic factory; and similarly, that an unattractive and poorly organized product is a product which has not had the care it should have, and showing this neglect goes to market under a serious handicap. Smoke became a symbol of incomplete combustion, dirt a sign of sloth, darkness a handicap, dangerous or unhealthy working conditions an unforgiveable economic waste; and an awkwardly planned product became an evidence of incompetence or carelessness.

At the same time and in the same type of minds, the quality of housing in which men, especially those without high earning capacity, are forced to live; the planning of the towns of which this housing is a part; the planning of highway systems which will determine where men live in relation to their work and where the work is to be done in relation to its market—all these problems of general concern became matters of acute personal interest. The amount of intelligent study given to these problems of living in the past twenty years, first in Europe and now here, exceeds all the care given them in all of preceding history; if the results in tangible achievements are not yet conspicuous, it is only because the task of reconstruction is so enormous that the small beginnings it has been possible to make so far are lost in the general welter. But the beginnings have been made and the movement to rebuild our environment on more rational lines has gained steadily in momentum—until now the frantic outburst in Europe threatens it with interruption.

Thus a new craftsmanship of the Machine Age has arisen, aiming again at rightness in things and in living conditions achieved by means of the tools at hand, re-establishing our self-respect through skill in work and asserting again our ability to deal successfully with our environing world. The problem confronting us is enormous—the design of an environment in which human life can flourish as it should, no less—and whatever design we make must be carried out in materials as specific as steel, concrete and glass; its ultimate form must be given it by means of the vast Machine Age equipment we are just mastering.

Assuming that we shall succeed in continuing an orderly advance, we have arrived at the point of requiring formulas whereby the physical work we have to do can be planned and checked. Obviously this must be a new procedure of a kind unknown and not needed in a world of handicrafts: we require a technique of design far more self-conscious and exactly understood than anything our forefathers practised. Our need is urgent for a restudy of the laws of design, and their restatement in terms of the tools, materials and techniques we have devised for our work; so that they can be applied with ease to this task of environmental reconstruction we still hope, optimistically, to perform.

34

CHAPTER THREE: SOURCES OF FORM

"Whenever beauty is really seen and loved, it has a definite embodiment: the eye has precision, the work has style, and the object has perfection."

—GEORGE SANTAYANA

During the long ages while the work of the world was done by the handicrafts, the designer could rely on time as his ally. Working with his hands and the tools his hands made and controlled, the scope of his individual efforts was not large and commitments were not final; right form could be evolved through the slow process of trial and error, and order could be allowed to gestate through a long series of experimental efforts.

But this leisurely progress is not practicable in this age of ours—our way of working does not allow it. The endless slight variation which was characteristic of the handicrafts, leading toward a final solution by gradual approximation, is not possible for us: we work with machines that are capable only of precision and exact repetition. In the past an undertaking might be begun and finished by a single craftsman, or under his direct control: ours are the result of group activities in which many men and machines, only loosely related, are involved. These men may be working quite independently of each other on separate phases of a single job, and the man who gives the work its final form may never be in personal touch with any of them. Although he must understand the operations by which

35

the work is done, he may never see any of these operations performed. Instead of being able to alter and improve the plan as it progresses, he must take a chance and in all major respects abide by his initial decisions. In mass production he must accept the appalling responsibility for ten or a hundred thousand units in which no revision is possible. Vacillation, indefinite plans, uncertainty, tentative advances, are economically fatal in our scheme of work. The great cost of our machine tool equipment, enforcing strictest economy and keenest foresight, the long routine that intervenes between inception and completion, the multiplicity of operations required by even the simplest of machine-made wares, the vast duplication of units—all of these factors combine to require a new procedure based, more completely than ever before, on conscious planning and prevision.

Things made outside factories today must be planned with the same foresight as things made inside factories: there is almost no making today in which machinery and mass production are not controlling influences. Building now depends very little on small units of brick and stone which can be shaped and assembled at the site by the skill of independent craftsmen. Our new structural forms are fixed in factories remote from the spot where the building is to stand, and construction is becoming more and more a process of putting together large-scale prefabricated parts. Towns completely satisfactory for their own times, such as Carcassonne and old Nuremberg, could be squeezed into shape by the pressure of circumstances acting on all citizens alike; but we have found that this kind of cohesive natural force no longer exists, and our towns become unworkable and almost unbearable if their growth is left to unfocused individual initiative. There was a time when roads could be mapped by the wheels that used them, seeking the easiest way; but our highway system is an enormous engineering problem that only the ablest minds can cope with. In all these joint enterprises on which our communal welfare depends, we find that prevision and precision are demanded by our machine-age way of working. Any good thing we do is the result of conscious planning and not of mere natural evolution.

It is in frank and complete acceptance of these conditions that a new art of design is perfecting itself. It accepts the characteristics of machine production not as limitations but as means for the creation of new types of rightness, and it sees the machines themselves as tools of enormously augmented effectiveness in the humanizing of our world. It undertakes to meet the challenging demand for adequate foresight, planning, and exactitude, and thereby to use our gigantic resources in a manner worthy of their scale. Our problem is defining itself as the art of synthesizing a great many varied activities and operations so that the combined output has a unity which appears to—and does—proceed from one creative impulse and serves a specific human end: we see it as the art of producing serviceable order out of our great variety of sources and diversity of impulses.

Obviously in this the designer is not a free agent. If he is any good at his work, he will not pluck his designs out of the air or out of the private storehouse of his own invention. The imagination which makes him competent is not inclined to fantasy: it is the kind of imagination which enables him to apprehend needs and feel himself into forms, gives him a sense of the nature of palpable materials and the feel of the processes by which they are worked; and it makes him sensitive to the relationships that exist between parts of a whole, revealing potential unity in elements not yet integrated. Visionaries may dream of Utopia, but it will be built by men whose estimate of subjective values is constantly corrected by

37

experience with tangible realities: the thought of their minds will be stimulated and guided by the work of their hands.

For the type of orderliness that will satisfy us in the world, or in any small thing in it, will not be invented and it will not be enforced according to any blanket theory. It will be evoked, painstakingly, out of each thing itself by the purpose for which it is created. Implicit in any man-made thing is the ultimate form that will most perfectly satisfy its maker and serve its user, just as the color of our eyes and the shape of our hair are latent in the uniting cells with which our life begins. Our budding cells, under right conditions, will develop spontaneously and, in time, barring accidents, arrive at maturity. But not so right form in design. Some man by his own conscious thought and effort must supply the vital force that brings ultimate form to birth, and he must act as midwife in delivering it.

This is no perfunctory task. Only patient effort directed by knowledge and skill, and illuminated by a kind of creative insight, will ever succeed in extricating right form from the envelopes in which it is hidden. In fact it may elude us, retreating before our advancing approximations. But under the conditions facing us and the exigencies of machine and mass production, our advance must be accelerated to the limit of our powers. So far as is humanly possible, our conscious intelligent planning should eliminate trial and error, and experiment should be confined to the laboratory stages of our work. Our mistakes may be disastrously expensive. Our responsibility as designers of a new world to be built in new ways is heavier than designers ever have borne before, and it demands proportionately broader equipment.

A mastery of design adequate to our responsibilities will not be acquired by accident, or easily, or by any narrow range of specialized experience. We cannot learn enough from any single application of the laws of design to guide us in other applications. The factors controlling form are too many, too varied and some of them too variable for any limited observation to give us an understanding of their workings. They must be studied over a wide range of times and circumstances, the operations of cause on effect observed in the widest possible variety of instances. The world and the ages must be roved in pursuit of those forces that have controlled the endless variation of men's work. And because our tools and materials and techniques are new, we should not make the mistake of thinking that the same forces are not still operating.

Behind all design are certain constants, as imperative here as in Greece or medieval France. When we are able to see identical laws controlling the forms of a Greek temple, a Gothic helmet and a Yankee Clipper, and at the same time understand why the operation of these laws results in such widely varying expressions, we can turn to the problems of our own day and environment with, at least, a somewhat greater degree of competence and confidence.

The laws of design are constant, and the standard of rightness is constant. There is but one standard of rightness, Greek, Gothic, or Modern, and whatever we do must be judged by that standard. Our aspirations may be better defined than our ancestors', and certainly they are different, but I doubt if they are higher. Our effort today is continuous with the effort of the past. Unless we appreciate the continuity of our racial aspirations and tap the reservoirs of racial experience, we shall be hopeless bunglers. There is no time and we are not big enough to treat design as if we had invented it.

But recognizing only one set of esthetic laws and one standard of judgment, we are still confronted with the endless variety of ways in which people have satisfied their needs. It is obvious that there are variables which lead every race, age and craft to produce a type of rightness peculiar to its own conditions and stamped with its own character.

To separate the variables from the constants in all design and so in our own special problems, and assign to each its own role in the shaping of right form, is the first sensible step in equipping ourselves for the work we have to do. This calls for an analysis of the art of design—the art of enforcing order on material substances for our service and satisfaction—to be made in terms of our own special circumstances. Without it we cannot hope to reduce the element of trial and error in our work, or develop in ourselves that perception of right form which should in practice guide our planning with almost intuitive insight. Unless we understand what we are supposed to do, we shall flounder as the Nineteenth Century did, and get no further with the organization of a decently humanized world. We are going to make a try at such an analysis in this book.

We shall begin with the first source of all form, which is also an incessant variable. And this is the principle of:

I. FITNESS

Which itself is divided into three phases:

Fitness to Function

to Materials

to Techniques

It is because of this principle of Fitness that the ultimate form of any object—natural or man-made—is inherent in the object itself: it must be evolved naturally to suit the function which the object is intended to perform, the materials out of which it is made and the methods used in its making.

Our first study is the needs of our times, the work that must be done to enlarge the rule of order in our world and advance our racial welfare: a sound conception of these needs will give us a sort of datum plane, a base of reference, to use in defining the function of the things we are called on to make. In a given instance, the first step in design is a complete and intimate study of the purpose our work is expected to serve, so that we can arrive at an adequate and exact definition of its functions; and to meet the need we have defined, we must proceed in complete familiarity with the materials and methods available for our use.

We deliberately ask ourselves: "What is the purpose of this thing we are making? What shall it be made of? How shall it be made?" And we must be especially careful that our answers to these questions are correct, in these days when so many of the things we need to make are without history or precedent and our materials and tools are equally new. When we commit ourselves to a specific form it will be an answer to these questions, whether or not we intend it to be. It may be a wrong answer—like so many the Machine Age has produced in the past—but it will be an answer nevertheless; and if it is too far wrong, the result may be economically and socially calamitous.

This analysis of fitness is not, by any means, as easy as it sounds. The function of an object, especially a newly invented object, may not reveal itself at once in its entirety; or, as in the case of housing, for instance, it may involve so many considerations never dealt with before that we are only hampered by our traditional conception of its requirements. Materials can be understood only through experiment, and the partnership between science and industry is handing us new materials with disconcerting frequency. Technologies change and advance as they are practised, and engineering is continually revising the whole aspect of our problems by making possible what previously had been beyond our powers. This is why ultimate form is approximated only step by step even under machine and mass production—big steps and rapid, but still steps. And this is why we are not to be censured if we do not produce the ultimate answer to any need at one grand initial delivery. We are to be criticized only in so far as we fail to use with relentless logic all the means and all the knowledge available to us at the time: a limitation which still leaves nearly all of us, and in fact nearly all the designers of all times, open to some censure.

The questions as to function, materials and techniques indicate form, but this form still must be organized and integrated. It must be made into a unity, with its parts bound together in harmonious and rhythmical relationships—workable, simple, clear, symmetrical, instinct with grace. The elements of a design may be indicated by the principle of Fitness, but a swift and sure integration of these elements is accomplished only by application of the

II. LAWS OF RELATIONSHIPS

Here we have another group of factors influencing form, and these are the constant elements in all design.

The Laws of Relationships are unchanging, universal, the same in all arts and all epochs—Greek, Gothic or Detroit. They derive their validity from the structure of the universe and the structure of our perceiving minds. It is conceivable that in another kind of universe, inhabited by a different kind of sentient life, the Laws of Relationships as well as the laws of mathematics might be different. But as there is no possibility of our being landed in any such unfamiliar scene, the question is purely academic. For us the Laws of Relationships have the same kind of universal application as the laws of mathematics, to which they are closely related. It is even probable that they are identical, although no one has explored them with sufficient thoroughness to complete the identification.

The sum of our knowledge of relationships is derived from age-old experience, and is to the effect that certain interplay of masses, areas, forms and colors, certain arrangements of shape and line are workable, give us satisfaction and even delight, while others do not. We know that this rightness derives from relationships existing within and between these elements rather than from any intrinsic character of the elements themselves. We know too that exactly the same types of relationships can be found in nature, giving us satisfaction there just as in our handiwork; and this fact is the source of substantial comfort and confidence.

Of the Laws of Relationships, the basic principle is the principle of Unity: all the Laws of Relationships are directed to the achievement of Unity. Every organism to be satisfactory must be conceived as a whole, and all its elements controlled and determined by their relationships to each other and the whole. Design is extended in space as music is extended in time, and the elements of design must have a rhythmic structure which satisfies the eye as the relationships in music satisfy the ear. These rhythms are the binding force creating unity, and the evidence of sound construction and complete effectiveness of the organic whole. They may exist between masses, areas, forms, lines and colors.

Proportions are our principal means of creating rhythms, and proportions are commensurable mathematically. Consequently various mathematical schemes for perfecting or testing the rhythmic relationships of dimensions, areas, lines and colors have been evolved. These can be most useful in training the accuracy of our eyes, or checking what our eyes have decided to be right. But a feeling for rhythmic relationships must be active in us, and our eyes as "sovereign judge" should create rhythms intuitively without the aid of scale and compass. In no other way can our work be lifted above dull correctness to a level of spontaneity and vitality. The fair world we hope to build will not be built by slide rule: it will have the charm and gaiety of the unexpected, and a stimulating variety within its unity.

If we today succeed in creating Unity in the things we make, we inevitably will have endowed them with the virtue of Simplicity. We will forego any unnecessary elaboration, strip off non-essentials and avoid irrelevancies. No matter how structurally complex our work will be, it will not satisfy us until its form has been stripped and revealed in a virginal simplicity. Other ages have not felt the force of this necessity as strongly as we feel it: but for us, in design as in science, no solution of a problem can be right so long as a simpler, more direct, and equally practical solution can be found.

The perfection of our rhythms demands the Dominance of a single theme or motif; to be effective they must be constructed within a comprehensible Scale, and they must be marked by Accents that lead the eye to perceive visual relationships as sequence enables the ear to perceive aural relationships. In adjusting and organizing the elements of design the subtle interplay of these factors of Dominance, Scale and Accent provides resources of inexhaustible variety. In the internal harmonics of visual design we have as much scope as in the harmonics of aural design in music, and we need the same order of skill in their handling. All music is bound together by the same laws of aural harmony, and yet is infinitely varied; all visual design is correlated by these universal laws of visual harmony, but there are no limits to the variety of needs to which our forms can be adapted with exact accuracy and satisfying rightness.

44

In solving our problems of Fitness, creating our rhythmic relationships and choosing the types of form and line and color out of which they are constructed, we inevitably give our work a character peculiar to itself and different from the work of other times. This special character is evident in all the work done at a particular place and time. It is called, dangerously,

III. STYLE

The word Style is hazardous because it has been lavishly misused, and may convey the idea of a surface appearance applied as a sort of masquerade to the exterior of the things we make: as, the buildings we have built in "the Georgian style," and the furniture we have made in the "style of Louis XV." We have engaged in this kind of charades only because in the recent past we have not had any strong, dominating preferences of our own, no clear conception of the kind of environment we wanted to make for ourselves; and it has been easier to borrow from periods that did know precisely what they wanted than to crystallize our own desires. We were led astray by our superabundant knowledge of the arts of other periods, and seduced into attempting forms and effects that may be historically interesting but are actually alien to our own natures as well as to our needs, our tools and our techniques. There has been an enormous amount of this archaeological pilfering in the past few generations—and there still is—making it difficult to re-establish honest practices. But until we learn to admire and study our antiques without wanting to produce them all over again, our work will be hopelessly ineffective in meeting our needs.

However, as we begin to seek accurate solutions to our own special problems, letting our own needs, tools and processes determine the forms we give to the things we make, it is inevitable that authentic Style shall reappear in the world. We are clarifying our ambitions and beginning to see what it is we want to make of our world; we are gaining a sense of mastery over our tools and a better understanding of what can be done successfully with them. We are honestly attempting to fit the forms of the things we make to our needs and to what we have to make them with. And, partly intuitively but with increasing awareness of what we are doing, we are beginning to integrate our work into a satisfactorily unified pattern. Of necessity, a degree of harmony is spreading through our work. And this of course is one of the essentials in any orderly scheme that we may carry out in the remaking of our environment.

It is not wise to think too much about Style, and it is never wise to try actively to apply it, or to identify it with specific forms. It can be defined exactly only when it has ceased to live and change. Our Style is still evolving and it will not be tomorrow the same thing it is today. It is authentic only when it appears as the result of a sincere concentration on the essential factors of our problems. We find then that the common considerations affecting everything we do in these days, and the pervasive likes and dislikes we all share to some extent at a given time, are producing a sort of family likeness in all our work. Certain characteristics, setting it apart from the work of other times, are appearing with interesting frequency. We choose instinctively lines and forms that suit our purposes, and these have acquired special significance for us. As we look at our work we find that it is inclined to have a geometrical precision, a precise definition, more than a trace of severity. There is in it a kind of clarity and classical reserve that relate it more closely to the art of Greece before the Fourth Century B.C. than to anything since, and the individualism that came in with the Renaissance is being suppressed in favor of an impersonal austerity. It seems that we are more ambitious to create a serene, harmonious order in our new world than to find expression for our relatively unimportant personalities.

But the designer's personality is still effective, if not in the exhibitionist sense. He must contribute to his work something that for want of a fresher, less hackneyed word, we can call

IV. INSPIRATION

In evoking rightness of form, conscious effort needs the illuminating help of insight and intuition. The power of creative imagination must play a part, if work is to be lifted above a pedestrian level. "Order and proportion when they are the whole story are soon exhausted; economy in itself is a restrictive taskmaster," observes John Dewey; and so, "Equally necessary is unexpected combination, and the consequent revelation of possibilities hitherto unrealized."

This kind of Inspiration cannot be exercised at will; it cannot be acquired by study. But it cannot manifest itself effectively except through mastery of one's craft: it needs an equipment laboriously and consciously acquired, to be automatically employed. And it is a sobering fact that the very greatest talents of all time—Phidias and Ictinus, Michelangelo, Leonardo, no less—have been unwilling to forego any aid which the most intensive study and profound analysis of their art could give them.

Assuming that we acquire an approximate mastery of the art of design, we have before us a thrilling

V. PROSPECT

And on this prospect the designer's eyes are always fixed. Before us stretches the gigantic task of rebuilding our whole environment to meet the complex new needs of men today, a fair and orderly environment in

47

which life can be lived with dignity, serenity and ample scope for our human potentialities. The task is so great and so immediate, its phases are so concrete and so close at hand, that we can afford to concentrate on the tangible problems as they present themselves, and keep our sense of humor and our sense of proportion by dealing always in realities rather than in theories. There is no better way of avoiding a touch of Messianic complex, and all the distortion of values it induces, than by constantly testing our powers against the intractable factors of concise, material undertakings. In the years ahead there is every opportunity to keep our minds on the constructive phases of the work, and derive endless excitement and satisfaction from slowly emerging, visible, tangible results; there is no reason to become doctrinaire about what we are up to, or think too much about the good that may result from it.

To set out deliberately to do good to our fellow men is a terrifying commitment. Much of the most tragic suffering in history and in the world today has been caused by men who thought they knew exactly what was good for other men. Some of the most unpleasant personalities ever known have been inspired by the most completely altruistic motives. It is fatal to assume that we can define any ultimate objectives for human progress except in the broadest terms, and the method of advance can be outlined only in the most tentative and obviously factual manner when we come to constructing a

VI. PROGRAM

The designer copies the method of the scientific investigator who never says, "This is positively so," but confines himself to conceding that, "From the data so far obtained we are led to conclude that the truth is approximately this." Both designer and scientist are satisfied to advance a step at a time, confident that the new vantage ground will indicate where one is to go from there. In a world full of pressing problems, it is possible to find enough definitely indicated tasks to occupy all the available talent without resorting to theoretical mapping of objectives. Our towns are unfit for human living and do not work; our housing is inadequate and generally far below the standard our present knowledge and resources make easily attainable; our systems of travel and transportation, on which the unity of the world depends, are antiquated and inefficient; a great improvement of living conditions and of living quality can be effected by supplying clearly evident needs, and these needs are both in the large scale and the small scale classifications. If we confine our Program to those objectives which are attainable and indisputably indicated, we can work in full confidence that the Program will enlarge itself at least as rapidly as our successful accomplishment. And first of all we need to insure, as far as we can, that our work shall really produce some accomplishments that can be called successful.

With this aim in mind, it is time we examined in more detail the various Sources of Form we have been listing. And when we have done that, we still shall have no more than an outline of an analysis of the art of design, interpreted in Machine Age terms. Perhaps the outline can be filled in and the analysis completed as we work on this environment of ours that so sorely needs doing over.

CHAPTER FOUR: FITNESS TO FUNCTION

"Now, a chair is a machine to sit in.
A home is a machine to live in.
The human body is a machine to be worked by will.
A tree is a machine to bear fruit.
A plant is a machine to bear flowers and seeds.
And, as I've admitted before somewhere, a heart is a suction-pump. Does
    that idea thrill you?"   —FRANK LLOYD WRIGHT

In the early eighteen-nineties, Louis Sullivan announced to an inattentive world that "Form follows Function," and laid down the principles of an architecture based on rational solutions of our own practical building problems rather than on the echoes of other ages' solutions of their practical building problems. And at the same time in far-away Hammersmith, William Morris was prolonging an Indian Summer of medieval craftsmanship of which he alone was the hot and extraordinarily potent sun. In singlehanded revolt against the whole tide of machine production Morris revived a dozen handicrafts and aroused a small army of willing workers at looms and potters' wheels, printing presses and forges. Of them all he was the mightiest hero and the tale of his labors is fabulous. In addition to the incredible flood of wall papers and tapestries, furniture, rugs, stained glass, printed books and printing types, and the rivers of placid verse that flowed from this fountainhead, he found time for cart-tail speeches on socialism and platform lectures on the salvation of man through skilled handiwork. With great power and effectiveness he preached the value of rightness, of honesty and simplicity and candid humble utility, to an age that went in for a practically universal application of fig leaves in art as well as in morals and regarded mere naked utility as somehow shameful. (They painted wood, as H. G. Wells once remarked, to look like other woods, or even like itself.)

The Victorian era had reason to blush at utility, for most of the utilities offered it by an adolescent Machine Age were indecently hideous. It was easy for Morris and his converts to set these crude mechanical products in humiliating contrast against the suave works of the old handicrafts, not stopping to think that the craft forms stood at the end of a long process of evolution while the machine forms stood at the beginning of another. The perfect adaptation of the older products to the uses for which they were intended, their simple, honest effectiveness and the deep-rooted, organic source of their beauty were serenely evident, and Morris' campaign had a brief prosperity. It could not succeed because it was a mere eddy in an irresistible current, a last revolt against destiny.

The object of work is not only its own joy. While there should and must be joy in work, its object also is the increase of material aids to the comfort and richness of life. Machines are capable of making more things and better things, making them faster and cheaper and available to more of us, than is possible through handwork alone. The end that Morris held most dear, the communal happiness of mankind, required that machine production should prevail, as a later generation of social revolutionists in Russia clearly realizes. But Morris did a great constructive service: he was one of the first to revive appreciation of sound and honest work and to re-establish rightness as the aim of all our mechanical endeavors. He made utility respectable and demonstrated the compatibility of utility and beauty. He maintained with lusty force the venality of ugliness and he convinced a considerable portion of an astonished public that a frame of satisfying beauty for the normal human life is not only possible but actually essential to our self-respect.

But it was Louis Sullivan who was the real prophet of our mechanical renaissance, he and the inheritor of his mantle, Frank Lloyd Wright: Sullivan re-proclaiming the ancient truth, received by his day as a new revelation, that function determines form, and form expresses function; Wright preaching the same gospel of functional fitness, with an added insistence on materials and processes as factors that also influence form, and a frank championship of machines as potential sources of rightness; both with their eyes on the world around them instead of the past, both heartily accepting the given conditions of their times as the basis of a new craftsmanship. After gaining momentum slowly for the better part of a generation, this new craftsmanship of the Machine Age is practised now by most of the alert and young-minded workers in Europe and America—architects, engineers, designers—who are attempting to devise forms to fit the functional needs of our times more exactly than any we inherited from the past. In all the fields of communal interest—cities, building, housing, transportation, manufacturing and public works—this modern school is practising a craftsmanship aimed at the creation of order by means of our own special equipment to meet our own special needs. It is attaining the ideal of honest workmanship at which Morris aimed, but by the very means that he thought hopelessly evil.

For the spirit of craftsmanship is independent of its tools. It can work with steel presses and milling machines as well as with hand planes and chisels, if its aims are honest and its intelligence adequate. As modern engineering has advanced in mastery, designing for purely functional ends alone, it has created examples of perfected order that meet all the high standards of Sullivan and Wright, and it has done it often without ever having heard of these gentlemen. In the superlative rightness of certain modern airplanes, power plants and machine tools, parkways and bridges, nothing has been admitted which did not contribute to performance, and forms have been determined solely by efficiency, materials and processes; while an accurate integration of all the parts in precise relationships has been achieved by the pressure of necessity. As a result these things approach a classical, abstract beauty of form which advances toward perfection with each new advance in functional efficiency.

This is inevitably true, that as a thing becomes perfectly adapted to the purpose for which it is made, and so approaches its ultimate form, it also advances in that power to please us which we call beauty. Use is the primary source of form. The function of a thing is its reason for existence, its justification and its end, by which all its possible variations may be tested and accepted or rejected. It is a sort of life-urge thrusting through a thing and determining its developments. It is only by realizing its destiny, and revealing that destiny with candor and exactness, that a thing acquires significance and validity of form. This means much more than utility, or even efficiency: it means the kind of perfected order we find in natural organisms, bound together in such precise rhythms that no part can be changed without wounding the whole. Our own bodies acquire their beauty, when they have it, from strength and virility in the male, fecundity and promise of delight in the female, grace and vigor in both. We are thrilled by the body's revealed structure as a working organism, the mechanism of bone and muscle beneath its surface, balancing, thrusting, restraining in its complex interplay, the flooding of vitality and sensitivity through its tissues giving bloom and color to its skin and light to its eyes. As a revelation of abundant health and life we delight in it; as a flaccid, devitalized thing it revolts us.

So it is with all design in nature, and in the things we make. It is *rightness* that gives us pleasure, entices and thrills and satisfies us, and rightness is a revelation of the function for which a thing is right; a revelation too of the skill and soundness with which it is made, and its adequacy to perform its function. When we find all these factors of fitness evident in a thing we have made, it delights us with the complacent knowledge that we have added something to the total of humanized order in the world.

The function of a thing may be trivial or magnificent; it may serve a very humble or a very exalted end. It may be a model of a four-masted schooner inside a bottle, serving no other purpose than to display the maker's skill and tickle our fancy; or it may be a forty-thousand-ton liner, carrying thousands of people swiftly and safely and in great comfort across perilous seas. The potentialities of beauty in a thing are in direct proportion to the importance or the wonder or the worthiness of the end it serves. As we admire the function, we derive pleasure from its revelation. This is not to apply an ethical standard to art: it is merely to state a simple rule of consequences. A temple to a god or the capitol of a state has greater possibilities of stirring our responsive emotions than a service station or a garage; an airplane can be more beautiful than a trolley car.

But we are also influenced by the degree of success with which a function is performed. Complete adaptation to a humble station in life, perfect fulfillment of a modest destiny, may be far more admirable than meretricious performance in a more exalted role. Hence there are plenty of good service stations and garages which are more beautiful than any number of banal temples and capitols with which our land is dotted, and there are

54

super trolley cars now building which are more beautiful than the older and cruder planes. We respond to the importance of the purpose for which an object is right, but we respond even more definitely to its degree of rightness.

It is easy to overlook the value of this simple homespun self-respect in design. It is done every day: an object's social rating appears lowly, and so its design is falsified in an effort to lift it above its proper station. This method of face lifting, in architecture, was invented by the Romans and enthusiastically practised by them and their artistic descendants, the designers of the Renaissance in Italy. The Romans would let almost nothing speak for itself; today we can accept very few Roman works with as little reservation as the magnificent aqueduct at Nîmes, called the Pont du Gard: a purely practical work of engineering designed frankly to carry a water channel across a river valley, and probably considered too utilitarian to deserve a veneer of applied pilasters, panels and cornices. It stands today in naked majesty, three tiers of bare, purely functional arches, a testimony to the genius of Roman engineers and a rebuke to Roman architects.

The Renaissance went further and established pretense in architecture as a conservative virtue: perhaps the most remarkable of its great and marvelous works. There were giants in those days, but they were very often frauds as well as geniuses.[1] We can accept the lively architecture they painted on flat walls as an amusing prank deceiving no one; we can even tolerate the equally false architecture they built in such profusion against simple sustaining walls, and the elaborate but not too serious pretentiousness of so much they did. But it is not so easy to forgive their

---

[1] Geoffrey Scott's brilliant defense of baroque practices in his delightful *Architecture of Humanism* proves only that they are indefensible.

55

having established the Beaux-Arts tradition that design is something to be derived from precedent and applied to the outside of things in the same way you smear stucco on a wall. This doctrine has been upheld in modern times in the most conservative circles and taught in the most respectable schools; and strange to say a taint of radicalism has attached to the reviving cult of candor and honesty, which maintains that design is evoked from within its object, that it derives its validity from its revelation of function, materials and processes, that while these may not be exalted the design will be still less so unless they are frankly acknowledged.

It is true that the respectably pretentious are now in retreat, but their long dominance has given their traditional approach to design an influence difficult to escape. Our subconscious tendencies are apt to betray us, and it must be admitted that human nature itself readily falls back on habit in preference to continuously fresh adjustment of its attitudes. Herbert Spencer says in his delightful polysyllables that "primitive human nature deviates into novelty only through unintentional modifications." It seems that we are all somewhat primitive. We find beaten paths easiest to follow and we take them even when they go in the wrong direction. It requires an effort of will, beyond the powers of many of us, to maintain an alert attitude toward all the problems of construction that come before us, solving each by a fresh study of its factors, uninfluenced by tradition.

We can appreciate the way that tradition hampers us in spite of our best intentions, if, to take familiar examples, we contrast the rates of advance in the design of airplanes and of automobiles. Airplanes, luckily for them, had no background in history, and so have been able to progress unhindered by deeply grooved habits of thought. To stay in the air at all, the form of a plane must be adapted with great exactness to its function of flying, and so the designers of planes have been forced, willy-nilly, to advance toward ultimate, unadulterated functionalism. As a result we have produced these thrilling organisms that have more power to move us esthetically than almost anything else this age has created.

Automobiles, on the other hand, inherited a carriage tradition thousands of years old, and almost any contraption can be made to run on four wheels. So the carriage tradition dominated automobile design and held it back for a whole generation. It was only when the memory of graceful, horse-drawn vehicles had grown dim that we could analyze the automobile's function in its own terms and evolve a rational form to suit it.

Not only tradition, but a number of other influences—fashion, supposed market preferences, mere imitativeness—have all distracted the automotive engineer from pure engineering into irrelevant bypaths and so delayed a solution of his problem. Most effective of all, however, was an impediment for which he could not be blamed, one which exists in practically all fields: the difficulty of accurately defining a function, and definition's habit of retreating before our approach.

When internal combustion engines were first substituted for horses as a means of propelling vehicles, the full implications of the change were far from revealing themselves. The engine was looked upon as a substitution merely, and it was only as the engine began greatly to surpass the horse in speed and endurance that it became necessary to revise the vehicle too in the interest of safety and comfort. A carriage that had been the height of luxury at ten or even twelve miles an hour became decidedly uncomfortable and unsafe at twenty or twenty-five. Continually greater speeds demanded progressive adaptations, and these speeds, with the increase in driving, demanded a new system of highways. The new highways made still greater speeds practicable, and a network of service stations removed the last restriction from practically unlimited travel. By

57

1930 we were driving millions of automobiles at cruising speeds ranging from forty to seventy and eighty miles an hour, with the limit not in sight. Yet these automobiles were still adapted carriages and the engineers had not yet begun to approach a simple and accurate definition of their problem. Gradually we have come to regard the automobile simply as a vehicle to carry passengers over the highways in the greatest possible comfort at speeds limited only by the factor of safety, and at a minimum of expense. Since 1930 an enormous amount of groundwork has been done preparatory to designing a motor car which shall exactly fit this definition, and in this study almost every part of the car has undergone drastic revision: the construction of the frame, the relation of motor to passengers and to driver, the contour of the body as it affects the passing flow of air currents, its construction and its trim, windows, seats, method of springing the wheels and of steering. New factors are continually making their appearance, but in the last ten years we have made substantial advance in clarifying our conception of the automobile's function and in devising a form to fit it.

In another field, the force of tradition and inaccurate definition are largely responsible for retarding our homes a century or two in development. We are incurable romantics in regard to our homes, unabashed sentimentalists, and rightly so: a home should be lovely and lovable and the inspiration of tenderest sentiments. But because romance and sentiment attach so strongly to things remote in time and place, we are apt to confuse our values and think that by giving our homes a character "remote in time and place" we therefore make them more lovable. So we have been deliberately planning our houses in imitation of houses which were functional in other countries or times but are not so here and now. The plan of these houses we imitate was determined by factors no longer

58

valid. In the historical "periods," the only practical method of heating houses was by means of attractive but highly inefficient open fires confined in niches in the walls; floors, at least above the ground, were framed of wood, and the span of timbers was short; glass was expensive, and too much of it added to the heating difficulties; the house required almost no mechanical equipment except locks on the doors and cranes in the fire-places; domestic life was governed by formal codes, and domestic help, if required, was plentiful and cheap. These conditions resulted in a house consisting of cubicles of moderate size, lighted by small windows, and so arranged that each could be isolated from the others to confine heat within it.

Today we can maintain an even temperature in our houses throughout the year, keep approximately the same degree of humidity in the air, and filter the air free of dust; and all this can be done automatically with practically no attention from the occupant. This degree of air-conditioning is still a luxury, but so for a long time were central heating and sanitary plumbing; today they are required for low-cost housing, and so air-conditioning will be in time. Steel and the cantilever principle of construction make it unnecessary to use bearing walls at such frequent intervals, and glass can be used in large areas, either in sheets or in translucent blocks. The mechanical equipment of a house—wiring, plumbing, heating, cooking, laundry—costs approximately as much as the structure itself and is just as necessary. We live with great informality, and domestic help is scarce and expensive.

All these changed conditions force us to examine the function of a house with fresh eyes. Freed from many limitations that used to control our house plans, we can adapt them much more exactly to their purpose of providing shelter and privacy for the processes of daily living—cooking, eating, sleeping, sexual intercourse and the rearing of children, relaxation, pastimes, and pleasant social relationships with our family and friends. We have been reluctant to abandon the traditional scheme of cubicles arranged, generally, around cross axes for purposes of access. Most houses in the world belong to this type, of course: we are used to them and many of them are delightful examples of the art of their times, worthy of careful preservation. But when we start from scratch today we find we can devise a much more flexible, practical and convenient plan if we study the actual requirements of our life as we live it today, the relationship of our domestic activities to each other, ease of circulation and ease of house-keeping. The result is an arrangement in which life flows easily and smoothly, and while shelter and privacy are still controlling considerations, we find that we can remove the solid barrier between indoors and outdoors when we want to and let sunshine, fresh air and ourselves flow in and out without hindrance.

It is obvious that the purpose of all housing is to provide for gracious and healthy living, and this has been accomplished in the past in very little expensive housing and in almost no low-cost housing. The affluent can be expected to use available resources and devise a satisfactory scheme of living for themselves, but the many whose earning capacity will never be high cannot do this for themselves. It becomes a social responsibility to study the function of housing and devise adequate machines for living well and happily, to be had by everybody at low cost. The preservation of low costs depends, of course, on the removal of housing from the field of commercial speculation. People are gregarious, and low-cost housing especially must be constructed in reasonably compact masses, with plenty of open space and yet with easy access to employment. And so the planning of functional low-cost housing involves the planning of functional

Simple rightness of form gives us pleasure, and we call it beautiful.

GERMAINE MARTIN, FROM ARTS ET METIER GRAPHIQUE ⟫→

Adaptation to the specific functions of the male and female
animal is the source of beauty in the human body.

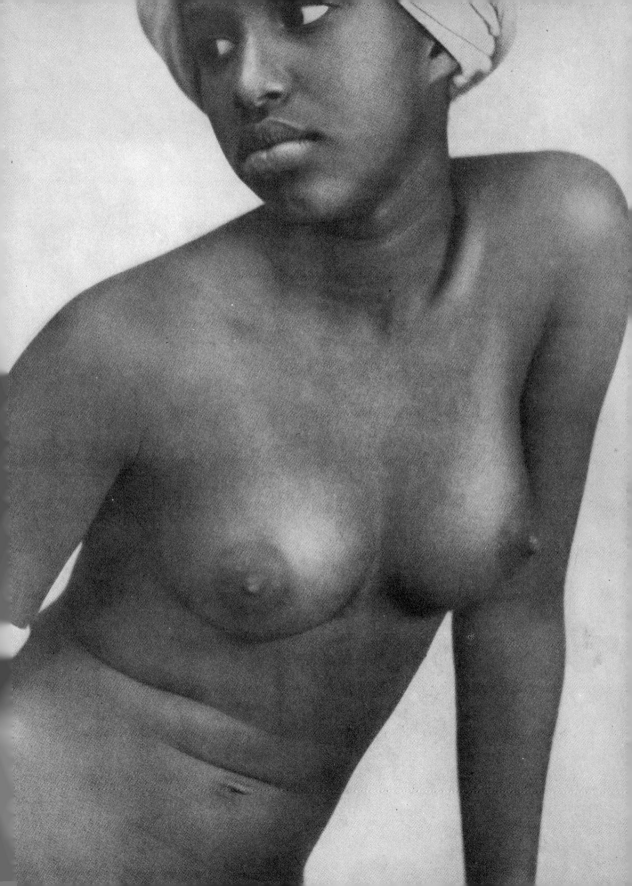

As they are more closely adapted to their functions, many of our modern forms acquire a classical, abstract beauty. Bridge of the "Queen Mary."

20

Use is the primary source of form, with materials and techniques determining all its developments. Detail of Westinghouse Portable X-Ray Unit.

21

We seek today to achieve decorative beauty by purely functional form, without embellishment of any kind. Garden Stairs, Ford Exposition, New York World's Fair.

23

22

Simple utilitarian construction becomes beautiful through careful organization for efficiency. Water tower and powerhouse, Chevrolet Motor and Axle Division. Designed by Albert Kahn. DAMORA

In certain products, especially those that move at high speed, right form has been evolved by necessity. Nose of Douglas Transport Plane.

25

Many of our great engineering works attain a superlative rightness of form through exact functional adaptation. Spillway, Boulder Dam.   U. S. BUREAU OF RECLAMATION

24

26

Man's first flight in a heavier-than-air machine, motor driven. Wilbur and Orville Wright at Kitty Hawk, Dec. 17, 1903. Below, DH-4B type U. S. Army plane remodeled to cross the continent in 24 hours, 1921.

First load of contract air mail was flown in this plane Feb. 15, 1926. Below, the swift evolution of functional form in airplanes, within a single generation, is brought down to 1939 in this transport plane.

ACME

27

UNITED AIR LINES

Henry Ford in the first car built by him, 1896, marking a definite break with the carriage tradition. Below, Barney Oldfield and Henry Ford with the "999" (record holder at 91 miles per hour), 1904.

But automobile design was long involved with the traditions of carriage building. Lord Northcliffe in his touring caravan, 1903. Below, Thomas car, "fully equipped," 1909.

PHOTOGRAPHS FROM BROWN BROS.

By 1931 high speeds and high efficiency had been attained, but functional adaptation of form was still retarded. Cadillac 16, January, 1931.

January, 1931, the Marmon 16 appeared, a consistent effort to simplify automobile body form and adapt it to the flow of air currents. Designed by the author and Walter Dorwin Teague, Jr.

In 1932 a special body built for Col. Howard Marmon took the next logical step in functional adaptation, again influencing later developments.

Body designed in 1938 for rear-engined car forecasts future trends. Clear vision, extra seating capacity, built-in bumpers, no projections, form adapted to air flow. Both designs by the author and Walter Dorwin Teague, Jr.

31

PICTURES, INC.

32 The furthest in functional adaptation to high speeds on land and water, 1939. John R. Cobb's car in Utah (record holder at 368 m.p.h.) and Sir Malcolm Campbell's boat on Lake Coniston (record holder at 141 m.p.h.)

BRITISH PRESS COMBINE

communities and functional circulation. Fortunately low-cost automobiles have enlarged the range of daily travel for everybody, and motor transportation has freed many industries from bondage to railway tracks. Therefore there is a growing tendency to decentralize industry by returning it to the country, where clean and well-built factories need no longer be an offense, and employees can live more pleasantly than in congested cities. The cities must be thinned out and redesigned to relieve their circulatory systems (which are rapidly becoming static) but also to admit the country with its sunshine, air, and carbon-dioxide-consuming plants.

Along all these lines we have done a vast amount of functional study and produced a respectable body of intelligent, functional planning. But the sheer size of the task of rebuilding, and the enormous mass of actual ponderable materials that have to be moved, all of them owned and guarded with understandable jealousy by somebody, make progress painfully slow in comparison with our leaping conceptions and mighty resources. Functional design has advanced most rapidly in fields where the units to be dealt with are smaller and more easily and rapidly replaced. For this reason, air and highway transportation have forged ahead while the railroads have persisted in an almost fossilized state. And while our cities and the housing of our people, the whole scheme of living, working and bartering in fact, compose a vast mass of inertia which can be nibbled at only here and there, the mechanical equipment of daily life in both home and industry has advanced with an astonishing velocity.

Even the most slavishly copied of our Norman *manoirs* and Cape Cod cottages contain within their fancy dress any number of splendid examples of purely functional design. Their kitchens and bathrooms are almost wholly rational and by all odds the most satisfactory rooms in the house. This is because bathing as now practised is a modern invention, and the methods of preserving and preparing foods have been so completely revolutionized by industrial science as to be almost equally new. Hence design in these fields could start from scratch and solve its problems on a purely functional basis. It would be pretty difficult to disguise a gas range as a wood-burning fireplace, or an electrical refrigerator as a cold cellar, and so far no one has cared to try. Except for a few abortive attempts to introduce "period" effects into bathrooms, these utilitarian quarters have maintained an exhilarating degree of candor, efficiency—and beauty. Our gas and electric ranges, sinks, refrigerators, kitchen cabinets and bathroom furnishings are among the most satisfactory works of art of these times. And our basements with their laundry and heating equipment are rapidly attaining the high esthetic rank of our bathrooms and kitchens.

Our living and dining and sleeping quarters have lagged far behind in beauty and rationality. The weight of tradition rests more heavily on our tables and chairs and beds, and while the utilitarian parts of the house have been the subject of extremely intelligent educational campaigns fostered by the companies who have really admirable equipment to sell, our taste in furniture has been corrupted by stupid propaganda from manufacturers and the "decorating" magazines. Furniture has been treated not from a functional and esthetic point of view: it has been regarded as a mere means for creating picturesque, trivial and completely irrelevant effects. It has been subject to changing whims of fashion as inexplicable as the mysterious forces that originate women's hats. The movement toward simplification which none of us has been able to escape has reduced the quantity of draperies, plush, fringe and knick-knacks as compared with fifty years ago, but has left a mass of useless debris still to be cleared away. The automobile manufacturers have made, in the past few years, a greater contribution to the art of comfortable seating than chair builders had made in all preceding history. An increasing number of people are allowing good sense and good taste to determine how their living quarters are furnished and arranged, but they are still few enough to stand out conspicuously in the general mass of cream-puff and plum-pudding ensembles.

Industry is analyzing the functional requirements of its own plants and equipment with admirable acumen. Factories are growing lighter, airier, cleaner, better and more conveniently arranged; machinery is growing simpler in organization for use, as it grows more astonishingly competent and complex in its operations. A modern machine shop is often a sight beautiful to see, and the men who work in these settings respond to them with keen appreciation. The products of industry, too, are being approached quite generally from the standpoint of, first, an exact definition of function, and second, an adaptation to that function as accurate as possible.

Function is seldom uncomplicated, and there is always a tendency to seize upon certain outstanding characteristics and neglect others that are less obvious but still essential. It was in this way that automotive engineers so long ignored the need for economy through adaptation of the form to wind resistance while they were engrossed in increasing the speed and power of their cars. Almost all mechanical devices have subsidiary requirements aside from their principal functions. An amateur motion-picture projector must first of all project brilliant and steady pictures, but it should also operate silently and it should never burn the fingers of the operator. A gas range should cook well, but it should also be easy to keep clean, it should bend the cook's back as little as possible, and require a minimum of her attention; and it should fit into the bright, immaculate scheme of the modern kitchen. These secondary requirements have revolutionized range design in recent years, and not the demands of cooking alone, which after all was done quite successfully on the old-fashioned cook-stove.

Certain functional requirements recur again and again in modern mechanical products: ease of operation, for instance, and the *appearance* of ease of operation. Many products that are really quite simple were left by their producers with such a bewildering appearance of complexity that they terrified the novice and so became actually difficult to operate: today we reorganize these devices to fit their functional definition, suppressing unexplained moving parts and exposed mechanism so that only the essential controls are presented to the operator's eye and hand.

Another recurring requirement is that a product should provide as little lodgment as possible for dust and dirt. This alone has helped eliminate vast quantities of "ornamental" detail from all sorts of things from typewriters to skyscrapers. Silence is another: if all our mechanical devices were designed without regard to the noise they make, our homes and offices would be unendurable bedlams. Compactness, lightness of weight, durability, automatic operation, low operating costs as well as low production costs, are almost universal functional requirements. To neglect any of these factors is to fail in achieving that ultimate rightness which is the aim of design.

The profession of industrial design in its brief career has developed a technique for analyzing the function of a product, and has set up standards for judging functional fitness. It has applied these methods and standards to innumerable objects ranging from domestic and office appliances to automobiles, ships and trains; and to industrial and commercial buildings, offices and shops, and the expositions in which industry explains itself to the public. It has set up a procedure which must be followed in devising housing that shall approximate our cars in efficiency and low cost; in developing a system of transportation whereby our planes, trucks, cars, highways and railroads can be co-ordinated into one smoothly functioning system for the distribution of goods and people; and in creating forms of community living which shall supersede the present unworkable town and city plan.

None of these problems will be solved automatically. They cannot be left to mere natural evolution. It is true that in certain products, especially those we have cited that move at high speed, right form evolves by necessity: any deviation from purely functional form is disastrous and the engineer is forced into functional design because he has no choice. In machine parts, too, the same compulsion operates and we have the marvelous abstract perfection of these forms—a beauty which makes Mr. Brancusi's sculpture seem somewhat trivial. But while the *parts* may be beyond criticism, the assembled machine may not be: as the form grows complex the possibilities of variation increase and often arrive at confusion.

Perfection of form is achieved automatically only when necessity leaves no choice in the matter. In all other cases conscious design must supplement engineering, and these other cases are the vast majority of all we do. The perfection of these naturally evolved functional forms proves that exact functional adaptation is the only proper aim of all design. In no other way can such vital distinction, such moving significance, such satisfying rightness be evoked. And exact functional adaptation of course implies adaptation to materials and processes of manufacture as well as the unification of the whole. It is impossible to disentangle these phases of the design problem. They interact on each other, and one cannot design successfully with an eye to function and ignore materials and processes; while satisfactory structure is impossible unless relationships have been accurately adjusted. Functional design requires that all phases of the design problem be dealt with simultaneously, and the ultimate form must be a composite answer to many subsidiary problems. If we discuss and analyze these phases separately, it is only because our minds are not built to hold much more than one thing at a time and it is quite necessary that no aspect of a problem be overlooked.

CHAPTER FIVE: FITNESS TO MATERIALS

"Old architecture was found out by men working in stone. A cathedral was, as it were, a natural growth from a quarry." —W. R. LETHABY

"There is no effect of form which the effect of material could not enhance."
—GEORGE SANTAYANA

The kind of materials available has determined the kind of work men do and the kind of civilization they attain, from the Stone Age through the Bronze Age and the Iron Age to this Age of Steel.

If the Athenians had not had quarries of exceedingly fine-grained marble near at hand on Mount Pentelicus and Mount Hymettus, they never could have accomplished the subtle exercises in applied mathematics that have made their buildings on the Acropolis a marvel to the world: joints so accurately ground as to be almost invisible, lines curved an inch or so in a hundred feet, a controlling scheme so precise and so comprehensive that it is said there is no stone in the Parthenon exactly square and no angle anywhere exactly a right angle. Without a material that could be worked almost as accurately as steel, the Athenians would have had to be satisfied with the approximations that have contented other builders.

The Romans had in their neighborhood an ample supply of an earth called *pozzolana*, and this when mixed with lime made an extremely hard and durable cement. This cement enabled them to advance beyond the

67

"post and lintel" type of building practised by the Egyptians and the Greeks, in which big stones are placed on other big stones to be held in place by their own weight. The Romans were no longer limited to the span between supports that could be bridged by a single quarry stone: they could build with small stones, bricks and tiles bonded together by tenacious cement, and so they could perfect the arch, the vault and the dome to cover vast interiors. Cement made possible the Romans' spectacular achievements in structural engineering.

The Eleventh and Twelfth Centuries in France saw a remarkable advance in the making of colored glass, and of colored glass windows. The Gothic builders were eager to use this glass in larger and larger areas, as they built higher and wider palaces for Our Lady. So as they developed ribbed vaulting and the flying buttress they contracted their masonry walls and enlarged their openings, and in the end they succeeded in building great structures which are mere skeletons of masonry framing huge screens of glass. Gothic glass was chiefly responsible for the most striking characteristic of Gothic buildings, their attenuated skeletal structure.

We in our time have found it possible to support even bigger structures than the Gothic builders attempted, by substituting for masonry piers and arches a far more tenuous framework of steel. In our steel buildings masonry lingers on, quite anomalously, only as an inefficient screen against the weather. Without having fully developed the potentialities of our new materials, we are already practising a building technique like nothing the world has ever known before.

We are far less dependent than other ages on the resources which nature has happened to put in our way: we are not limited to the materials we can find at hand. Our modern partnership between science and industry, with the great expansion of research laboratories and experimental stations through which it works, is able to meet our needs with reasonable promptness whenever these needs become sufficiently urgent. Out of the simple natural materials to which former ages were limited, and out of many others they found useless, we make an endless variety of special adaptations, combinations, refinements and syntheses, so that our repertoire of available resources is far more extensive than any possessed by designers heretofore. Because of this facility with which we devise means to satisfy our needs, it is hard to say whether our greatly expanded activities are due to the expansion of our material resources, or whether our activities invading new fields are responsible for the increase in our range of materials. But the two are inextricably involved, and conditioned by each other. Our work today takes its character from the means we have at hand for doing it, and materials added to our needs and our tools compose the forces determining the forms of what we make.

Design today as always is directed by the interplay of materials, methods and functions, with forms determined by materials almost as much as by function, function affecting the choice of materials and materials influencing the scope and type of possible functions, materials instigating and hastening the devising of new processes. These forces whose power we feel are not novel: they merely move more swiftly and so with greater impact, and they vary their direction more frequently, than they used to do. The peculiar difficulty of our position is that this interaction of forces is accelerated almost beyond our ability to keep pace with it in conscious mastery of our resources. The times are moving too rapidly for us, and compressing into our single life-span what once would have been long ages of change and slow adaptation.

Through the centuries preceding the Industrial Revolution the enlargement of the craftsmen's resources, in materials especially, proceeded almost imperceptibly. He had stone and wood for building, with bricks and tile baked from clay where clay was available; clay again for pottery, and wood for furniture; glass in small panes for windows, and for blowing small vessels; cotton, wool, flax and the silkworm's cocoons for textiles; first stone, then bronze, iron and finally steel for weapons, and for implements where strength and temper and a fine cutting edge are required; tin chiefly as an alloy, and brass, copper and lead for uses where corrosion would destroy less expensive metals; marble and other rare stones for enrichment, and gold and silver for adornment and the satisfaction of pride. Through thousands of years the list of available materials was scarcely larger than this, and it had only a few additions in the France of the Revolution that were not known in the Rome of Augustus. Only the commonest and cheapest materials were used in any great quantity. In America in 1789 it is estimated that there was less than half a pound of steel in use per person, and this served for swords, knives, scissors, gunlocks, needles, and such intimate tools; while today there are more than nine tons in use per person, in buildings, bridges, railroads, automobiles, ships and a vast proliferation of machines, tools and appliances.

Here we see the older craftsman's advantages and our handicap. In such static conditions there was time to get the feel of materials and to master them, to try out all their possibilities and perfect the techniques of their use. As there was time to develop one's tools and gain skill in their handling, there was also every opportunity to discover what could best be done with the stuff in hand and to weed out all inappropriate or impractical applications of it. The problem of fitness to materials, like fitness to function, worked itself out naturally without hurry, but with a very satisfying certainty.

But the Machine Age in its multitude of inventions has not only included our long repertoire of new materials—it has enormously increased the number and kind of things we can do with materials, old as well as new. It is not surprising that as a result we have fumbled very clumsily with many of our unfamiliar stuffs, while we ran wild in inept uses of those our forefathers understood so well.

Tradition has been a source of confusion, and not a help. It might have been supposed that the store of experience accumulated through working in such primitive substances as wood and iron would still be available to guide us aright in their use. But we were applying new tools to their shaping, and new processes demand new forms. In devising new forms to fit our new processes we have been and still are hampered by our constitutional reluctance to "deviate into novelty": the instinctive impulse of man faced by a new thing is to take refuge in the familiar and regard the new merely as a substitute for the old. So we looked upon our new machines simply as a faster and cheaper means of doing exactly what we had previously done by hand. Now this, as we shall see when we come to consider processes, is a misconception: machines by their very nature are adapted to do something quite different from anything that can be done by hand, and their imitation of handwork is a feeble failure. Our old materials needed to be restudied with reference to their adaptability to machine production, so that machine forms which would bring out their special qualities and individual beauties could be devised. Until this fresh study had been accomplished, the confusion of thought in the crafts was deplorable.

We have clarified our objectives in many classifications of materials, but not in all. We can feel superior now to the designers who, discovering that cast iron made a practicable building material, cast their first structural iron in forms simulating carved stone, faithful even to the joints in the masonry and the Corinthian capitals on the fluted columns. But we too have not yet fully extricated ourselves from the influence of tradition in this field of building, where tradition is strongest, and we have not yet devised a form of structure which can be built of our characteristic materials by our characteristic techniques, with the efficiency we display in so many other phases of production.

When steel was made practicable for building and so increased the possible height of structures, it forced the development of that other essential in tall buildings, the swift and safe elevator. It also impelled the invention of a long list of new appliances, devices, equipment, materials, and methods, until the building art today is something quite different from anything ever practised before, and the designer enjoys a freedom without precedent. All these new developments are expansions of a basic vocabulary of steel, reinforced concrete and glass, and together they make almost all the traditional forms of architectural design meaningless or at best irrelevant.

Not quite all, since a man still passes very comfortably through an opening about three feet wide by seven feet high, our beds and tables are still mostly rectangular and fit most conveniently into rectangular enclosures, and it is almost as unpleasant to let too much light into a room as too little. But the designer today is free to plan his solids and his voids, his circulation and his enclosures, for functional ends, without being hampered unduly by the law of gravity which has restricted his predecessors; the improvement of insulating materials—there are insulating slabs one inch thick which have the same coefficient of heat transmission as a sixteen-inch brick wall—and the improvement of the art of heating, ventilating and air-conditioning have made the climatic limitation negligible; we realize the importance to health and comfort of proper acoustical conditions and efficient lighting, and we have acquired a partly scientific and partly pragmatic knowledge of both these subjects with the means to apply what we have learned; there has been an amazing proliferation of plastics, laminated compositions, composition boards and sheets, roofing and flooring materials, durable finishes and rustless metals, standardized mechanical, sanitary and culinary equipment, all enabling the designer to create a range of forms and a degree of comfort and rightness beyond anything dreamed of by previous ages.

So far as our material resources are concerned, there is nothing to hamper us in developing new forms exactly suited to our needs: but we continue to build our tall buildings on principles originally derived from timber framing, and in housing we have not yet succeeded in obtaining any of the advantages of increased efficiency and low cost which we enjoy in so many fields of production. Our handicap in this latter field is not one of materials, but of the application of processes. We have failed to extend to the final stages of the building art those advanced methods used in the production of our building materials and equipment. We build our refrigerators and heating plants on an assembly line and produce actual miracles of efficiency and economy, but we continue to build our houses on the site by the old unit-production system which would make a Ford car cost about $17,500—just about the cost, significantly, of a modern house that in its own field would be comparable to a Ford car in functional quality.

It is obvious, of course, that a house is not a mobile unit and that houses probably never will roll off the assembly line every forty-five seconds and be delivered to the site complete. But it is equally obvious that we should find ways of fabricating, by modern production methods, standardized, interchangeable building units which can be shipped easily and can be assembled quickly and easily on the site: the total cost per dwelling should be cut in this way to a mere fraction of present costs. This is a problem of first importance, which must be solved before we can advance very far with the construction of a rationally organized environment. Satisfactory housing is in fact the first requirement—after ample feeding—in a satisfactory world, and the amount of intelligent study now being applied to this subject leads us to hope that in time even those of us in the lower income brackets can be housed as well at home as on the highways.

It can only be done by discarding the traditional methods of unit construction—which still prevail today even when a builder commits the appalling offense of constructing hundreds or thousands of dwellings exactly alike. These atrocities that blight so many of our towns and cities and suburbs are cheap and inefficient and stultifying in quality, but they are still excessively expensive in cost. But if we extend machine and mass production into this field, and fabricate our houses in the form of a relatively small number of standardized panel units which can be assembled to compose a room or a house of any size or shape, we shall have low cost, flexibility, and high efficiency without tiresome uniformity or rigidity of plan. These panel units, dimensioned on a module system as the Japanese have built their houses for centuries, will be designed to embody all we have learned about insulation and about modern living requirements. They will be durable and attractive, and varied to the point where a designer will be conscious of no constraint in adapting his plan to the function of his structure; but they will be transported with ease, and assembled with no more time or trouble than so many of our knocked-down products today. In addition to low initial cost and upkeep, flexibility of plan, and functional efficiency, houses built in this way can be altered or enlarged with the greatest of ease, or taken down and reassembled on another site in a matter of hours.

Technical advances along these lines must precede any really adequate utilization of the material resources we now have available. In the interval of experimentation, it would be unfortunate if we congealed a new vernacular for our new materials before we had acquired technical mastery of their use, and there is a danger that we may do just that. Flat roofs and ribbon windows wrapped around corners, cantilevered balconies and unexpected lally columns have become as hackneyed in the work of the International School as mansard roofs and molded cornices were in other days. The International School has appropriated the leadership of modern design and its achievements are formidable and often admirable, but the characteristics it has made so familiar do not make a design necessarily adequate and they are not necessarily the characteristics we shall see in the more fully organized production of tomorrow. It is a fatal mistake to give our loyalty lightly to externals. Adequate design is based on a fresh, intensive study of the use to which a structure is to be put, and the materials and methods to be used in its building: it must issue as an exact adaptation of plan to use, and materials and methods must be so employed as to give the highest possible degree of satisfaction to the users.

Such an approach and such an aim will give a new form to our tall steel buildings as well as to our housing. Tall buildings were first created for the purpose of crowding more people into areas already overcrowded, and it is popular today among critics whose social conscience is stronger than their imaginations to damn the skyscraper as an abomination in the land, as though an ill-used tool should itself be evil. Acuter vision has foreseen

75

the skyscraper's true function in freeing the land of a crowding world for other purposes than building. A large part of the population in time will live high up in the sunshine and fresh air of tall towers, widely spaced in a land of gardens, parks and playgrounds.

When we succeed in adapting their form to their materials and techniques, these skyscrapers of the future will no longer have their present box-like masses, inert and dull no matter how skillfully they are piled up. So far we have supported these structures on a framework of columns and beams derived from the principles of timber construction, and as a result the whole skeletal structure is buried and invisible within the building, where it creates inconvenient obstructions and enforces a harsh rigidity on the plan. But look at our bridges—their lightness and dynamic vitality, with all their structure clearly revealed and their stresses and strains evident to the eye. Here is a prototype of external structure which foreshadows a more rational use of steel in our buildings. When building codes no longer need to deal with fire hazards, when non-oxidizable, high-tensile-strength steels are less expensive,[1] we shall put our structural supports outside our weather-screens and suspend our light and airy structures from overhead trusses. The esthetic advance of such a method of building we shall discuss when we consider the values of rhythmic and expressive line, but we should emphasize here the importance of such an adaptation of form to the properties and values of the materials used. Most steel supports are still used in compression because masonry cannot be used otherwise and wood cannot easily be framed in tension, but the tensile strength of steel is its distinctive virtue and gives it an adaptability

[1] This may come about not only through lowered cost of the formula and processes with increasing use, but also through the greater tensile strength of non-corrosive steels. These demand less tonnage than equivalent tensile requirements in carbon steels.

no other building material possesses. The logical line of development in steel building is toward a greater utilization of steel's tensile properties.

In the furnishing of our houses, it was inevitable that our early machine-made furniture should attempt to repeat the success of the skilled cabinet-maker and carver—and repeat it very badly. As machine production grew into mass production, the urge to simplify operations and so reduce costs resulted not in the elimination of superfluities but in lowering the quality of workmanship. Most of us have painful childhood memories of those startling concoctions of pressed "carving," jig-saw work and glue which were produced in the eighties and nineties as bedroom and dining room "suits"—the absolute low-water mark of American taste. The Grand Rapids type of product has gained in finesse since that time, and slowly in fundamental honesty and simplicity.

Gradually there has emerged a realization that wood itself is a beautiful substance, in its virgin purity, unravished and untormented. With the world-wide exchange of products characteristic of these times—at least in years of peace—the number of beautiful woods available to the manufacturer has greatly increased, and this in itself has stimulated our appreciation of the material's possibilities. As a result, there is a growing realization that the perfectly simple, undecorated, geometrically controlled forms most practicable and economical in machine production are also well calculated to bring out the native beauty of any wood. As a result of this trend we have seen magnificent walls of matched Macassar ebony or rift oak or holly, with no break whatever in the expanse of their polished surfaces and glowing with a subdued richness of natural pattern and color on which any sort of decorative irregularity would have been an impertinent intrusion. At the other end of the economic scale we have seen inexpensive furniture built in simple, graceful forms with no adornment

77

whatever, and only a treatment of thin shellac to preserve the original quality of the wood, composing in its ensemble a gracious and highly civilized setting for life as we lead it today.

In the same field, it became evident in the last century that furniture in mass production could be made very economically of metal. The tyranny of familiar forms was so great, however, that it occurred to no one that metal furniture could do any more than imitate wooden furniture. Exactly the same shapes were stamped out of sheet steel or cast in iron or aluminum. Even the same type of post and panel construction was faithfully imitated, though the actual assembly of parts might be according to an entirely different system. These metal products finally were painted and grained to simulate the exact appearance of wood, often so accurately that they were a rude shock to the sense of touch. So long as metal furniture was made thus it could have nothing more in its favor than a shamefaced economy—not an honest, thrifty economy but the kind of apologetic penny-saving which tries to pass unnoticed.

In recent years we have discovered that we can make metal furniture frankly as such, with no disguises or reservations, provided we design it in entirely new forms and use the material in ways natural to itself rather than to wood. And this furniture says clearly, "I am what I am; I cost as much as I should cost and there is no need to compare me with anything else; I have sparkle, grace, charm, lightness, comfort, durability. If these are enough for you, all right; if you want other virtues, try something else." This forthright attitude has won its way in the world with a success that should be a lesson to manufacturers and designers. It is a right and intelligent use of material, leaving wood exactly where it was before, with all its great beauty and appeal, but proving that metal also has a definite field of service in furniture.

78

Our fumbling progress toward rational forms in furniture, where there are thousands of years of experience with both materials and functions to guide us, and only our processes are new, is indicative of the labor pains we have suffered in the fields of design where functions, materials and processes are all unfamiliar. Chemists, physicists, metallurgists and engineer-inventors are the most powerful influences in modern industry—more important than either capital or labor, since they could continue to produce without the aid of capital or labor, and these would be helpless without the scientists. Their most important work is done in the field of new and improved materials, and they lay a very heavy burden on the designer, who cannot specialize but must keep in touch with all their achievements. From them come the materials most characteristic of our times—new materials for which the designer must find the right forms and the right applications. To them we owe our light-weight metals—aluminum and magnesia alloys; our non-corrosive metals and finishes—stainless steels, chrome and cadmium plate and the anodizing of aluminum; safety glass and many forms of structural glass; the whole wide field of plastics derived from cotton and wood fibers, resin, soya beans, milk and many other surprising sources, plastics that can be molded into almost any form, pressed or laminated into sheets and extruded as rods and tubes; the quick-drying lacquers which are superior in beauty and durability to any preservative finishes known heretofore and which can be applied in a tiny fraction of the time formerly required for a satisfactory paint job; the wide range of fine textiles developed by chemical processes from cotton and wood fibers and now from glass and coal; numerous highly effective insulating and sound absorbent materials; improved light sources, especially the "cool lights" employing as luminous media various fluorescent gases; a whole catalogue of compositions supplied in large sheets for wall sheathing, both inside and out, and compositions provided in various forms for floor and wall coverings, all having desirable properties for certain applications.

To use these materials successfully the designer must become so familiar with them that he gets the feel of them, knows their peculiarities, virtues and limitations. This is no easy task when the research men are producing so rapidly that a man's time is pretty well occupied in keeping up a speaking acquaintance with their achievements.

Yet each new design problem today requires a special material study, made with a conscious effort to select the best substance for the purpose and to get at the true nature of that substance. This material may be indicated by custom or necessity, or it may require a fresh selection. In any case it must be tested against the functional requirements it must satisfy, and the method of working it if that is predetermined. In these days such a study very often results in a discovery that the material traditionally used for a specific purpose is not the best now available. We find instances where a molding compound may be more economical or more adaptable than metal or wood, where a light-weight die casting may offer advantages over sheet metal or a machined part, or where a non-tarnishing metal may be available to replace one that requires constant care to prevent corrosion.

Often to get at the true nature of a substance it must be disentangled from the disguise in which it comes to us. Our constitutional weakness has caused a surprising number of the most valuable achievements of the scientific researchers to be presented to us as cheap substitutes for some familiar but more expensive material. Most plastics, those ubiquitous, versatile and indispensable aids to modern life, were originally promoted as simulacra of wood, marble, mother-of-pearl and ivory. They were not very satisfactory imitations. They never deceived the knowing, and the only success of this effort at confusion was to obscure for a time the special qualities and possibilities of their true character, not possessed by wood, ivory, marble or any of the older materials. Intelligent designers are extricating plastics from pretense and giving them an honest status. There is no need to apologize for a material that can be molded in the most difficult forms, is hard, durable, colorful, light, pleasant to the touch and relatively inexpensive. The designer's problem is only to understand his plastics and use them intelligently: he must know where the slight inevitable tendency of molded plastics to shrink and warp can be tolerated and where it cannot (although it is probable that the busy chemists in time will remove even this limitation). But chiefly he must know how to mold his material in forms which will bring out its sparkle and color and arouse pleasant tactile sensations in the beholder. Properly understood and applied, plastics may crowd wood and metal out of many more fields of use—in furniture, appliances, utensils, the interior finishes of buildings— not as an imitation of better stuff but as the better and cheaper stuff itself.

Plastics have made "safety-glass" possible, and now there are plastics that are even more transparent than glass and at the same time are tough, flexible and non-breakable under ordinary shocks. They are not as hardsurfaced as glass, but again the chemists are working to remove this disadvantage and probably will succeed. With safety-glass and transparent plastics the designer can bring the beauties of transparency, brilliancy and light into places where until now it has been excluded. We are finding that glass doors need not have frames, that chair seats of Lucite do not get hot in the hottest sun because heat rays pass unabsorbed through the plastic. These are indications of the expanding freedom of the designer—

freedom from almost every restriction but the appropriate use of his material.

Transparency suggests light, and light today is one of the designer's materials as much as plastics, glass and steel. By making his walls of clear glass, he can use daylight in his interiors to any desired proportion, or by making them of glass blocks he can have privacy and insulation where they are needed. He can use electric light with extraordinary subtlety and variety, since it has dawned on us that we need not isolate our light source from inflammable materials. For years after their invention our electric lights were placed on hanging chandeliers or in sconces just as we had placed candles and gas, but there has been such a reaction from this custom that we are now in danger of forgetting that the light source may itself be beautiful and need not always be concealed. Similarly we need to remember that shadows are beautiful and give added value to light, both in our rooms and in the open night. The exterior night-lighting of our buildings will gain enormously in effectiveness as we apply this knowledge, use light as accents and refrain from wiping out the architectural form with flood-lights.

The designer's work in materials has only begun when he has selected the material most suitable for a specific use. He has to extricate it from any masquerades in which it may come to him and study to obtain the maximum effect from its individual qualities. Then he still must consider the forms in which he will shape it, with reference to the processes by which it will be fabricated. This is just as true of the materials which have been in use for countless centuries as of the latest invention, since our processes are either wholly new or have not yet been studied with sufficient thoroughness. The tool leaves its mark on whatever it touches, and this applies to our enormous complex tools of today as it did to the carver's chisel. The tool—any tool—can do certain things very well with certain materials, but to force it to do anything else is to produce a sorry result. We shall not be able to put our environment in order until we learn not only how to make the best possible use of our material resources, but also how to use our tools to fabricate these materials in the most useful and satisfying forms.

CHAPTER SIX: FITNESS TO TECHNIQUES

*"In the labor of engines and trades, and the labor of fields, I find the develop-
    ments,
And find the eternal meanings."*   —WALT WHITMAN

An aged and masterly shipwright once showed me his proudest possession, a plane made by himself some forty years before of a piece of name-
less wood he had obtained on a voyage to Cuba. The wood was beautifully
grained, of a rich rose color with a tone of amber underneath. Years of
handling had softened its lines and smoothed its surfaces until it had the
feel of amber as well, and instinctively one's palm passed over it in prolonged caresses.

A good craftsman often made his own tools, used them for years, and
knew them and loved them as if they were a part of himself. His tools
were in fact extensions of his own hands, and it was necessary that he
should know subconsciously exactly what each slightest manipulation of
them would accomplish. In themselves they had no exactitude; they would
never approximate the same effect twice unless the skill of his hands held
them to the mark. Try as he would, there was always an element of slight
variation in his work. He strove incessantly for an ideal precision which
he was never able to achieve, and in that effort's never quite attaining its
goal lay the endless charm of his work.

This ideal, unattainable by the craftsman, became the basic condition of machine production: precision is the essential characteristic of machine operations, exact repetition is the machine's reason for being. Now the value of an ideal, *as an ideal*, lies in its elusiveness: so long as it remains safely beyond our reach it retains its directional power and may successfully polarize all activities that are within its sphere. But the instant it is completely conquered and becomes a familiar possession, even an unavoidable condition, the whole aspect of the problem changes. A new set of values comes into existence. With this achieved ideal as a starting point, a necessary limitation if you will, we are compelled to direct our efforts toward the new ideal which has become visible from our new position. We are forced to strive for a new set of qualities in our work.

The quality of precision in machine operations has had more effect on the character of modern design than any other one factor. Our unprecedented inventions have demanded new functional forms, our widened choice of materials has had its own influence on these forms, but the actual quality of line and shape and surface, the range of permissible elaborations in design, have been determined most directly and most drastically by the exactitude of the machine's processes. To it can be traced our new primitivism, our devotion to utmost simplification, our abandonment of historical ornament, our application of mathematical formulas to design, our reliance for beauty on the adjustment of geometrical relationships. It has made it not only possible but necessary for us to erect a new ideal toward which our efforts can be directed, and it has therefore brought into existence a new and authentic kind of rightness of which we are the exponents.

It has taken a long time for us to comprehend this truth and allow it to have its way with us; a long time measured by human lives, but in the history of art not really so very long. A century and a half is not an excessive period for this slow-moving race of ours to extricate itself from hundreds of centuries of tradition, and form basically different habits of thinking and working. We have had to abandon our custom of "deviating into novelty through unintentional modifications" and hasten the birth of new forms by conscious effort and often painfully rational analysis. This sort of experience is always accompanied by growing pains, a kind of adolescent upheaval marked by conflict and heartburnings. Hence the battle of schools and the rash of "Secessions" and "Independents" which have kept the world of art overheated during the past century, while objectives suited to our way of working and our habit of thought were slowly being defined. These objectives have by now emerged with sufficient distinctness to be described with a considerable degree of accuracy and accepted with confidence. As a result, a style peculiar to these times is spreading a new harmony throughout our work, and at the same time spreading traps for the unperceiving who mistake its superficial characteristics for its essential character.

Machine production, as we have said, was regarded at first and for a long time only as a means of doing more rapidly and more cheaply exactly what had previously been done by hand. There was no thought of new designs for machine-made products except in so far as it was found absolutely impossible to duplicate handwork. An enormous amount of ingenuity was spent on this problem of exact reproduction, devising machine operations to produce effects which had no functional value and were only desired because they were customary. If all the processes of imitating this or that were extracted from our industrial activities even today, their volume would be appreciably diminished; for we are still very largely obsessed by this idea of cheap substitution and find it exceedingly difficult to think of a new thing except in terms of something older and similar.

It is not surprising that our grandfathers in design, suddenly finding themselves possessed of machine tools, found this feat of disassociation quite beyond them.

Instead of devising a new kind of chair for machine production, for instance, they found it easier to build a machine which would turn out a Louis XV chair leg with ogee curve and modeled surface complete (even twelve such legs at one time); another which could carve or press a passable semblance of the carved garlands with which the original chair-back was adorned; another which would weave a recognizable imitation of the tapestry with which it was covered. And they made all this effort without asking themselves whether it was worth while to go on making rather poor Louis XV chairs now that that morose monarch had been so long in his grave.

The Nineteenth Century was the "heir of the ages" to an unprecedented and lamentable degree. It developed an archaeological habit of thought and a mass of archaeological knowledge such as had never been known before. No other age had ever had equal facilities for studying the past. Lithography, photography, half-tone and four-color-process reproduction made it possible to compress the art of the world almost into a five-foot shelf. But the shelf didn't end at five feet, nor at fifty: it expanded into vast libraries and enlisted in its service an army of patient ant-like workers busily piling little antiquarian fact on little antiquarian fact to make a prodigious dust heap. Out of this great accumulation of knowledge the designers and producers of the world plucked this and that random precedent and set machines to work reproducing them. Even the layman acquired a glib familiarity with styles and periods and prided himself on his facility in allocating any given product to its proper antique source.

The habit of collecting and the great growth of public and private museums gave a dignified sanction to this practice of looking backwards. Collections and museums are not strictly a modern phenomenon, but they have had their greatest development in our day, and while they may for a time have confused our practice, they will perform their greatest service to the future. The intense interest of the Nineteenth and Twentieth Centuries in the arts and crafts of the past is unquestionably due to our awareness of a changing world. In the midst of revolution we clutch at vanishing values and seek to preserve the disappearing treasures of an ancient, dear, but dying order. The crafts exist today only as vestigial survivals serving a luxury market, and that a diminishing one. It is possible that they may vanish entirely in time, as some have already done. In the great public museums of the world, expanding always in size and number, their fruits will be preserved for the future. And as we acquire confidence and mastery of our own new crafts, and realize the continuity of artistic standards in spite of all changes in techniques or forms, we begin to appreciate the enormous service these storehouses of past achievements can render. We are learning to extract from our antiques the values that are permanent and pertinent to us, without being confused by those that were relevant only to their own time of origin.

For the emergence of our own style implies no break with the past. We have, it is true, new needs, new resources and new techniques; but in adapting our forms to these conditions we are following the precedent that all good craftsmen have set us. If we study our tools and do with them what they are capable of doing best, we shall be upholding the one tradition of craftsmanship that counts more than all others.

Since precision and exactitude are the essential characteristics of machine operations, and machines are unquestionably our tools, precision and exactitude must be the basic characteristics of our design. The waver-

ing variation, the gentle incertitude, the delicately expressive individualism which are the charm of handicrafts must be foregone; also that wide
range of decorative elaboration which was restricted only by the taste, the
patience and the manual dexterity of the craftsman. These are positive
values, delightful virtues, but they are not the only ones, and they are not
for us.

It is our destiny to explore the values latent in precision itself, and
from it as a starting point create a new ideal of mathematically exact
relationships. We can perfect the relationships within our designs to
achieve a unity beyond anything possible to the handicrafts, and approached before us by only one people in the whole course of history.

The esthetic values of exact relationships have always been known and
felt, but they have in the past been familiar to mathematicians, musicians
and physicists more than to craftsmen. A certain type of mind has always
felt the profound beauty of mathematical truth, and the relationship between mathematical and musical beauty has been movingly evident to
many. This perception was especially keen in the Greeks, who had a
mathematical sense more highly developed than any people before or
since, and it was natural that in their visual arts they should attain a
precision of relationships such as no people had reached before or would
reach again—until our time. Without machines and without a mechanical
bent of even normal proportions they achieved a "machine-like" quality
simply by their intense appreciation of the beauty of exact relationships.
Their incomparable precision originated in mathematics, and produced
in the Parthenon, for instance, a masterpiece of idealized mechanics; our
precision has had its origin in mechanics and will flower, unquestionably,
in an art of idealized mathematics.

There was a time when "machine-like" was a derogatory epithet, implying an uninspired repetition, and with the usual persistence of a habit the words are still so used. But our sensitiveness to the abstract beauty of machines has grown steadily with the progress of the machines themselves, and it is possible to use the words "machine-like" today as a term of exalted praise. We are all machinists today of one sort or another: machines are becoming more and more the constant furniture of our daily lives, and our boys are growing up in an intimacy with motors and their ways as close as a farm boy's familiarity with the cattle of his barnyard. The character of machine operations has come to represent an ideal of ultimate efficiency; and the geometry of the machines themselves has gotten into our minds and into our eyes and affected all our preferences and tastes. It is becoming easy for us to appreciate the fitness of those things which machines do most naturally, and to welcome in the products of modern industry the unique values of the machines themselves from which these products issue. We are growing not only content but enthusiastic in our acceptance of stark functional simplicity; we are not only ceasing to hanker after the elaborate gracilities of other days but are actually resenting them as fussy intrusions when—as they too often do—they still appear in our products. We get a kind of athletic thrill from the stripped, hard, trim but beautifully appropriate forms in which our countless mechanical products are presenting themselves, and from the tightly integrated relationships we can create within these forms. Line, shape and surface, stripped of irrelevant complexities and reduced to the absolutely simple versions which are all that functional necessities require, can be knitted together in a rhythmic unity thrilling in its perfection. These achievements in unity are coming to have an inspiring significance for us—a kind of material counterpart of the spiritual simplifications which have so deeply moved more religious ages than ours. We are deriving a profound emotional stimulus from these ultimate realities in our design.

When not long ago a collection of machine parts such as ball bearings, cams, coil springs and cylinder blocks were mounted on pedestals in the ecclesiastical atmosphere of a museum, the public's response to the abstract beauty of their forms was not so much the result of an unexpected revelation as of a delayed recognition. It was as if the people who crowded to see them said, "Unconsciously we have always known these things were beautiful; now we are delighted to see them in their proper setting and have their quality made clear to us."

But it is not only in these mechanical embodiments that pure simplicity conditioned by necessity has stirred our enthusiasm. From them it has passed over into all our machine-made goods and we find ourselves responding to exact relationships alone, uncomfortable in the presence of any vagueness, any lack of distinctness in the organization of the things we make. We are recovering the Greeks' power to appreciate the pure beauty of our materialized Euclidean theorems.

We have rediscovered the moving power of a straight line and an exact angle; the meeting of planes is again dynamic; a curve acquires value if it is a definite arc or parabola; the relationship of visual forms and lines reveals the harmonic possibilities of musical chords; and above all we require that these things should derive their sanction from something more necessitous than a designer's fancy.

The designer today will never acquire the intimacy with his tools that the shipwright gained from forty years' handling of his home-made plane. Machines are multiple, complex, remote; other hands than ours will control them and we may never once perform any of those operations we decree. But we can concentrate our study on the character of the operation, and familiarize ourselves with that as our actual tool. The basic operations in machine production are not too many or too complex to be thoroughly mastered in so far as they affect our forms. We can learn the limitations and the scope of die stamping, of die and sand casting, of the various types of riveting and welding, of the various types of the machining of metals, of plating and lacquering and other methods of preserving metals against change and deterioration; and we can go on to the techniques of plastic molding, of woodworking, of glass blowing and textile weaving. An alert mind stimulated by a real interest finds it increasingly easy to assimilate the essential characteristics of machine operations and the quality of result they are fitted to produce. Provided these qualities are realized with sufficient vividness it is possible through careful planning to elicit them in the finished product. This experience in perceiving a desired quality, and in producing that quality as the end of a series of planned operations, must take, in the modern designer's equipment, the place of the craftsman's virtuosity with his tools.

It is evident that in directing machine processes the designer's work cannot be successfully disentangled from the engineer's; nor, for that matter, in achieving fitness to function and fitness to materials. Design and engineering are in fact inseparable, and where form is completely controlled by functional necessity, as in airplanes, speed boats, machine parts and other instances we have cited, there is no occasion to separate them. But unfortunately the range of possible variation compatible with reasonably efficient function is quite wide in most products. And here the designer who specializes only in design has his field of service. For the specialist engineer is burdened with the demands of an enormous technology; concerned primarily with problems of operation and of production, he can hardly be expected to master also the difficult art of evoking rightness of form. A mastery of design demands a breadth of study and

The influence of materials and techniques in the adaptation of form is illustrated in the history of steel construction. The Park Avenue Hotel (1869) was built of cast iron simulating masonry. Louis Sullivan's early skyscrapers (Guaranty Building, Buffalo, 1895) were designed in forms suggestive of the steel skeleton beneath the masonry.

33

But eclectic architects were loyal to "styles," finally concentrating on Gothic because of its verticality (Hood's Tribune Tower, Chicago, 1922); until Saarinen's design in the Tribune Tower Competition revived the approach indicated by Sullivan.

*Hood advanced swiftly in command of his medium and with John M. Howells
produced the Daily News Building in 1930 and the McGraw-Hill Building in 1931.
In the latter the importance of glass as a co-material with steel was recognized.*

Rockefeller Center displays a less stylized manner than Hood's earlier buildings, with attention to the relationship of neighboring structures prophetic of future city planning. Archi-
36 tects, Reinhard and Hofmeister; Corbett, Harrison and MacMurry; Hood and Fouilhou

Elimination of present restrictions may make it possible to reveal the steel structure of future buildings, with a great increase of vigor and interest. The United States Steel Building, New York World's Fair, was a modest forecast of this possibility.

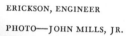

The steel skeleton of the Perisphere and Trylon (Harrison and Fouilhoux, Architects) was more beautiful than the finished forms. The wall of the entrance court, du Pont Exhibit, was arrested at this stage because the steel was too interesting to hide beneath stucco.

The pattern of rivets on a main tower of the Golden Gate Bridge, San Francisco, is extraordinarily effective, although in the future steel may be all welded without rivets.

ORVILLE LOGAN SNIDER—TRIANGLE ⟫⟫⟶

The revealed engineering of the Gothic builders and of our modern bridges
has the same high esthetic value. Chartres, and the Triborough Bridge.

40

M. H. W.

The influence of materials and techniques is illustrated in the contrasting forms of the steel piers of the Harlem River Crossing (lift bridge), Triborough System, and the reinforced concrete piers of the Kill Van Kull Bridge.

43

ALBERT KAHN, ARCHITECT   JOHN POLLINA

The plastic character of reinforced concrete, poured in
forms, has introduced a new simplicity in contemporary design. Spiral ramp of the Road of Tomorrow, Ford Exposition, New York World's Fair.

Interior of the ramp opposite. This elevated roadway is
prophetic of much highway construction of the future. Designed by the author, with Charles Colby and Russell Kil-
burn as associates.

44

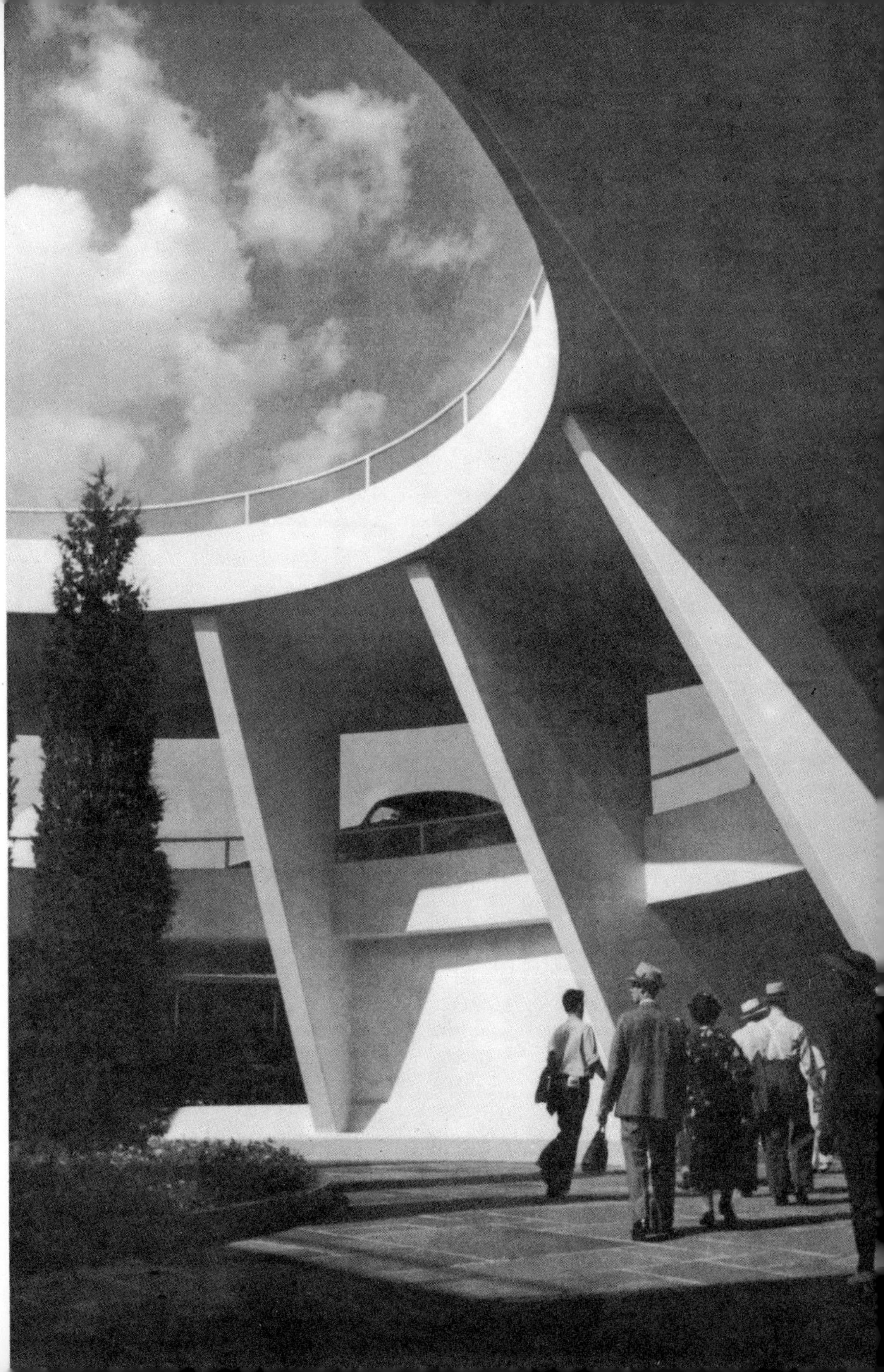

HENRY REID

EUGENE GERBEREUX, ARCHITECT

PHOTO—WURTS BROS.

Glass as a factor determining form. Above, plate glass wall of Hall of Light, Kodak Exhibit. Glass block wall of Entrance Hall, Ford Exposition, New York World's Fair. Opposite, light as a factor in design. Garden Court, Ford Exhibit, San Diego, 1935. Author's designs.

ALBERT KAHN, ARCHITECT

PHOTO—JOHN MILLS, JR.

47

48

Today the designer's repertoire of materials is greatly enlarged over his predecessors'. Chair of aluminum and transparent Lucite. Wall and doors of unframed Herculite glass, table of plate glass, in Executive Lounge, Ford Exposition. Author's designs.

STUDLEY   DAMORA

experience in many fields not usually familiar to the technological expert. This mastery of design is the equipment which the designer brings to his partnership with the engineer, and a partnership it must always be, sincere and whole-hearted.

Good design, like most products of this machine age, is the result of group activity. The engineer in this group is responsible for the performance and the manufacture of a product. The designer therefore must draw constantly on the engineer's technical knowledge, not only that functional requirements may be fully met, but that he may discover in all their details the factors which will determine and give significance to his form. The engineer is the designer's reservoir of knowledge, his guide and mentor.

The designer on his part holds engineering to its proper course, steering it away from irrelevancies and digressions, evoking the form which is a satisfying revelation of the product's function, its materials, and the techniques by which it is made. It is his business to perfect those adjustments between elements which produce coherence, so that the product issues from all the multitudinous sources contributing to its creation not as an assemblage of parts but as an organic unity.

This partnership between engineering and design is spreading its control over an ever-widening proportion of modern activity. Its technique is being perfected through practice, and where it was first consciously applied, a few years ago, to some of the minor but more popular output of machine production, it is now being exercised even on the machines themselves, to improve their organization and their efficiency. From early successes with small-scale wares it has gone on to larger and more important undertakings, until there is almost nothing in the reconstruction of our environment that now would be considered outside its scope. It

93

is, of course, the inevitable solution to the problem of controlling our gigantic Machine Age equipment so that it will serve the ends of order and human well-being. In no other way, except by this union of diverse talents, can we get from our machines the fair and beneficent world they are physically quite capable of building. One talent, expert in machine technologies, insures the efficient operation of the machines themselves and the functional value of what they create; the other, also familiar with machine technologies but preserving always the viewpoint of the people whose needs the machines must serve, controls and molds the output so that it is exactly adapted to its end and becomes an effective part of the harmonious world we need to build.

This partnership between engineering and design has acquired a genuine mastery over its tools, as we have said, a mastery of this incredibly complex mechanism of Machine Age production comparable to the craftsman's control of his simple hand-tools. Our machines can be directed with the utmost accuracy and delicacy to produce almost any predetermined result: there is almost no limit to the quality, efficiency, and ingenuity of the work they are capable of doing. They place no bounds to our creative activity: the exact rightness of the things we do will be conditioned only by our ability to envision it and give it definite form in our plans and blueprints. Any fault in their production is no fault of the machines: it is due to our own failure to know, and foresee, and definitely visualize the results they should be getting for us.

In quantity as well as in quality, the machines are capable of meeting our demands. They have effected an extension of mankind's capacity to do work, to a degree that has an awesome approximation to a divine "Fiat lux." We have multiplied our productive powers to the point where the rebuilding of our entire environment to fit the needs of decent human living is delayed only by our own wills, not by our ability to do the job.

I do not mean that we have the equipment ready and waiting: our entire existing productive capacity is inadequate, as the Brookings Institution has shown, to supply all our people with even the minimum quantity of goods required to raise life to a level of decent comfort.[1] And hence the shame that any of our wheels should not be turning, that our production should be restricted and our men idle, while millions are underfed and underclothed and poorly housed even by standards that make no allowance for any of the graces and richness all life should possess. But we have the knowledge and the facilities and the resources to expand our equipment, and to undertake whatever constructive enterprise we definitely plan, and decide to be desirable. Our productive capacity is incomparably greater than the race ever possessed before, and would be inconceivable except for that extension of our own individual human powers we call machinery.

To do an adequate job of world-building would require a great increase in the mechanical equipment we now possess, but an increase entirely feasible; it would require also an increase in human activity that would leave no room for idleness or unemployment. And even all the work we can do would need to be supplemented by a much greater mechanization of operations and an extension of automatic controls, beyond anything yet seen. To produce five or ten times the quantity of goods we now produce will be no child's play, no mere matter of pressing buttons and throwing switches, however much the buttons and switches are multiplied. To raise the general living standard to the level demanded by

[1] This is a book on design, and not on economics; but when a statement such as the above is made, and especially when it is made by a designer, it should be substantiated without delay. Since its truth is basic to our contention that environmental reconstruction should engage our efforts and would solve our ills, the reader is referred to Appendix B for verification.

human dignity will require the concentrated efforts of the whole race. It will, however, accelerate the tendency already strong in industry to shift the proportions of mental and manual labor; brains and skill will steadily advance in importance, as they are already doing, and mere muscular effort will diminish relatively, as it is replaced by mechanical devices for lifting and pushing and carrying. To design and build and operate the equipment of a completely mechanized world will absorb the labor of a vast army of scientists, investigators, engineers and designers. This army is already being recruited; each year sees it expanding in numbers and consolidating its influence in the industrial scene. It is gradually and quietly going into action on the side of environmental reconstruction even while the air is filled with the battle cries of frantic ideologies.

Ideologies are the distractions and the obstructions that delay constructive advance. No ideological solution of our racial problems, so far devised, has in it more than one or two reasonable premises in a great proliferation of futilities; none certainly has even a small portion of adequacy as a chart of future advance, and most are fantastically evil in their potentialities. No merchant of words will ever succeed in planning a world fit for human living; not even men actually busy at the task can see the way for more than a short distance ahead. It will be done by men who painstakingly deal with the immediate and evident tasks, extending the rule of order a little further, in confidence that by this success the direction of a still further advance will be revealed. Each triumph of order extends our vision and clarifies our objectives a little more. We suspect we are beginning to know what kind of towns we want to build, how we want to be housed and what arrangements we want to make for working and playing. The lines are vague and certainly not final, but we believe the course of advance we are following will ultimately lead to a clear and precise conception of what we want to make of our world. Once that conception is present, the obstacles to realizing it in concrete reality will have vanished with the mists.

We think we are defining it more sharply as we study our needs and our tools and our materials, and acquire skill in using the means at hand to augment the proportion of smoothly functioning, serviceable order around us. Our building of superb planes and highways and domestic equipment, our experiments in housing and town planning and the correlation of industrial work with pleasant living, all our work in laboratories and experimental shops and design studios, are not only immediately productive, but are also effective as a training course. We learn how to build well by building well, we define our functional needs with greater accuracy, we explore the possibilities of our material resources, and we acquire skill in using our mechanical equipment to obtain the results we want.

At the same time we explore the possibilities of that exact unity which machine precision establishes as the ideal end of our creative efforts. One thing we are confident we know about this world we hope to build, and that is that it will be free of the confusions, wastes and frustrations we can see all around us today. In its small and great elements, and in its dominating scheme, we believe it will have a serene harmony and a smoothly functioning unobtrusive organization which will give the individual full scope to exercise whatever capacity for enjoyment of life and for fruitful activity he possesses. It will have the perfect integration of parts we see today in some of our products and that machine production makes possible in all of them.

CHAPTER SEVEN: UNITY

"Every part is disposed to unite with the whole, that it may thereby escape from its own incompleteness." —LEONARDO DA VINCI

Every living organism is a kind of world of its own, moving among other little worlds similarly demarked and isolated, as a planet moves among its fellows in space. There is an inward-turning character in any living thing, relating all its parts to each other and to its own life impulse in an attitude of defense against all the rest of the universe. It is set apart in its own identity, and the preservation of its existence has forced upon its complex scheme a "one for all and all for one" subordination that is very nearly absolute. Complex it is, regardless of its size or place in our human scale of values: if it has any sentient life at all it is almost inconceivably complex. Yet the nature of life itself compels unity in this complexity. Unity is a condition of identity and of existence, unity obvious even to our crude vision; so obvious that we recognize its necessity instinctively and perceive any flaw in it as a disturbance of a fixed scheme. The tearing of a flower's petal or the misplacement of a bird's feather, or any loss or maiming or malformation of a part, is felt immediately as a fault in a coherent design. And when we pursue the organization of a living thing down from such evident levels through its microscopic structure we find the same coherence prevailing until the limits of our perception are reached.

The nature of life demands unity for its own vital ends, and art similarly demands unity as a condition of vitality and identity in its works. The instinct of the craftsman has always made this clear to him. He has sought coherence in his designs since he first began to make things and long before he analyzed its nature: without unity the product of his work was unfinished and inept and gave him no satisfaction. There must be in his design the same inevitability we find in the design of a living thing, the same acceptable order, so that a misplaced or intrusive part, a disproportion or a broken line, is uncomfortably evident. This happy state of coherence wherein all the parts of his creation are bound together in a whole is the goal he seeks in his efforts to achieve complete fitness to functions, materials and techniques, and it is the sign that he has attained that goal.

The reason there can be no finality in design without unity is to be found—as are the reasons for all our basic laws of design—in the structure and limitations of our perceiving minds as they attempt to hold their own in a difficult universe. The world presents an enormous number of objects to our attention at any one time, but our attention is capable of dealing with them only one by one or in comprehensible groups. All of us in this sense have single-track minds. We cannot listen to two pieces of music at once, or two conversations. If we think we do, it is only because we shift our attention with great rapidity from one to the other. We have all experienced the fatigue of this kind of nervous effort. Most of us too have played a parlor game in which a number of unrelated objects are displayed for a short time on a tray—a spoon, inkwell, champagne cork, key, match, coin, pencil, and so on to the number of two dozen or so—and the players are then asked to list as many as they can remember. Because of the complete lack of relationship between the objects, most memories

99

are incapable of retaining more than a fraction of the total. The excessive fatigue which visitors carry away as their strongest impression of museums and world's fairs is due, similarly, to the great number of unrelated objects offered to their interest and the incessant shifting of their attention across chasms of disconnection. The only thing that makes such experiences endurable at all is that some degree of classification has been effected in these exhibits, and the more skillful this classification the easier for us. Even so, the experienced museum visitor gives his attention to only one class of objects per visit.

Where conflicting claims are made on our attention we instinctively look for relationships, we attempt to make our own groupings, in order to ease the strain upon our nervous system by reducing the number of reactions or attitudes required of it. The keen mind, the "quick thinker," confronted by complexity, will be most adept in sorting and arranging his impressions and so dealing with them successfully, while the nervously unstable may be thrown into a state of helpless exasperation often highly uncomfortable both to him and those about him. Both minds, the quick and the slow, will be conscious of an effort and some degree of fatigue.

When a great many objects of the *same* kind are presented to our attention we follow a similar course and endeavor to relate them in patterns so that we can perceive as many as possible at one time and with a minimum of effort. If we can discover these patterns we feel a certain pleasure, partly a sense of relief and partly that satisfaction which recognition and mastery always give us. It has often been pointed out that we grouped the stars in constellations to satisfy this urge, and most of us are still thrilled on a starry night by our recognition, among the uncountable myriads, of Ursus Major and Minor, or the immense figure of Orion with his scabbard at his belt. I recall the pleasure I felt when as a youth I was painting fields

100

dotted with shocks of wheat set up at random, and discovered for myself that these haphazard shocks always arranged themselves in a kind of unsymmetrical pattern.

When identical objects are arranged in a fixed pattern, such as spots on wall paper, we immediately, if we see them at all, group them in sub-patterns. We see them as forming vertical or horizontal or diagonal lines, we see them maneuvering as squares or diamonds or crosses, and these perhaps grouping themselves into larger squares and diamonds and crosses. Skillful designers of repeat patterns deliberately assist us to make these combinations. The builders of early skyscrapers gave us no aid in this process of simplification and punctured their walls with hundreds of windows equally spaced. A wiser generation tied windows together in vertical or horizontal bands with noticeable relief. Skillful designers have always been considerate of our limitations in this respect and attempted to group their details in manageable combinations. They have been aware both that we derived pleasure from the recognition of these relationships, and that the number of units we could assimilate without effort in a single act of perception is strictly limited. Hence the penchant of architects of all ages for groupings of three and five—windows or courses or decorative details—and the combining of these again into larger groups of three and five.

If proof is needed that this practice is sound psychologically, it has been supplied by careful experiment, and Prof. Langfeld's summary of his findings confirms what designers' instincts have always taught them:

"Some of the earliest experiments in the psychological laboratory were devised so as to discover how many dots can be clearly perceived if they have no relation to one another other than the fact that they are visual stimuli of the same quality. Each dot was equally distant from its neighbor. It was found that one can perceive five or six such objects if they are exposed to the eye for only a fraction of a second, and that all beyond this number are not observed. The same was found for letters and numbers when arranged in meaningless order. They could be individually recognized up to six at the outside limit, with individual variations. That is, a nervous pattern can be formed and sufficiently integrated for five or six isolated units so that a single response can include this number of units simultaneously. When a series of similar dots, equally spaced, is exposed to the observer for a longer period of time, the mind has a tendency to arrange them into groups, but of not over six units each. There will be a certain quality in the awareness of these groups, a quality of form which makes one feel that the individual elements of the group belong together; and generally it will be observed that the spatial distance between groups seems to be greater than between individual units of the same group, although the objective distance was the same. When thus grouped many more units can be perceived, for each group is then perceived as a unit of a higher order. But again, these higher units cannot exceed six, and there is a limit to the formation of successively higher and more complicated unifications, which depends to some extent upon the experience and training of the individual. This psychological law, which is termed 'the span of perception' is applicable to all qualities of sensation. One can perceive and distinguish separately five or six sounds without counting or grouping them, such as the striking of the clock. Any number over that we break into groups, as for example, seven strokes into groups of four and three. In fact, in audition there is a strong tendency to subdivide even three or four units into groups. It is seldom ,that we can hear a short series of sounds without breaking it up into long and short groups with varying degrees of accent. The fact that the ear tends to group sounds and cannot hold more than six has been of fundamental importance in the development of music. . . . The same law obtains in touch, and is one of the reasons why the Braille System for the blind is based upon various arrangements of six raised points, which are felt by the fingers. Since not more than six points are used for one letter, each letter can be felt as a unit. This feature makes the system simpler for the user." [1]

While it is undoubtedly true that our perception will stretch to include six units at a time, designers have preferred with a right instinct to deal in threes and fives and even sevens because these odd numbers provide a balanced grouping in relation to a central axis, thereby assisting our recognition of their order.

This evidence of our method of dealing with multiple claims on our attention indicates a constitutional limitation of our minds, or, to put it more accurately, it reveals the technique to which our minds, as tools, are adapted. Here is the source of that urgent need to organize some kind of perceptible order in whatever we make and among all the things around us; it accounts for the necessity we feel to organize the complex things we make into an obvious unity, and to relate these things to larger unities, until our minds can find their way step by step, with ease and satisfaction, through the multitude of claims upon their attention. Confusion means frustration, defeat, exasperation; we wear ourselves out in attempting to find relationships and classifications which do not exist, and we escape from the resulting distress only by shutting our eyes to what they cannot perceive with satisfaction, and relaxing into disgust and apathy.

The disorder of the Industrial Revolution was more than we could

[1] *The Aesthetic Attitude*, by Herbert Sidney Langfeld, Harcourt, Brace and Company, page 161.

deal with, and we were forced into an attitude of callous indifference as an alternative to a complete nervous breakdown: in spite of all our efforts at defense, the nervous strain on the race has been terrific and has resulted in as handsome a crop of neuroses and mental and physical maladies as the world has ever seen. It is logical that our first attempts to create a new order to replace the old and vanished order should be directed toward manageable units of our reconstructed environment: the characteristic products of our Machine Age technologies, which are complex enough in all conscience but not too big and unwieldy to be dealt with successfully if we put our minds to it. By careful study and a measure of inspiration we can succeed in integrating the parts of these things into a unified scheme that can be grasped as a whole. There is relief and satisfaction in this, and the experience gives us confidence and trains our skill to attack the larger problems of organization in which these things must be related to one another and to our vital needs.

The training is not entirely inadequate, because even the task of creating unity in individual units is not simple. Most of the things we make are unavoidably complex, and many approach the complexity of a living organism. A chair has dozens of parts, and dozens of operations are required for its making. There are more than fifteen thousand separate parts in a Ford car, and several times as many distinct operations are needed to produce and assemble them. But no matter how complicated our products may be, our desire is that when assembled they shall convey an impression of coherent organization: their parts must relate themselves so closely that our minds need not deal with them as separate details, but can perceive them all at once as a body having an individuality and identity of its own. The designer in forming the mechanical products of this age aims to organize this kind of interrelationship among the diverse parts of which they are made. He must take the assemblage of castings, stampings, pipes, rods, gears, controlling instruments and what not which the engineers have found necessary for a machine's operation, and bind them together so closely that the resulting body can be dealt with in attention not as so many assembled parts, but as one functioning organism.

This unity we seek has many phases, and we instinctively demand that all be present even though we may not consciously define them. Without always knowing why, we are pleased by their presence and dissatisfied by their absence. In many different ways we seek to achieve our aim. The fitting of form to function is one of the basic requirements without which unity cannot exist, and we demand the unity of appropriateness between our forms and the materials of which they are made; while a perception of rightness in the way techniques have been applied to the production of these forms from these materials creates unity among all three.

But beyond these basic demands we require that the separate physical parts of a thing be bound together into one whole, as arms and legs and head and torso are seen to be controlled by their relationship to the whole human being, composing its identity. To achieve this kind of unity in anything we make, we play with the adjustment of its parts to each other, attempting to create felt relationships that will act as bonds between them. We seek symmetry and balance among them, accenting some and suppressing others; reducing their apparent number by simplification, and creating resemblances of form between those that must remain distinct; we draw their lines so that they flow into one another as the lines of the human body are blended, and we adjust our colors by repetition, balance, accent and contrast as we have adjusted our forms; and most subtly of all we strive to create the binding force of rhythmic relationships between the proportions of our masses and areas, our lines and dimensions.

During the past generation we have been able, as an object lesson, to watch this coherence of design emerging in one omnipresent factor in our environment. While we have been adapting—all too slowly—the form of an automobile to its functions, its materials and its techniques, we have been developing that form in the direction of a plastic unity which gives it the look of having been "poured in one mold." This has not been accomplished by distortion or disguises, but by creating, little by little, closer relationships between its parts: between its forms, its lines, its proportions, its functioning elements. This process has required a progressive simplification, the elimination of disturbing excrescences and non-essential elaborations, the adjustment of lines and proportions, the achievement of an asymmetrical balance, and a gradual emphasis of major elements with the suppression of less important details until the relationships necessary to its internal rhythms have been created.

The process is far from complete, and every year sees cars produced with distortions and excrescences, discordant proportions and awkward lines, faults of balance and accent; while the best designs are still far from that sleek tear-drop shape we believe will be their ultimate form—to be achieved, probably, about the time the need for building automobiles of the present type will be eliminated by the adoption of low-flying landplanes, or some such more mobile vehicle. But the improvement to date is obvious and the better cars of today make those of only ten years ago look like inexcusably haphazard collections of unrelated parts. They themselves represent a distinct contribution to the sum total of order in our world, even though we have not resolved the many disorders created by their disconcerting multiplication in numbers.

Their improvement has not been all the result of a conscious application of an intelligent design technique: it has been in large part the result of trial and error inspired by a mere unformulated sense of fitness. The wastefulness of leaving ourselves in this way to the mercies of chance and slow time has been proven throughout the whole history of Machine Age development, but we are at last aware of the greater speed of advance and reduction of waste when visual design, like engineering design, is controlled by knowledge, skill and consciously formulated principles. There is satisfaction in knowing we possess an innate sense of fitness which will compel design to evolve in the right direction even without benefit of competence, but it is far more encouraging to see the recent achievements of conscious skill in a hundred different fields—proving itself not only in cars but in highway systems and service stations and in the factories and machine tools that build the cars; in trains and towns and houses and minor features of our environment, all in vast numbers evolving with perceptible speed through simplification and coherence toward ultimate unity.

There are of course limits beyond which the process of simplification cannot safely be carried. A billiard ball or a brick have unity to an ultimate degree, just as a picket fence or an unending march-past of identical policemen have a very real order and even a certain impressiveness. But none of these things holds our attention for long: the sphere is quickly exhausted, the policemen run true to sample, and if we are compelled to contemplate them too long we grow restless and resentful. If there is one thing we hate more than excessive effort it is monotony and its resulting boredom. Boredom in fact is a kind of fatigue caused by too long continued calls for the same reaction. Our fixed and agonized smile at the dull interminable story, our anguished efforts to escape the person whose remarks can always be anticipated, are similar in mental origin to our revulsion from the long street of somber houses all alike and our rage at the man who habitually whistles the same two bars while he works. We get our pleasure from less quickly exhausted schemes: in fact our pleasure is proportioned to the number and variety and appositeness of relationships we can find within the frame of a single pattern. We demand variety within unity. Our world can never be regimented to the point of dullness, either politically or materially.

"Unity in variety, variety in unity": these twins are the Romulus and Remus of esthetic history. They are fundamental in successful design, as all craftsmen have realized even when they did not know the words. But we have so long been familiar with the formula because the Greeks not only practised a superb art of design, they also understood its psychological bases and stated them quite clearly for the guidance of later generations who were better scholars than artists. The Greeks in fact spent their enormous gifts in perfecting the unity in variety and variety in unity of a surprisingly small number of design patterns, realizing quite clearly that the attainment of perfection required an intense concentration of effort. The typical mass of a Greek temple is identical in form and very nearly identical in dimensions with many a totally uninteresting barn. As they perfected this design scheme they did not feel any need to enlarge it in scale or elaborate its basic and extremely simple form: they felt it only necessary to adjust and refine the relationships that exist between the essential elements of their pattern, until in the Parthenon they achieved a unity so complete that every detail is related in a definite mathematical scheme of proportions to all other details and to the whole. And yet this unity has inexhaustible variety because of the uncountable number of subtle and completely satisfying relationships of which it is composed, so many that no one has been able to discover them all, and each competent student reveals new ones. Thus it becomes a single fabric woven of a vast number of threads of almost imperceptible fineness.

Disunity is not only a cause of fatigue: the perception of unity is a positive pleasure, that pleasure in recognition which Aristotle realized was one of the characteristics of the human mind. We derive a keen satisfaction from perceiving meanings and meaningful relationships, and this appetite is gratified by variety in the separate elements which have been knitted into a whole. Our pleasure in fact increases in proportion to the number of relationships presented to our minds, so long as they may be dissected out of a scheme which first and last we perceive as a unity. The inevitable complexity of most of our Machine Age products thus becomes an aid as well as a challenge to the designer, because it provides him with the necessary diverse elements with which to orchestrate his composition. A Douglas transport plane presents a thrilling aspect of complete unification, an effect of vital integration of its members. There is a meaningful harmony of line and form, with a continual recurrence of the same type of parabolic curve, making its design appear to be determined by some life-force within itself—as in fact it is determined by the force of its functional necessities. Yet in spite of its superb unity there is no monotony whatever in its aspects, but lavish variety in the interplay of its lines and masses as we look at it from different points of view. As we walk around it at rest, or watch it approaching and passing overhead and receding in the sky, or—most effective of all—see it in flight from another plane at its own level, we receive a thousand different impressions, no two of them alike. In all its aspects, our dominant response is the recognition of its vigorous, powerful vitality—a triumph of variety in unity of design.

Airplanes by their nature are peculiarly and intensely thrilling to our modern spirits, and it may very well be that in such typical products of our modern art we are approaching the degree of perfection in design achieved by certain craftsmen of the past. But these craftsmen were not always building temples and cathedrals—they did utilitarian urns and ewers and armor and vehicles with the same superb skill and up to the same rigorous standards—and we are not always building planes and ocean liners and Boulder Dams. We have kitchen ranges and refrigerators, machine tools and service stations, typewriters and vacuum cleaners and thousands of other appliances to fit into our environment, and here we see the heartening triumphs of design organization producing a fine and rhythmic unity where unregulated chaos existed before. We have proven the possibility of order, serenity without monotony, in innumerable isolated objects that make up the furniture of our modern lives; now as we tentatively attack the larger problems of our communal living and the broad environmental backgrounds of our activities, we feel reasonable confidence in our ability, in time, to introduce a satisfying degree of unification into our whole disorderly and discordant scene.

In all this work, big or little, our first attack is on the enormous mass of non-essentials and superfluities in which the kernel of our problem almost always lies buried. As human beings we have a talent for the useless and the elaborate which seems to be unique in the animal kingdom. We spend vast funds of energy on overelaborations which serve no useful purpose, practical or esthetic, and almost as much on digressions that are not only unnecessary but definitely had better not be made. The first step in every one of our design problems is the separation of the essential sheep from the superfluous goats, a process we all approve in logic but find exceedingly difficult to complete in practice. We admit the value and the necessity of direct advance but we find bypaths extremely alluring.

It is difficult to adhere to a ruthless process of simplification which, discriminating between distracting and significant elements, eliminates the former and co-ordinates the latter into an essential unity. And yet there is no other method whereby the order we seek can be achieved.

CHAPTER EIGHT: SIMPLICITY

"Beauty, like truth, is never so glorious as when it goes the plainest."
—LAURENCE STERNE

There lived in England in the Fourteenth Century a monk named Occam, to whose philosophical mind occurred one of those bright ideas which make history: he formulated for the first time the basic principle that truth is not complicated beyond necessity; in other words, that no solution of a problem can be right if a simpler and more direct solution can be found. This principle has been known, for obvious reasons, as "Occam's razor," and by it centuries of scientific investigation have been shorn of avoidable complexities. The art of design also requires an Occam's razor, ruthlessly wielded, and never more so than now.

The more beyond enough, the enticing diversions which tempt every designer to go a little further than he needs to go, the weakness for adorning and enriching and thereby confusing what might otherwise be plain and clear, have always been and still are the cause of futility and waste in incredible quantities of earnest effort. For a designer to steer straight toward his proper goal, without digressions, and stop his work when he has accomplished the essential, is a feat beyond most men's self-control. But if he is incapable of this discipline, the designer will only add to the sum of confused and inept work already cluttering the world. Directness and simplicity are the basic virtues of design, without which there can be no satisfying order, and it is because these virtues are so difficult to preserve, not only in design but in all fields of human activity, that we find our world today a problem on our hands.

Fitness to function, materials and techniques, unity achieved through complete integration of elements, are incompatible with elaboration. Unnecessary embellishments, avoidable complexities, obscure the significance of forms and confuse the binding rhythms of any scheme. Today, unless we find simple and direct solutions to our problems of design we will not find any solutions at all. In the things we have to make and the work we have to do there is no place for even the attractive elaborations in which other times could, sometimes, reasonably indulge without reducing their efforts to confusion. In our work, simplicity is the essence of rightness, and this rule is enforced by the circumstances in which we live and work and which we cannot alter. We would not change these circumstances if we could, because on them—our system of machine production, our alliance of science with industry—is based our confidence that we can control our environment and rebuild it in satisfactory order. They give us our power to achieve rightness, and we are compelled to accept the conditions they lay upon our work.

Ours is a primitive art. The handicrafts, when they were superseded by machine production, had been perfected through thousands of years of painstaking cultivation, and it is probable that we stand at the beginning of an equally long period of evolution in the art of the machine. We today are exploring new territories, charting new lands and in general doing initial spade work. We have had to work our way back to first principles and remaster the abstract laws on which all arts have been based. We are living in an age of sources and origins, not of culminations. Instead of inheriting a tradition, we are initiating one. The inheritors of

113

traditions, like the heirs of rich parents, have had some of the most difficult if most instructive problems of life solved for them, and their means of livelihood has been handed to them on a silver platter. The inheritors of traditions receive the first principles of design already embodied in satisfactory forms and workable formulas, and it is only necessary for them to carry on with these in a worthy manner. But the founders of traditions are put to the labor of finding these forms and working out these formulas for themselves in terms of their own needs, materials and tools. It is pioneer work, and like all pioneering it is severe and self-denying labor productive of spartan rather than epicurean virtues. Now, when the world might expect to feel old, we find ourselves busy with this youthful task of trailbreaking.

Undoubtedly our own status as primitives is responsible for our keen sympathy with and pleasure in the primitive arts of other ages and peoples—a taste our forefathers do not seem to have shared. We are becoming constantly more aware that for our own nearest spiritual kin we must look backwards over long epochs of time, to the Eleventh and Twelfth Centuries in France and the Fourth and Fifth Centuries B.C. in Greece, when great schools of art were being securely founded, as we are founding a school of art—great also, we hope and believe.

We are especially conscious of our fellowship with the art of Greece: the "classic" quality of the best modern design is easily recognizable, partly because we are more familiar with early Greek than with most other primitive arts, and partly because the Greeks, like us, were extremely self-conscious in their practice, analyzing the abstract principles of design and formulating its mathematical laws. Their art had a quality of precision and a severe aversion to the merely ornate with which we find ourselves in active sympathy. The early Gothic builders, too, were exploring newly discovered engineering principles, just as we are doing, and embodying them in work of clear definition and great power, just as we are endeavoring to do. We have a keen understanding of the motives that inspired them and the ends they were attempting to—and so often did—achieve. But it is not only early Greek and Gothic art that interests us: we find our own preoccupations reflected in the first vigorous, inventive, exploratory phase of every great period of creative activity.

Artists in any changing civilization, confronted with new needs demanding new forms, with new tools and techniques and materials at hand, have had to make a return to first principles and proceed from there. They have had to deal first of all with abstract relationships and discover means of creating these relationships successfully in the new forms and materials, with the new tools. As a result the beauty they create is a fundamental type of beauty, deriving from the rhythms that can be composed between simple forms and areas and lines and colors. It excludes whimsey and caprice: precision and exactitude are its essence. It derives little if anything from associations or references to things past; it has no romantic glamour and no time for elaborations beyond the essential. Inevitably it is inclined to be austere rather than charming, reserved and severe rather than discursive, serene rather than vivacious. The values it seeks are universal values common to all great art and so it links itself across the ages with the arts of other primitive periods, often more closely than with its own later and usually decadent developments.

We are accustomed to call "primitive" the art of any people whose civilization we regard as decidedly lower than our own. This is not necessarily primitivism of the type we exhibit today, and the type we are discussing now. The arts of many people who live much closer to nature

115

than we do are very old, highly developed and traditional.[1] Successful formulas have long before been adopted and exploited as fully as the means at hand permit and the psychological needs of the people require, whereupon the art has become largely static. While it may be practised with great skill and vigor it often escapes for long periods of time the processes of change to which the arts of more advanced, more rapidly evolving civilizations are subject. It avoids, in fact, the decadence of elaboration and devitalization which seems inevitable in more sophisticated arts, and its more or less static formalism preserves its vitality intact. These arts of primitive people have certain characteristics, however, which relate them to our type of primitivism: they are highly formalized, and they are highly impersonal. The simple-minded savage or semi-savage has an almost unerring appreciation of formal values: he may deal with an elaborate system of ornament but it will be a stylized ornament of symbols and conventionalized forms which is as eloquent to us because of its abstract values as it ever could have been to its makers. He avoids realistic representation and personal deviations, not through incapacity, as many think, but through native discrimination.

Personality has played so large a part in western art since the height of the Renaissance that we are accustomed to think of it as an essential factor in all art. "Self-expression," "originality," "strong individuality" have been exalted for the past few centuries as high virtues, in complete disregard of the fact that the artist himself is of no consequence whatever, since any universal values there may be in his work are all that count ultimately, and are exactly the same as the universal values of all other art. During the long decadence initiated by the Renaissance, our creative

[1] Franz Boas' *Primitive Art* (Harvard, 1927) is a fascinating presentation of this developed and formalized character in the arts of savage or semi-savage peoples.

116

impulse satisfied itself with easel painting, since it could not build its work more securely into the fabric of its time. This addiction to activities that may be essentially rootless has given rise to a whole scheme of false values, and led often to an artist's merit being assessed according to the degree of his difference from other artists. Since the creative impulse of man is strong and will not be denied, some greatly satisfying comments on life and the world about us have been produced even by so detached a process. But if these works should survive a thousand years, certainly interest in the personalities which produced them will not; and they will be valued for their universal and not their individual qualities. Already the serener work of the older masters and the classic achievements of Cézanne, Van Gogh and Picasso are beginning to extricate themselves from the ruck of modern painting on just this basis.

In the arts of design, as our new problems drive us back to elemental virtues and we seek values which the artist can evoke but cannot safely distort, we find accidental impressions of the artist's personality being more and more successfully excluded from his work. The artist cannot play fast and loose with the laws of relationships any more safely than with the laws of mathematics, and if he seeks consciously to put his own trademark on his work he must inevitably sacrifice something of absolute rightness. His work tends towards anonymity, because his ideal leaves no scope for individual digressions.

Because his art is in its formative stage, he is restrained to simple forms, also, by the simplicity of his vocabulary. We have no thesaurus of accepted ornament to draw upon in the elaboration of our work. We today in fact have no ornament at all, and we, like those esthetic ancestors for whom our sympathy is keenest, can do very well without it. We have had a hard time learning that ornament cannot be arbitrarily created: it must grow with time, acquiring abstraction and symbolic value, or it cannot exist at all. A number of able men, chafing at being restricted to elemental forms, have tried to provide themselves with a scheme of ornament by sheer fiat: Wright, Claude Bragdon, even so great a man as Louis Sullivan have all tried their hands at this sort of thing with no success whatever. Sullivan could conceive his bank at Owatonna in fine simplicity and then transform its interior into a cavern hung with incredible and inexcusable stalactites. With growing discretion the modern designer is realizing that he cannot inflate forms or patterns with meaning if they have none.

Here again we probably have been led astray by the example of the Renaissance. That period, being essentially antiquarian and revivalistic, appropriated all the ornament it could find in Roman survivals, elaborated it with great ingenuity and used it with little restraint. The grace and gay insouciance of much of this work are its justification, and these it may readily be admitted are not virtues to be despised. Neither are they virtues to be mimicked successfully, and the worker today confronted by his more basic problems must achieve grace and insouciance if at all by other means than the juggling of arabesques and festoons.

It is arguable that ornament of any great degree of elaboration is inevitably a symptom of decadence. Certainly every great artistic impulse has confined its attention first of all to basic relationships, letting them tell their own story starkly and powerfully. Then, as it has grown more familiar with its method, it has found means of elaborating its rhythms by subdividing its forms and areas in ways which are functional in origin and are justifiably emphasized because of their binding power over the fabric as a whole: they serve to intensify through repetition and extension the rhythms which give the structure unity.

There is a point at which perfect balance seems to be attained in this use of elaborated rhythms, a dividing line between stark primitive austerity on the one side and decadence on the other. We find this balance perfected in the Parthenon, for instance, and in the southern tower of Chartres Cathedral. Greek design had inherited from the wooden architecture of early structures a certain vocabulary of forms which had been carried on into masonry building because of their effectiveness in the subdivision of areas, the revelation of forms and the creation of accents. Long before the Parthenon was built they had lost any imitative reminiscence and had become simple abstractions, enormously effective in skillful hands. It is true that the designer could have built his temple as a rectangular stone box with a peaked roof, and if usage demanded a porch it could have been supported on square or cylindrical shafts. Such a structure if well proportioned might have had a certain gaunt dignity. But he preferred to make use of the means that prior builders had prepared for him: he preferred to emphasize the forms of his columns by fluting them, and so setting up by means of sunlight and shadow a series of varied rhythms which made the rounded mass and upward thrust of the shafts vastly more evident than they would have been if not so accented. His moldings and metopes and triglyphs with their shadows he used to carry the major rhythms of his structure downward and inward in diminishing harmonies that are inexhaustibly satisfying, and even his sculpture served its primary purpose by varying his textures rhythmically and providing curved lines and forms to contrast with the dominant angularities of the whole.

We see here the point at which ornament is a powerful tool: we see a restrained use of significant and familiar ornament indulged only in so far as it will contribute to the unity of the whole. Beyond this point, where ornament begins to be elaborated for its own sake and valued as enrichment, degeneration begins its progressive course.

One may see in certain Norman structures of the Eleventh Century in France, such as William the Conquerer's Church of St. Stephen at Caen, the first powerful stirrings of the Gothic movement. In the nave of St. Stephen's we see a magnificent austerity that is a right expression of the men and times that produced it. But we find in the southern tower of Chartres this same great power and integrity of intent when it had fully mastered its methods and before it had relaxed any of its restraining principles. Here as in the Parthenon we see inherited forms utilized for the perfecting and extending of rhythms without any blurring of functional lines. Here is refinement that makes no detraction from strength, here is grace and subtlety and variety achieved within a scheme of perfect simplicity. "The greatest and surely the most beautiful monument of this kind that we possess in France," Henry Adams quotes from Viollet-le-Duc; ". . . where the effects are obtained, not by ornaments, but by the just and skillful proportion of the different parts." Here we have the characteristic that relates the work to the art of Phidias before, and to our courageous if not yet so successful efforts so long after.

Flanking this masterpiece at Chartres its companion tower to the north shows what happens when the impulse to elaboration has had its way and a period of art draws near its end. This northern spire was built four hundred years later than the other, after Gothic design had become a kind of necromancy producing that "lacework in stone" so much admired by many amateurs of architecture. In its bewildering complexity it does not lack a feminine kind of grace and charm, but it lacks strength, repose, dignity and simplicity. Subtlety has become fragility, refinement has become triviality. In its confused chatter there is none of the strong, singing harmony that satisfies us so completely in its elder brother—elder in years but vastly younger and fresher in spirit. To this state of febrile nervousness design descends when ornament becomes a thing of value in itself and "digressions," as Dewey says, "present themselves in the guise of enrichment."

We have not yet arrived at the state of mastery enjoyed by these builders of Hellas and La Beauce, and we may never reach it, but unquestionably we are feeling our way in that direction. We have not yet developed our technique of design to the degree of certainty and resourcefulness which made the utter satisfactoriness of their work a possibility. We have no ornament at all: no forms which have acquired abstract significance and become a familiar dialect of design, to be used at will in the building up of tightly knit and subtle rhythms. We are in the stage of recovering our mastery of relationships themselves, and our work if it is fine will inevitably have much of the grand gauntness of St. Stephen's or of St. Martin de Boscherville. As yet we dare not run the risk of sacrificing the unity of our designs by extending our rhythms beyond our essential forms, and as a result we preserve their simplicity at the price of a certain degree of barrenness. Hence the antiseptic grimness of much modern domestic architecture, and the too easily exhausted, utilitarian bluntness of some bigger structures.

There is danger that we may accept this barrenness as a virtue and confuse mere plainness or poverty with simplicity. The Parthenon and the southern tower of Chartres are perfect examples of simplicity for the reason that a single motive dominates every inch of both structures and their unity is complete: there is nothing extraneous, nothing dispensable, in either. Yet the rhythms of which they are composed are so complex and so infinitely extended that no one has yet succeeded in analyzing them all. When you have a building like these in which every stone is related to every other stone as though by nervous ganglia, you have the true goal of simplicity attained.

Simplicity demands the exclusion of every detail that does not contribute to unity. It requires that a scheme of rhythmic proportions be imposed on the whole and carried down through all its elements. But it permits this rhythmic scheme to be extended as far as it can be through relevant and meaningful forms: the more exact and subtle it becomes, the more firmly will the whole be knit together. As the designers of this age become more conscious masters of their craft and more familiar with their tools, it is probable that they will develop certain forms and methods of emphasizing form which will become familiar and significant through constant repetition. They will thus acquire a more flexible vocabulary and their work will advance in subtlety, losing the somewhat frozen rigidity of too much of our present work in favor of a more intense vitality.

It is this process of evolution which cannot be hastened voluntarily. The builders of the past did not consciously invent the abstractions which, at their great periods, they used so freely and so skillfully to give greater variety to their rhythmic schemes. These forms had had a purely utilitarian origin and they had become established in the vernacular of design through constant usage. As time passed and designer after designer contributed to their refinement, they had acquired an abstract beauty and a value as pattern which persisted after their original utility may have disappeared: they had acquired, in fact, a new utility as factors in rhythmic arrangements. In this way stylized ornament has always developed and had its justification, and it would be strange if the same process did not take place in our art. We already see a tendency to repeat certain forms in our modern design, an acceptance of what amounts to the beginnings of a vernacular: this tendency is often so strong as to threaten the purely functional solution of our design problems, crystallizing a style which certainly should remain plastic and formative for some time to come. But there is no reason to suppose that we shall not fulfill the promise of our beginnings and arrive in time at that state of balance between undue austerity and undue elaboration which is the triumph of design.

If precedent holds, we shall approach this apex through experiment and steadily growing mastery. We can see how other ages went through this same training period, and observe the immaturity of their school work in the Temple of Ceres at Paestum and in the church of St. Martin de Boscherville. Many of our own productions can stand comparison, creditably, with these efforts which preceded by two or three generations an absolute mastery of their type of design. If mastery was twice attained beyond this stage, it may be again.

Vastly more work must be done before we shall have had enough experience to use our media with complete assurance and success. The wide range of experimentation now going on is the most heartening portent of future achievement. The process of recasting our productions in forms that suit their functions and their making is proceeding in countless industries and activities, and in all the results of these efforts, as they approach success, we see a similar type of design emerging. It is marked by a fresh, new simplicity, a classic elegance flowering in refinement of line and fineness of form and proportion, a gratifying unity attained by the rhythmic integration of all the elements involved. Here, in these products coming off our assembly lines and building in scattered parts of the land, we see the harbingers of a world where simplicity, elegance, unity will not be isolated phenomena emerging in a scene of confusion: they forecast a world where serene order will bring all things into a similar gratifying harmony. No other age, even when they achieved mastery of their media, had the means to exercise this mastery over more than a very limited field of creation: we have the means to exercise it without limits, once it is ours. We have the means and, if we have also the vision and the will, we need nothing more.

We have, too, a conscious understanding of the factors constituting rightness in the design of our environment, a rational conception of design unequaled except for a few brief, bright moments in the far past. And it is conceivable that with this grasp of the problem, our tremendous powers, and a clear aim, we may postpone indefinitely the long autumn of decadence that has followed so soon after each period of mastery.

We feel a necessity to organize the complex things we make into an obvious unity.
600 H.P. radial motor, Dresser Manufacturing Co., as first built and as redesigned.

Characteristic products of our Machine Age technologies are being subjected to a process of organization and simplification. Old and new models of the Mimeograph Duplicator.

As a result, many familiar objects are acquiring a new degree of order, in our homes, shops and factories. Sales slip register, American Sales Book Company, as used for years and as redesigned.

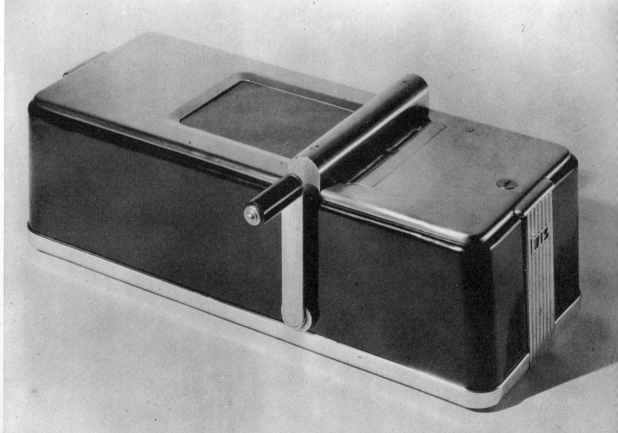

The new order invading our homes has established itself first and most firmly in our kitchens, bathrooms and basements. Lower photograph, kitchen designed by White and Weber.

Much domestic equipment has been given a new unity and simplicity to meet the new standards of the purchasing public, as in this combination coal and gas range, redesigned for the Floyd Wells Company.

Industrial products today are studied not only for functional efficiency, but for functional form, convenience, unity and simplicity. Super Kodak, Eastman Kodak Co., with coupled range finder and photronic cell automatically controlling the aperture.

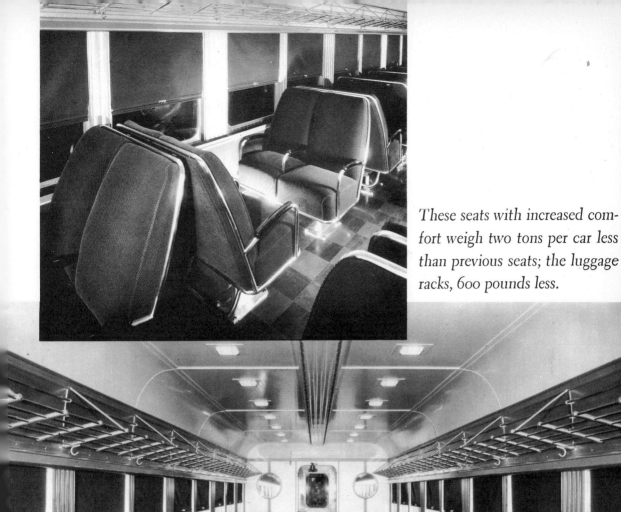

These seats with increased comfort weigh two tons per car less than previous seats; the luggage racks, 600 pounds less.

One of 150 Pullman Day Coaches in use on the New Haven Railroad, finished in blue, white, aluminum and vermilion. 25% lighter than previous coaches. This and preceding industrial products designed by the author.

55

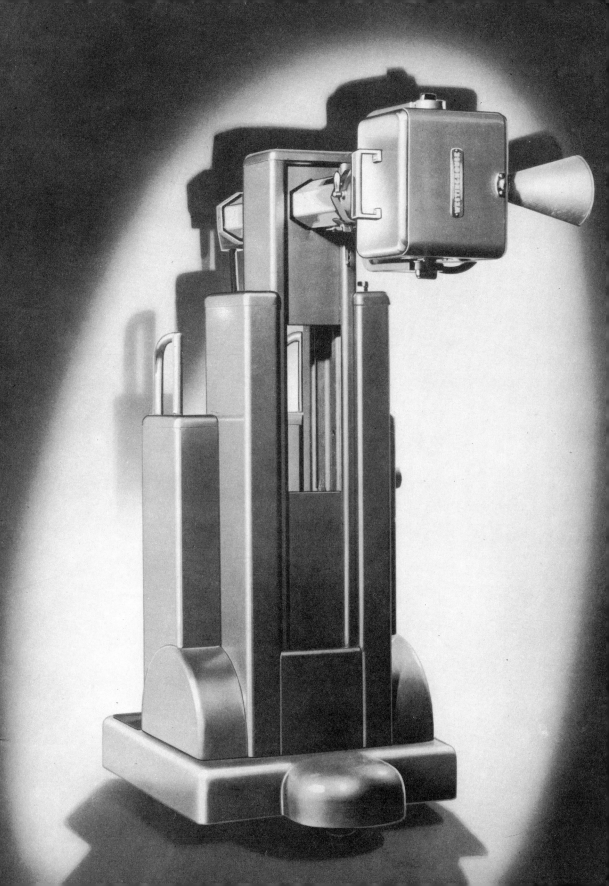

Scientific engineering, plus careful organization, results in the high efficiency and convenience of many modern products. Westinghouse Portable
X-Ray Unit, for hospital use. Controls above. Author's design.

PHOTOGRAPHS COURTESY OF TVA

Our gigantic engineering works often attain magnificently the same simplicity of form we strive for in minor products. Norris Dam Spillway and Powerhouse, opposite, and Gantry Crane, Pickwick Dam, designed by K. C. Roberts. (Compare latter with Plate 11.)

RICHARD AVERILL
SMITH

60

Industrial plants themselves are studied with the same care as the products made in
them. Plant of the Burroughs Adding Machine Co., Plymouth, Mich. Albert Kahn,
Architect. (See also Plate 16.) Opposite, the grand simplicity of the Bronx-Whitestone
Bridge, New York. Allston Dana, Engineer of Design; Aymar Embury, Architect. 61

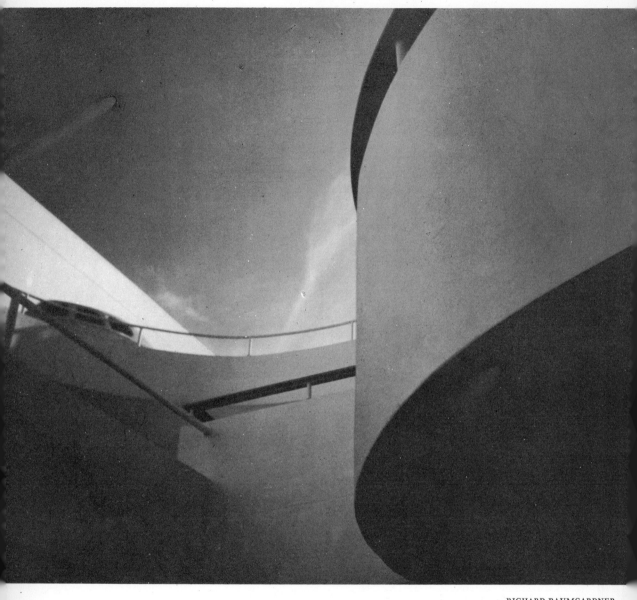

Our objective is the esthetic value of simple masses, integrated forms and rhythmic line. Detail of Road of Tomorrow, Ford Exposition.

Essential structural forms, if undisguised and simply stated, can be organized into effective and unified schemes. United States Steel Exhibit, New York World's Fair.

Beauty is present wherever a form ultimately right for its pur pose, without any blurring non-essentials, has been achieved. Elbow in cable anchorage, Triborough Bridge.

CHAPTER NINE: RHYTHMIC RELATIONSHIPS

"The first characteristic of the environing universe that makes possible the existence of artistic form is rhythm."   —JOHN DEWEY

Occasional attempts have been made to arrange perfumes in some significant order, and entertain an audience by exposing it to this series of odors. The efforts have been attended with no success beyond a mild amount of publicity, which probably was the only objective. It has never been possible to combine odors in an architectonic arrangement so that the relationships between them rather than their individual quality was the source of our pleasure, as we derive pleasure from the relationship between notes in music rather than from the notes themselves. This is the more remarkable since the sense of smell is the oldest of all our senses, and gives "either pleasant or unpleasant sensations in a more marked and universal way than in the case of vision or hearing." [1]

Cooking is unquestionably an art, and meals may be made to have a positively lyrical quality. Yet tastes are as intractable as odors: no one has ever succeeded in arranging them into an abstract pattern delightful for itself alone. No arts have ever been addressed to the senses of smell and taste as to the senses of sight and hearing. Writers on esthetics often have speculated on this fact, and produced a number of unsatisfactory

[1] *A Textbook of Physiology for Medical Students and Physicians*, William H. Howell, 1928, page 304.

reasons for it, usually having to do with a silly rating of senses as "higher" and "lower." The explanation, like the explanations of most of our human characteristics, is to be found in the structure and functioning of our physical organisms.

To stimulate the sense of taste, a substance must be in solution and must come in contact with certain minute hairlike processes which project from the "taste buds" of the mouth. In these the sapid substance produces a chemical reaction which communicates an impulse to connecting nerve fibers. Similarly, odors must penetrate the nose in a gaseous form and there "after solution in the moisture of the membrane act chemically upon the sensitive cells of the sense organ." [2] The sense of hearing, on the other hand, is activated by a direct mechanical stimulus. Sound waves are "alternate phases of rarefaction and condensation" traveling through the air, and the length of these waves, or rather the distance between phases, may vary in musical sounds from seventy feet to fractions of an inch. These waves cause the tympanic membrane of the ear to vibrate in consonance, and its vibrations are communicated by an elaborate and delicate mechanical device to sensory nerve cells in the inner ear.

Light presents a far more intricate problem than sound, and is not so completely understood. However, we do know that it has both vibratory and corpuscular characteristics. The frequency of the vibrations and the amount of energy in the corpuscles (or quanta) can be measured in the laboratory. Light rays leave an object and pass through the lens of the eye, which bends and focuses them on the retina in something like the arrangement in which they left the object. The retina is light sensitive: that is, it contains a great many small cells in which light produces a

[2] Howell, op. cit., page 303.

chemical reaction, instigating a nerve impulse. Here again we are describing in general terms processes of which the details are as yet uncertain. We do not understand why the grains of silver nitrate in a photographic emulsion turn dark after being exposed to light and then immersed in certain chemicals, and we are still further from understanding how the self-renewing sensitivity of the visual rods and cones operates. But we know that the vibratory impulses that affect these cells vary in length; we know that the shortest ones (of those we can see, since there are waves both shorter and longer than those to which our eyes are sensitive) give us a sensation of violet, while the longest give us a sensation of red, and, in between, the regular variations in length carry us through graduated sensations of orange, yellow, green and blue.

Thus we see that the senses of smell and taste are stimulated by solutions or gases which differ *qualitatively*: their reactions on our nerve cells are not related to one another in any proportional scheme we can detect. Sound waves and light waves, on the other hand, vary *quantitatively*: they can be measured, and they are related in a proportional arrangement. They can be combined in precise patterns, and these patterns can be expressed or notated by means of mathematical symbols. In this truth we can find the explanation of the arts, and of our esthetic reactions. We see here the reason why, in music and in visual design, we can create rhythmic relationships that give us a satisfying sense of order, unity, rightness— beauty.

Why rhythm should be so important to us we do not know, except that by integrating our own work rhythmically we are repeating the structural scheme of the universe in which we live. Rhythm is the principle of order in the world and in ourselves. "So far as nature is to us more than a flux lacking order in its mutable changes, so far as it is more than a whirlpool

127

of confusion, it is marked by rhythms."[3] But a flux lacking order and a whirlpool of confusions exist only to our own imperfect perceptions: there is no disorder in nature. From the dance of the electrons in an atom to the swing of the planets around the sun a rhythmic law is dominant. The waxing and waning of the solar systems are measures in a prolonged rhythm, and there is a theory that the universe itself contracts and expands in a mighty heart-beat. Modern science, in fact, seems to have reduced the universe to a series of pulsations in space. These are rhythms "obvious only to thought," but within the range of our consciousness a rhythmic order everywhere prevails. The procession of the seasons, accompanying the slow swing of the sun's path from low in the south almost to the zenith and marked by the upsurge of life in the spring and its subsidence in the autumn; the waxing and waning of the moon; the pulse-beat of light between night and day; the rise and fall of the tides and the beating of the breakers on the shore: all these and countless others are familiar rhythms by which men have ordered their lives since we knew any order at all.

Our own vital experience is composed of a multitude of rhythms, from the beating of our hearts and the breathing of our lungs to our life-cycle itself—birth, growth, fruition, decay and death proceeding in monotonous sequence through generation after generation. Walking and running, a series of orderly falls and recoveries, are perfect types of simple rhythms, and the repeated motions of many occupations and sports are similarly typical. There is a convincing theory that we sang before we talked prose, and certainly rhythmic utterance is common among other creatures, from katydids to jackasses. Since Freud has taught us to respect the influence

[3] *Art as Experience*, John Dewey, page 149.

of our sexual impulses on all our psychological processes, we realize that we must have been deeply if unconsciously influenced by the rhythmic character of our sexual experience: the rise of sexual desire, its satisfaction in a series of pulsating movements leading to a climax and a quick subsidence, to be followed by a growth of desire again; the cycle is complete and can be charted like a sound wave.

Our subjection to rhythmic influences keeps thousands of bands busy far into every night, and fills the same number of badly ventilated rooms with spasmodically gyrating human bodies. "I got rhythm, you got rhythm": no truer words were ever spoken. Jazz and swing may be barbarous by the standards of Bayreuth and La Scala, but they are as authentic as the music of the spheres and the same god is responsible for all three: whatever power determined the structural principle of the universe. No matter how moronic a dance-crazy crowd may appear, its frenzy is proof that men are never so drunkenly happy as when they are putting their bodies, as exactly as they know how, into active harmony with this basic principle of the world they live in.

The rhythms of jazz and swing are simple, obvious, repetitious, easily expressed in the movements of our bodies. The music of Bach and Beethoven is no less rhythmic in structure, but the rhythms are subtler, more complex, more varied. Lovers of "classical" music are often scandalized by the rude simplicity of "popular" music, and this attitude is frequently sincere; but while they are expressing violent distaste their feet are often tapping the rhythms they cannot abide. Rhythm is the essential factor in all music, without which it cannot exist.

The distinctive characteristic of a musical note, pleasant to the ear, is that its wave lengths shall be equal; sounds of unequal or irregular wave lengths are merely noises, and often unpleasant. Dr. Howell states this fact more scientifically: "When these [sound] waves, whatever may be their form, follow each other with regularity—that is, with a definite period of rhythm—a musical sound is perceived provided the rhythm is maintained for a number of vibrations. So that regularity or periodicity of sound waves may be considered as the underlying physical cause of musical sounds. Non-musical sounds or noises, which constitute the vast majority of our auditory sensations, are referred, on the contrary, to non-periodical vibrations."

The note of a tuning fork may have a perfectly simple wave form, but "when a single note is sounded by the human voice, a violin or any other instrument that has a characteristic quality, the trained ear can detect a series of higher tones, the upper partial tones, or harmonics, or overtones, which indicate that the note is really compound, and not simple." [4] This type of compound wave form is due to the fact that the vibrating string not only vibrates as a whole, but in its aliquot parts: its halves, its thirds, its fourths or its fifths may each vibrate separately, each giving out a simple tone which blends with the note of the whole. So long as these vibrating fractions are equal divisions of the whole, as stated, the overtones harmonize with the fundamental. Similarly, when the rates of vibration of two different tones are the same, or when they bear a simple ratio to each other, as one to two, they form the most perfect harmony. The octave of any note has this one to two ratio, the double octave one to four, the twelfth one to three. These intervals give absolutely consonant sounds, but the ratios of two to three (the fifth) or four to five (the major third) give less perfect harmony. When three notes vibrate in such a simple ratio, as four to five to six, we have a chord. This four to five to six ratio of

[4] Howell, *op. cit.*, pages 399-400.

the major chord means that one note vibrates, for instance, 128 times a second, another 160 times, and the third 192 times.

If these three waves are charted it will be seen that at no time do their crests or hollows fall together. The waves blend into one compound wave having no exaggerated peaks and valleys. If, however, we combine a note of 128 vibrations a second with one of 136—a ratio of sixteen to seventeen—we find that crests and hollows coincide eight times per second. As a result we have eight beats a second or the effect of unequal wave lengths, a discord or dissonance, and we create a most unpleasant reaction in most people. Seeking an explanation for this phenomenon, which everyone recognizes, we can only conclude that our nerves are not adapted to the reception of these irregular stimuli. A flickering light is similarly unpleasant to the eyes.[5]

Music is presented to us in time: that is, its intervals are time intervals, which follow each other processionally and separately, so that they can be exactly measured; and harmonic relationships are precisely stated no matter how complex the rhythmic structure may be. But visual design exists in space, with all its parts and intervals presented to us simultaneously. For these reasons the rhythmic structure of visual design is less readily perceptible, it may become far less legible than the most intricate musical composition: it exists not in the one dimension of time, but in four, including time; it may be constructed not of one material alone— musical notes—but of many expressed in lines, areas, forms, textures, colors, light and shade. It is probable that we would not be aware of visual rhythms or feel their necessity at all, if it were not for the special way in which we see things. The eye by its structure and method of observing,

[5] A discussion of the structure of musical sounds will be found in *Science and Music* by Sir James Jeans (Macmillan, 1938) and *Music, A Science and an Art* by John Redfield (Knopf, 1928).

if properly guided, may supply the time intervals in which rhythms become perceptible.

A kodak film is equally sensitive all over its exposed surface, and a kodak lens is designed to give as nearly as possible equal clarity of focus all over the area of the film. But our eyes are constructed according to a different principle: there is only one tiny spot on the retina where vision is exactly clear. This spot is known as the fovea centralis, and actually there is one minute spot within itself, the foveola, where the utmost acuity of vision is attained. All around the fovea is a peripheral region in which vision diminishes in distinctness as the distance from the center increases. Color, as well as light intensity, is accurately perceived only within the fovea, while the peripheral regions are progressively less sensitive to color rays.

This clever structure of our eyes, together with the fact that we are bilateral two-legged animals, is probably responsible for the fact that we have any visual art at all. If our visual field consisted of a large area of equal distinctness, like a motion picture screen, it is hard to believe that we would ever have recognized relationships in nature or felt an urge to create perceptible relationships within our works, and none of the laws of fitness, simplicity, unity and variety would have had any validity for us.

Built as we are, our vision includes a wide field awaiting attention, as it were, but present to our consciousness. If there is a movement within the field, a flash of color, or any other appeal to our interest, we instantly direct our attention to that point by turning our eyes so that the light rays fall on the fovea. We see the whole visual field only by directing the fovea toward one small point after another. When we look at an object with attention, it is as if we *felt* it over with two tiny fingers of light, following its lines, touching its prominences and exploring its recesses, slipping over its surfaces, *feeling* its masses and recording its colors. During this process the lenses of our eyes are constantly adjusting themselves to changing distances so that the point of attention is always in focus, and the iris is expanding and contracting delicately with varying light intensities. At the same time our two eyes are constantly changing their angle of incidence to their own medial axis, so that the two lines of vision always meet at exactly the same point. This changing angle formed by two lines of vision, together with the diminishing size of objects as they recede from us (perspective), gives us our sense of distance and of the third dimension. By all these subtle accommodations we *feel* an object as we see it, repeating its form as if by means of a special code within our organs of vision. Simultaneously our tactile senses are aroused: from past experience we know how these forms feel to our hands, and we are conscious of the smoothness or roughness, the rotundity or flatness, the softness or hardness, and the weight of these surfaces and masses over which our vision glides, just as our hands might do.

Thus by a process extended in time, just as the hearing of a series of rhythmical sounds is extended in time, we come to know an object, know it as a whole in whatever dimensions it may have, but know too the elements of which it is composed and the relationships that bind them together. Our seeing and handling are sequential, progressive series of perceptions, passing from one feature to another and back again, enabling us to detect whatever rhythms exist among lines, forms, colors and proportions. These relationships create unity in design, whether in nature or art, and their recognition, being the recognition of order in the universe and in our work, gives us a sense of satisfaction mounting at times to delight.

A progressive method of seeing makes it possible for us to feel rhythms, because rhythm basically is a regular recurrence of expected intervals, and it is from the fulfillment of these expectations that our pleasure is derived. John Dewey has defined rhythm as "ordered variation of changes," and he then proceeds to disparage as inadequate the "tick-tock" or "tom-tom" theory of rhythm. It is true that mere repetition of simple units, or even fixed groups of units, at fixed intervals, is an extremely elementary and obvious form of rhythm and insufficiently describes the more complex rhythms of design. Yet intervals and recurrence are essential to rhythm, and from the simple we may approach an understanding of the more subtle. The ticking of a clock is definitely rhythmical, but under most circumstances not particularly exciting. But anyone who has sat through a performance of *The Emperor Jones* realizes how deeply moving the beating of a tom-tom may become when kept up for an hour or so. We are quite ready to believe that when maintained in the jungle for days and nights it might produce almost any degree of frenzy. A picket fence is not particularly inspiring, though under certain circumstances it may be very pretty and satisfactory. But a colonnade, where the rhythmical scheme is almost as simple while the form becomes glorified, may be enormously moving.

The interesting point about both the fence and the colonnade is that in all such cases we feel under compulsion to place our units at uniform intervals, and find the whole decidedly disturbing if they are not so placed. There is really no very sound practical reason why the spacing of pickets in a fence should not vary within reasonable limits, and in the post and lintel type of masonry building it might even be more convenient if we spaced the columns according to the length of the lintel stones as they are most easily quarried, rather than insisting that all lintels be cut to a uniform length. But if builders followed any such practice we should describe the results, and the builders likewise, as crazy. Our sense of order would be offended. No matter how simple in structure a rhythm may be, we are satisfied if it is present and disturbed if it is not.

A finely proportioned colonnade has power to move us not only because its rhythmic units are larger than human scale: its rhythmic relationships include much more than mere repetition of units at fixed intervals. Its rhythms are built also of opposing forces in whose interplay we feel alternate tension and release, incipient fall and recovery. Columns that support nothing may still be graceful, but they lose most of the power to stir us emotionally that they possess when they are properly loaded. Not overloaded: columns in the base of a skyscraper are not satisfactory, because the mass above them is too great and they seem inadequate. We must feel that their strength is adequately proportioned to their task, as when there is an architrave and pediment of sufficient but not overpowering mass above them. We feel then their upward thrust against the weight they support, and feel that the tendency of that weight to fall, as it accumulates across a void, is intercepted and counteracted at the proper intervals. We are pleased by the stability attained, and the spectacle of forces of nature successfully controlled.

Stability is profoundly important to us, and its maintenance is one of the functions as well as one of the satisfactions of rhythmic structure. Behaviorist psychology maintains that the fear of loud noises and the fear of loss of support are the two terrors we bring into the world with us, and subconsciously at least we never escape from them. The fear of falling, says Leo Stein, "is quite possibly the feeling that enters most importantly into rhythm, which is the satisfaction in recovery from an incipient fall. Nothing is more unpleasant than a fall which does not promise recovery, but a fall which does holds within itself the essential quality of excitement." Here probably is one of the basic reasons for our pleasure in rhythmic exercises of walking, running and dancing, composed as they are of a series of incipient falls and recoveries. This experience is symbolized in many forms of rhythm, the downward curve and upward surge of a wave being the simplest and most typical. But we find it present, although less obviously, in the alternation of voids and solids with their recurring light and shadow in building, the piercing of windows in walls according to a recognizable pattern, the regular placing of supports, and the patterns of many forms of historic ornament.

We find this principle of tension and release, fall and recovery, expressed in the egg-and-dart and similar moldings, the fret or key patterns, the swags and festoons so popular in the Renaissance, the metopes and triglyphs of the Greek frieze, the fluting of classic columns and interwoven arches of the Gothic builders. But architectural ornament, where it performed a real function and was not merely an exuberance of the designer's fancy, has always played a part in rhythms larger and more structural than those it contained within itself. Ornament marked subdivisions of areas and created contrast of surfaces, thus creating those recurrences of proportions which are the most subtle and binding form of rhythm. The essence of rhythm is not in the recurrence of units, simple or complex, but in the recurrence of *relationships*; so that when it is apparent that all the lines, masses and areas of a design are related in a definite scheme of proportion (as the notes in a musical chord are related in a simple ratio), that the lines and forms recall one another in character, and the colors compose a harmony, we find that the most satisfying unity has been achieved.

Phidias or Ictinus—whoever designed the Parthenon—not only felt his rhythms but understood them clearly and regulated them with the utmost mathematical exactness. A whole book would not be enough to explore all the interlacing of proportions in this one relatively simple structure. But glance for a moment at the function performed by the metopes and triglyphs of the frieze: they repeat in themselves the proportional scheme of the whole façade, and mark their contribution to it by asserting a contrast in texture with the plain surface of the epistyle below them. The vertical grooves of the triglyphs carry the proportional scheme inward a step further, at the same time that they recall the vertical lines of the columns and emphasize by contrast the horizontal divisions of the epistyle and cornice above and below. The severe verticality of these triglyphs are the upward thrust of recovery between the tangled complexity of the sculptured metopes, and the details of the regulae and guttae all play their parts like grace notes in a musical theme. The position of the frieze marks a rhythmical division of the entablature as a whole, serving to establish certain boundaries of the proportional scheme; the frieze is subdivided rhythmically, and holds an amazingly complex arrangement of rhythms within itself.

The flutes of classic columns, while uniform in size, could never be seen as such: they formed a rhythmic crescendo and diminuendo of light and shade across the visible surface of each column, emphasizing as nothing else could have done the roundness and competent mass of these supports; while their vertical lines accented their upward thrust as they dealt with the dead weight of the horizontal masses above and below. The subdivisions of the grouped columns of the Gothic builders were rhythmic after a somewhat similar fashion; but they also served to carry down to a firm foundation in the earth all those lines of the vaulting ribs above, gathering them up into chords at regular intervals along the nave and aisle, combining them into larger and larger groups as they descended, but keeping them always within a human scale. Reversing the direction, these columns carried the eye upward in their straight slim flight to the spreading fountain of interlaced arches into which they burst. The interlocking rhythms, endlessly repeating themselves in columns, arches, windows, towers, pinnacles and buttresses within the fabric of a Gothic cathedral, are beyond the power of anyone to count or to analyze, as they were beyond the power of any one man to create. They are not, fortunately, beyond our power to feel.

These subtle but powerful forms of rhythm accomplish a perfect symmetry in which all the parts are referable to the whole and can be interpreted in its terms, while the whole can be similarly interpreted in terms of its parts. As Leo Stein says, "There must be no separation and yet the separation must be distinct; there must be no parts, and yet the parts must be definite." Which is like the status of a chord in music: it must be clear and pure, and yet its sole value lies in its place in the theme of which it is a part; while the theme itself must hold all its parts in complete subjection to the pattern of the whole. In accomplishing such an integration the artist, as John Dewey puts it, "selects, intensifies, and concentrates by means of form: rhythm and symmetry being of necessity the form that material takes when it undergoes the clarifying and ordering operation of art."

In subjecting our materials today to "the clarifying and ordering operation of art" we do not have, as we have said, the resource of developed ornament on which designers of the past relied so heavily in marking the divisions of their proportional areas and in creating harmonies, contrasts and rhythmic repetition of line and texture. We are in a stage where we must deal with the starkest elements, the most essential forms, and create our rhythms, unassisted, by means of the relationships we set up between these basic elements. This may be no handicap: that an art is in its early stages of development may simply mean that its vitality is greater and its intention purer, while it can be strong in dignity, resourcefulness and charm. If we contrast the art of Giotto with that of Raphael, or St. Stephen's at Caen with St. Maclou at Rouen, we can be reconciled to our own equipment. When we begin to acquire a generally accepted vocabulary of ornament, we may know that our youth is over.

What the designers of the developed periods of the past accomplished with the aid of accepted ornament, we can still attempt without its aid. We have means to effect the same proportional relationships between areas and forms, the same harmony and opposition of line, the same rhythmic diversity of surface and texture, the same accentuation of significant structural elements, the same symmetry, balance and repose, the same permeation of rhythms throughout an organism. We possess the fundamental resource, to which the ornament of more mature periods was at best an adventitious aid and too often a means of evasion and disguise: we have the geometrics of design.

Design, to paraphrase a sentence of Claude Bragdon's, is geometry made visible, as music is number made audible. If rhythm is the basis of order, and rational relationships are the essence of rhythm, we have all the mathematical means for perfecting these relationships that any age ever possessed. It is more important that rhythm should be felt than that it should be analyzed, and it *is* felt by many who are intellectually unaware of its existence. Rhythms are created, too, by the native sense of rightness of a good craftsman or designer oftener than they are consciously organized. But the designer is in a far more masterful position if he not only feels his rhythms, but also understands their structural principles and is able to control them by intention. No one else, I think, has ever achieved the exact mastery of Ictinus or Phidias, but innumerable

139

designers have felt the need of conscious controls and sought mathematical means of disciplining their native instincts. This understanding and these technical skills are as important to the creator of visual order as to the composer of music.

CHAPTER TEN: RHYTHM OF PROPORTION

"Proportion is not only found in numbers and measurements but also in sounds, weights, times, positions, and in whatsoever power there be."

—LEONARDO DA VINCI

Design is geometry made visible, and "Euclid alone saw beauty plain." But design is one art, and geometry is quite another. For a certain type of mind the fascinating and inexhaustible relationships of numbers and quantities have a narcotic allure: their study may become such a consuming passion that the student is permanently diverted from making any constructive use of what he learns. Many of those who have undertaken a study of the geometry of design are of this susceptible type, and have ended by studying not design, but mathematics, endlessly.

Design is a straightforward art. There may be a long preparatory period in which the designer familiarizes himself with all the determining factors of function, materials and techniques, but the form in which his design finally emerges is usually shaped swiftly and surely by his sense of rightness operating on these factors. There may follow a period of adjustment and revision, when he perfects his order and knits his rhythms more tightly. But at no time is there any slow process of building bit by bit, which would make it possible to apply elaborate and erudite mathematical formulas to the creation of simple unity. The designer's innate but trained and experienced sense of rightness selects the one right form from among

141

innumerable alternatives, and while he may experiment for a while with first one possibility and then another, there is never any doubt in his mind as to whether he has found his solution: when it presents itself to his mental vision he recognizes it immediately, and as a whole. Once seen, it need only be given physical reality—sometimes a long and difficult process requiring both patience and tenacity, but never lacking exact direction. During this period of painstaking work which makes a vision real, the designer has time to measure, compare and revise; but unless his first-seen form is right, having order, unity and completeness, no amount of pulling about of its parts will make it successful.

For this reason, whatever tools the designer uses in actual creation must be a part of his own mental equipment, to be used automatically and without conscious effort. The geometry of design first of all must be in his eye, in fact in his mental eye, and if later he consciously applies design formulas to his realized vision, it must be as a simple and straight-forward means of clarifying and correcting his intention. It cannot be stressed too strongly that mathematical formulas never help a designer to create. They serve but two useful ends: first, to train the designer's mental and physical eye in right proportions, and second, to test and correct the proportions his eye has established.

"Proportion," according to the men who write dictionaries, is an equal-ity or identity between ratios. "Ratio" expresses the comparative value or magnitude of two quantities, "proportion" is the sameness of such com-parative values. Thus if we have a panel two feet wide by four feet high, and another four feet wide by eight feet high, we say they are in propor-tion, because the ratio of height to width (two to one) is the same in each. Now proportion is the most effective means of creating unity among the diverse parts of an object or organism, both in art and in nature: if we feel or see a rhythmic recurrence of the same ratios among lines, dimensions, areas, masses, colors, we feel that these elements are bound together indissolubly in one identity, so that no part can be removed or altered without disturbing the rhythm of the whole. So we try instinctively, in every form of design, to create right proportions among the elements with which we must work.

Since we are dealing with quantities, and ratios of quantities, it is obvious that there must be mathematical formulas which will express the result we are aiming at. But it is also obvious that we cannot begin our work with these formulas, any more than a composer of music can begin by considering the vibration-ratios of the tones he proposes to use. The composer's ear must be trained to know true harmony of tones, and the designer's eye must be trained to see right proportion of lines and areas; the composer has simple means of training his ear and testing the accuracy of his tones, and the designer's means of training and testing his sense of rightness must be equally simple and as easily applied. Also it must be equally unobtrusive, and keep out of his way until needed.

It is to be expected that the Greeks, intellectually and mathematically gifted as they were, should have paid attention to the geometrical bases of continued proportion in design; and we need not be surprised to find that they discovered what is, in all probability, the fundamental design principle on which Nature bases the scheme of growth in living organisms: exemplified, as modern research has shown, in the proportions of the human skeleton, the growth of plant forms and shells, the arrangement of seeds and countless other manifestations of the life force.[1] Bota-

[1] On the Relation of Phyllotaxis to Mechanical Laws by A. H. Church, Oxford, and On Growth and Form by D'Arcy W. Thompson, Cambridge, are important works on this subject. Prof. Church, for instance, points out that the seeds of the sunflower are arranged in two series of intersecting curves, and that these curves can always, in normal growth, be counted in numbers of

nists and conchologists observed the recurrence of this design scheme throughout nature, but it remained for an American artist, the late Jay Hambidge, to show that the Greeks, for a short time during the Periclean age, applied these same principles to the perfection of intricate internal rhythms within their works. Whether the knowledge of this method was restricted to a cult or guild of artists, as Mr. Hambidge suggests, we do not know. But in any case the method was lost or its practice abandoned after a time, and less satisfactory mathematical methods of achieving rhythmic relationships were used by the later Greeks and all other artists since, until Mr. Hambidge revealed the results of his studies. He called the system Dynamic Symmetry, the word "symmetry" being used in the root sense of analogy, to signify "the relationship which the composing elements of form in design, or in an organism in nature, bear to the whole"; [2] and "dynamic" being used to distinguish this type of design, which is characteristic of certain growth processes, from the "static" type of symmetry found in crystals, the cross-sections of stems and fruits, and in the design schemes of many schools of art.

That Mr. Hambidge's system was actually used during the bright noonday of Greek art there can be no doubt. Of all the efforts to explain the design scheme of the Parthenon—and every competent student has sensed the presence of some proportional system to which all its internal relationships have been adjusted—this is the only one to provide a key so complete, adequate, exact and simple that there can be no doubt of its

the summation series (which we shall soon discuss): that is, there will be 34 long curves and 55 short ones, or 89 long and 144 short, etc., according to the size of the head. He cites many other instances of the occurrence of the summation series, and extreme and mean proportion, in growth forms. Two remarkable books, *Nature's Harmonic Unity* and *Proportional Form*, both by Samuel Colman and C. Arthur Cohn, and published by Putnam in 1912 and 1920 respectively, contain a huge collection of information on proportional schemes in nature and art. Their character is partly mystical and partly scientific, not always convincing, generally bewildering but curiously interesting.

[2] *Elements of Dynamic Symmetry*, Jay Hambidge, Brentano's, page xiv.

144

conscious use by the designer. In addition, the basic logic of the system, backed by the ample sanction of nature's own practices, unquestionably would have appealed to the supremely logical minds of the Greeks.

But we will not minimize our great debt to Mr. Hambidge if we doubt that his system was used quite as he outlines it. In spite of his disclaimers, he was by temperament more interested in the mathematical subtleties of his Dynamic Symmetry than in its creative use: he was by nature more of a student and analyst than a creative artist. Therefore it seems to me that he followed his theories up many alluring but devious alleys which I am sure were ignored by the Greek artists, however much they may have attracted the Greek geometricians. In studying Mr. Hambidge's analyses of Greek designs, one is often overtaken by doubt that a Greek artist would ever go to such bewildering lengths to obtain an essentially simple result, and one wonders how, if such a scheme could be planned in advance, it could possibly be applied to three-dimensional objects by means of any devices the Greeks possessed. This overelaboration is unfortunate, because there are certain relatively simple and highly useful tools embedded in Mr. Hambidge's system of Dynamic Symmetry, and if we can extricate them and use them with ease we may adjust the internal relationships of our designs with some of the accuracy the Greeks attained.

Mr. Hambidge says, "Fortunately, we have the use of a tool which the Greek artists did not possess. That implement is arithmetic. By the use of a little adding, multiplying, dividing and subtracting, we may expedite our progress enormously." [3] We may also get in so deeply that our activities cease to have anything whatever to do with design. We may become so engrossed in intricate calculations that we might as well be spending our time on crossword puzzles or chess, so far as esthetic results are con-

[3] *Op. cit.*, page 31.

cerned. The fact that the Greeks knew only geometry, which is a form of design, and deals entirely with relationships, may be the reason why Dynamic Symmetry was a constructive tool in the hands of Greek artists for a generation or so at least. The interpretation of geometrical relation-

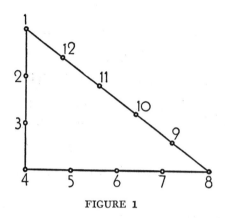

FIGURE 1

ships in the more facile but purely numerical symbols of arithmetic, as Mr. Hambidge and his school consistently do, may be the reason why Dynamic Symmetry has not been more conspicuously helpful in the hands of modern artists.

The Greeks were an extraordinarily lucid and rational people—more so than any other people in history—at least for the generation or two immediately after the Persian wars when their genius reached its fullest development. They had learned from the Egyptians a purely practical art of measuring areas by means of a knotted cord. The Egyptians were compelled to re-survey their flooded fields every year after the Nile returned to its banks, and they discovered that if you tie the ends of a cord together, and tie eleven other knots in it dividing it into twelve equal spaces, and then stretch that cord into a triangle with the first, fourth and eighth knots at the corners, the fourth knot will be the apex of a right angle.

This simple device enabled them to recover the square boundaries of their flooded fields, and incidentally to square up their pyramids and other structures. If the string is knotted accurately this is as good a way as any to make a square corner. In handling their strings they discovered a number of other facts about triangles and squares.

But when Thales, according to tradition, brought this string trick back to his homeland, it came into its own. We must remember the Greeks' delight in logic, but we must also remember that the Greeks had almost no mechanical gift: any man who had the ability to figure out an instrument or a machine thought it beneath his dignity to build the thing, and besides, what was the use of building it once you had proved conclusively by logic that it could be built? So they had no instruments and wanted none. But anyone can play with a piece of string, and tipped off by the Egyptians to the possibilities of the game, the Greeks proceeded to perfect the science of geometry: all propositions of which can be demonstrated by means of a piece of string, a couple of sharp points and a smooth expanse of marble, slate or sand on which to make scratches.

It should be borne in mind that the Greek designers who used "dynamic symmetry" certainly used no more elaborate equipment than a string and points, square, level and straight-edge. They did not possess our ready means of dealing with arithmetical fractions, and the metric system which enables us to analyze their proportions so glibly was more than two thousand years away in the mists of the future. By means of decimal measurements we are able to discover in their schemes many intricate relationships which were unknown to them, and which, if known, they would have dismissed as diversions from their sole purpose. By using decimal fractional equivalents for their spatial relationships we are diverted from their aim, which should be ours as well. Their aim was quite simple: they wished to divide their forms, areas and dimensions into parts which had a constant proportion to each other and to the whole. They wished to create rhythms binding their work together as a unit, and they used the means necessary to this end and nothing more.

In trying tricks with his string, the first thing Thales is reported to have discovered is the fact that any triangle drawn within a semicircle, with the cord for its base and its apex touching the arc, is a right-angled triangle. This seemed to be a delightful and highly useful discovery: given the diagonal of an area you could always square its corners. Thales then discovered that if you drop a line from the apex of the triangle perpendicular to its base (that is, if you divide a right-angled triangle into two right-angled triangles) the dropped line will be a mean proportion

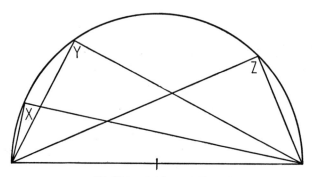

FIGURE 2. X, Y and Z *are all right angles.*

between the two sections into which it cuts the base: AB will bear to BC the same relationship that BC bears to BD (Figure 3). This was still more fascinating, because here he had a means of establishing a constant ratio of proportion in the length of lines: the same sort of thing as when we say that two is to four as four is to eight, and four is to eight as eight

148

is to sixteen. In dealing with these whole numbers, the smallest ratio that can be used, one to two, doubles every time and gives us such rapid increases that the quantities quickly get out of hand and the sense of a

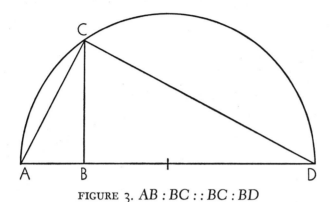

FIGURE 3. $AB : BC :: BC : BD$

constant ratio is lost. But with the string method of creating a constant ratio, these steps can be kept as close together as one likes and still their proportional increase will always be the same.

I think it must have occurred to someone about this time, or soon after, that if a designer wants to bind his quantities together there ought to be a better way of doing it than by this mean proportion method; something closer, more tightly interlocked. Suppose, for instance, you could divide a line or an area in such a way that the lesser part is to the greater as the greater to the whole? There you'd have a self-contained interlocking rhythm, complete within every two adjacent intervals, and thus twice as effective as the mean proportion method. It could be extended indefinitely, always returning on itself, and it could be read either way between any two adjacent quantities.

I think the desirability of such a scheme of proportions must have occurred to the Greek experimenters before they discovered how to do it, and it must have been a great day in Athens (or wherever) when they found that a square drawn within a semicircle gives the answer. The vertical sides of the square cut the base line of the semicircle at two points, and each short end of the base line is to the side of the square as the side of the square is to their sum. Thus, in Figure 4, AB : BC : : BC : AC, and CD : BC : : BC : BD.

But suppose you had only the line AC given, and not knowing how long AB or BC might be, you wanted to divide AC in this extreme and mean proportion. The Greek geometricians found that it could be done easily if AC is made the side of a right-angled triangle, in which the short end is one-half as long as AC: swing out from one end of AC a line half its length to form the right angle, draw the hypotenuse EC, and swing the line EA through an arc to intersect EC at F; then swing the point F

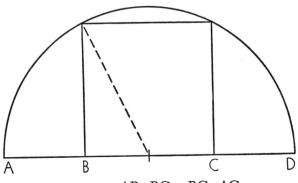

FIGURE 4. *AB : BC : : BC : AC*

back across the line AC, with C as a center, and it locates the point B. Now AB : BC : : BC : AC, once more (Figure 5).

What can be done with lines can be done with areas: if a rectangle is erected on AC, with a height equal to BC, a vertical line through B will divide the area into two portions of which the smaller is to the larger as the larger is to the whole. The larger portion, obviously, will be a square (Figure 6).

In this method of dividing lines and areas the Greeks had hit upon

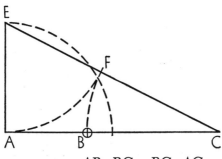

FIGURE 5. $AB : BC : : BC : AC$

a basic principle which, they were quick to see, is used by Nature in her own proportional schemes. They fully appreciated its importance as a fundamental and essential principle in design. It has been called the

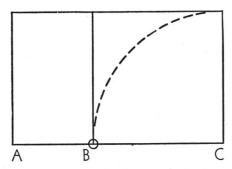

FIGURE 6. *The smaller area is to the larger as the larger is to the whole.*

"golden section," but Plato referred to it simply as "the section," as if no other type of section was of any importance. Greek designers during their greatest period made the golden section the integrating element

151

in their work, the measure of their rhythmic relationships. They realized that it creates intervals which are visually harmonious, as the simple ratio of a musical chord creates audible harmony, and they saw that satisfaction and beauty are found in it as inevitably as in the even vibration of a pure musical note.

The principle of the golden section as applied to lines, or distances, has never been lost: as applied for a short time to the division of areas in design it was quickly forgotten, and not rediscovered for more than two millennia. Lines in design are chiefly significant for other attributes than their length, and, in proportional schemes, areas are the designer's first concern. So the golden section principle was not conspicuously useful until we learned again how to apply it in the creation of rhythmic relationships among our areas. There is, however, a series of numbers which approximates a continuous series of extreme and mean proportional relationships, and these are useful in the arrangement of numbers of units. Nature uses them in this way, and they are a ready and reasonably accurate means of approximating extreme and mean proportion among a series of whole numbers. These numbers are known as the Fibonacci series, after an Italian mathematician, or the summation series, because each number is the sum of the two preceding. The series begins as follows, and may be extended indefinitely: 1-2-3-5-8-13-21-34-55, etc.

If equations are formed of any three adjacent numbers in this series, as, 1 : 2 : : 2 : 3, or 2 : 3 : : 3 : 5, it will be seen that the statements are inaccurate. We recall from our high school algebra that the product of the means must equal the product of the extremes, and the product of the extremes in the first equation has an error of -1, and in the second equation an error of $+1$. This error of alternately -1 or $+1$ will be found in every equation of the series, and while it is substantial at the beginning of the series it grows proportionately smaller as the numbers in the equations grow larger, until finally it is very small indeed. The error is always present, however. There is no other series of whole numbers starting from unity which makes so close an approximation to accuracy; it is in fact impossible to express the ratio of extreme and mean proportion in whole numbers, since it is a never-ending fraction. The familiar approximation used by Mr. Hambidge and others—.618 : 1 : : 1 : 1.618—is more accurate than the lower equations in the summation series. But the latter, with a constantly diminishing margin of error as they are carried higher, eventually become more nearly accurate than the Hambidge equation. And when we are dealing with indivisible units, fractions however accurate are no help to us.

The Greeks realized that unless the designer was dealing with combinations of separate units—such as columns, windows, courses, steps—he had no business to be concerned with numbers at all. It must always be remembered that the Greeks, like nature, disapproved of fractions, and had no use for them. When adjusting the internal divisions of an area such as the façade of the Parthenon, there was no room in it for fractions: if a scheme of rhythmic relationships is to be successful at all, there should be no portions of one's areas left out of it—no little fractional parts here and there that do not fit in. So the wise Greeks stuck to their geometry, with which they *could* express extreme and mean proportion with absolute accuracy and inclusiveness. By means of their string and points they could subdivide their areas as intricately as they pleased, maintaining always a constant ratio, and including in their proportional scheme every vestige of their surface and every element in their design.

The square within the semicircle was the foundation of their system. If a rectangle is completed, its length the base of the semicircle and its

height that of the square, we have two golden-section rectangles overlapped to the extent of the square. The area X (Figure 7) is to the
area Y as Y is to the sum of X + Y, and Z is to Y as Y is to Y + Z. Both

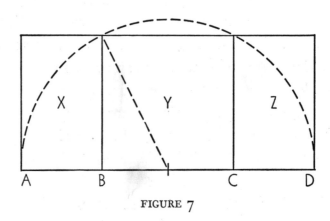

FIGURE 7

X and Z are exactly the same proportion as X + Y and Y + Z—both are
golden-section rectangles. If a square is drawn in one end of X or Z
(Figure 8), the portion left over is another smaller golden-section rectangle. This kind of subdivision can be carried on to infinity, or until
you are dizzy.

But in X + Y + Z we have a new rectangle that has amazing properties
and possibilities of its own. Its height and length are incommensurable:
that is, if the end is considered as one, or unity, the side is a never-ending
fraction. But the Greeks found that the side and end are commensurable
in square: that is, a square erected on the side is exactly five times the
area of a square erected on the end. So if the end is one, the side, in our
arithmetical parlance, is the square root of five, a never-ending fraction.
Mr. Hambidge calls it a root-five rectangle, and we don't know what the
Greeks called it. What made it so vitally important to them as a factor

in design was its construction as a double golden-section rectangle, reading both ways.

If the diagonal of this rectangle is drawn, and a line is then drawn from one corner (D) and perpendicular to the diagonal, extending through to the opposite side, this side will be cut at its fifth point (E). By this means the rectangle can be divided into five equal rectangles, and each of these is exactly the same proportion as the whole—each is a root-five rectangle, and each may again be subdivided in the same way, as in the subdivision W, Figure 9. The smaller rectangle of the same proportion as the larger is called a reciprocal of the larger, and again you could go on cutting it up to infinity: it would always fit, always come out even, and the ratio would always be maintained.

If a square is drawn in the center of any of these subdivisions as at o, Figure 9, it of course forms part of two golden-section rectangles and

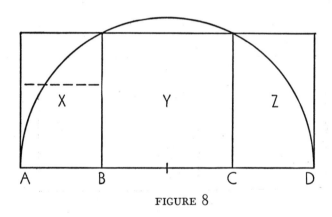

FIGURE 8

leaves a golden-section rectangle on either side of it. If a square is drawn in each end of a root-five rectangle, the space between is composed of two squares and a root-five rectangle, as in Figure 10.

155

If a square is replaced in the center of the large rectangle, and the center space of Figure 10 drawn both ways across it, we see that the square is cut into four squares in the corners and a smaller one in the

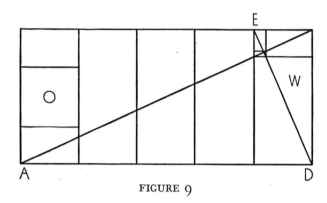

FIGURE 9

center, with four golden-section rectangles separating them; or the whole square may be considered as filled with four golden-section rectangles, all overlapped to the extent of the cross in the center (Figure 11). You

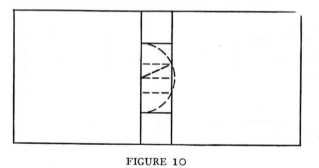

FIGURE 10

can figure out a number of other combinations for yourself, if you wish.

If the diagonal of a golden-section rectangle is drawn, and the perpendicular to the diagonal, as in Figure 12, the square and its golden section

156

Post and lintel construction of the Parthenon. Simple, direct, accurate
engineering, lending itself to the clear statement of rhythmic relationships.

Column bases of the Parthenon. This machine-like precision and simplicity of construction makes possible an accurate adjustment of relationships.

66

Corner of the Parthenon, illustrating the adjustment of proportions in stylobate, columns, entablature and pediment.

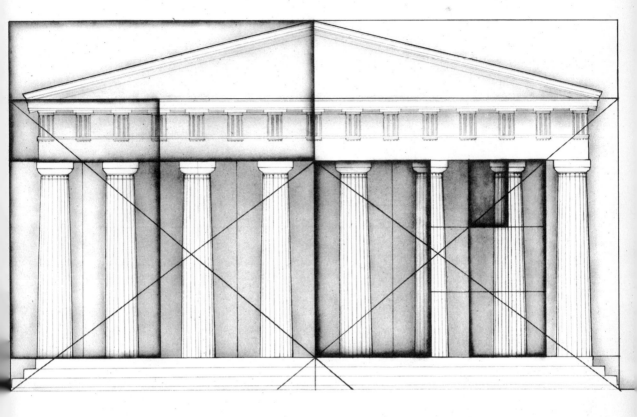

Proportional scheme of the Parthenon, based on the
square, the golden-section rectangle, the root-five
rectangle and their diagonals. The Golden Section
is the basic proportion. For an analysis of the scheme
see Appendix A, page 263.

68

The Greek designers felt their way toward the perfection of their forms and proportions, just as we are
doing. The awkwardness of the Temple of Ceres,
Paestum (B.C. 550) contrasts vividly with the serene
mastery of the Parthenon (B.C. 454-438).

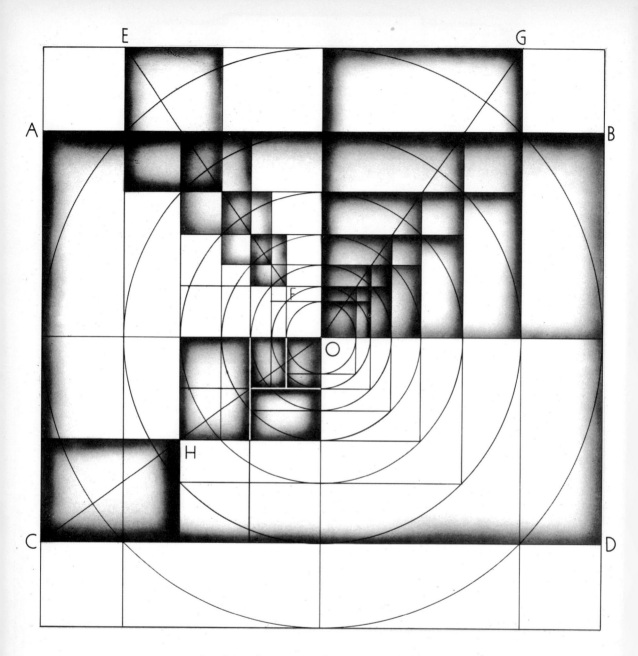

Circle-and-square scheme of rhythmic proportions used by many Roman, Renaissance and modern designers. Each square is drawn with sides tangent to the circle it encloses, and its diagonal is the diameter of the next circle. In reality it is an arrangement of the root-two rectangles of Dynamic Symmetry. CH, HO, OB are all root-two rectangles; OG and EF are series of overlapped root-two rectangles; all proportions in the scheme are based on the ratio of one to the square root of two.

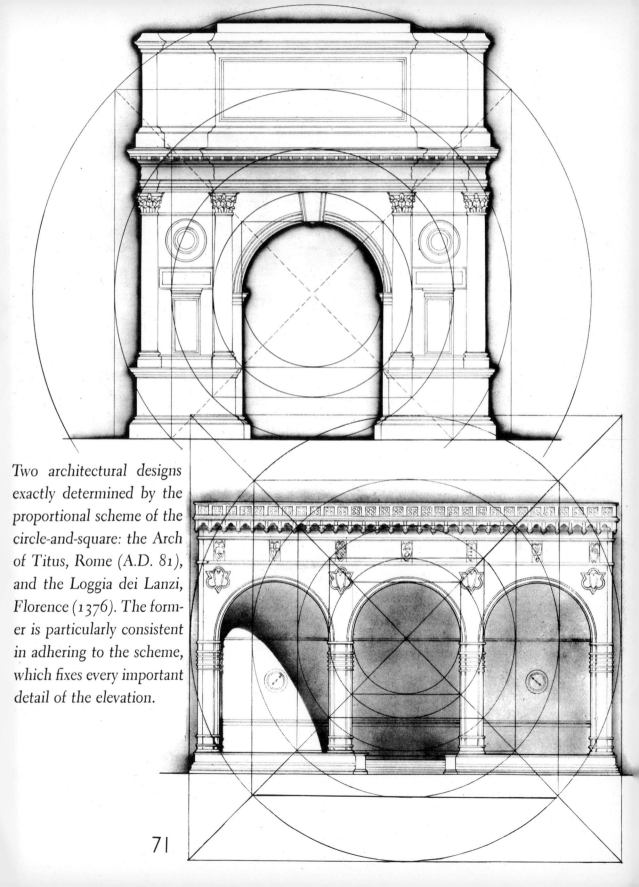

Two architectural designs exactly determined by the proportional scheme of the circle-and-square: the Arch of Titus, Rome (A.D. 81), and the Loggia dei Lanzi, Florence (1376). The former is particularly consistent in adhering to the scheme, which fixes every important detail of the elevation.

71

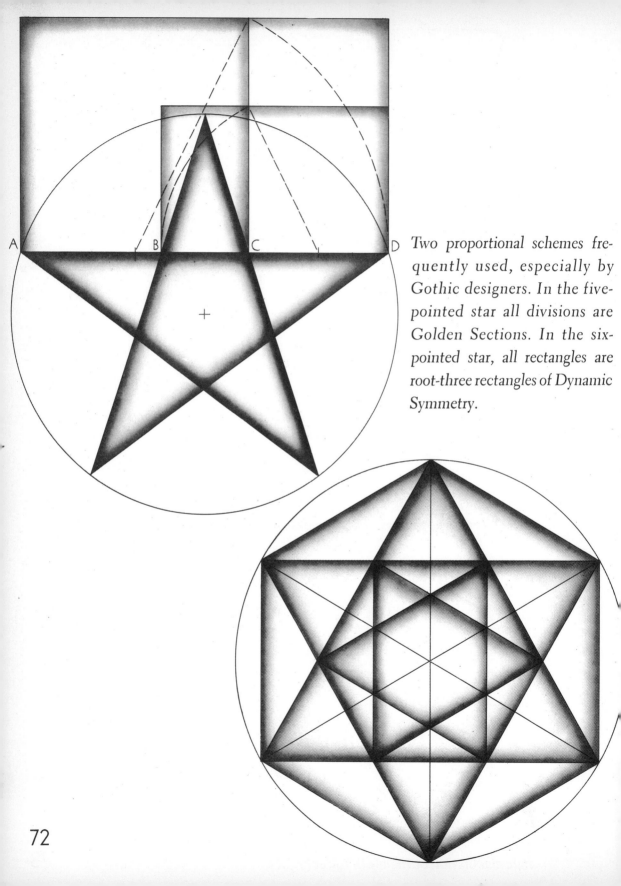

Two proportional schemes frequently used, especially by Gothic designers. In the five-pointed star all divisions are Golden Sections. In the six-pointed star, all rectangles are root-three rectangles of Dynamic Symmetry.

A   B   C   D

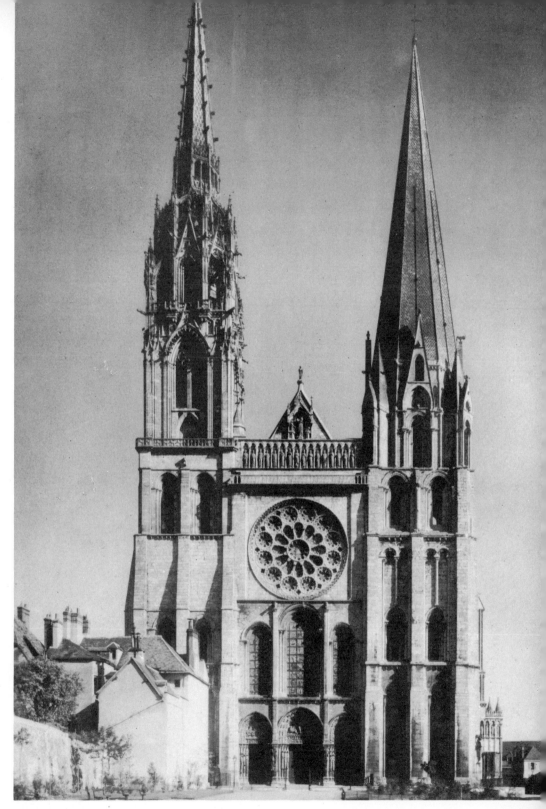

West front of Notre Dame de Chartres, contrasting the rhythmic perfection of the south tower (1107) with the nervous and effeminate elaboration of the north tower (1506).

73

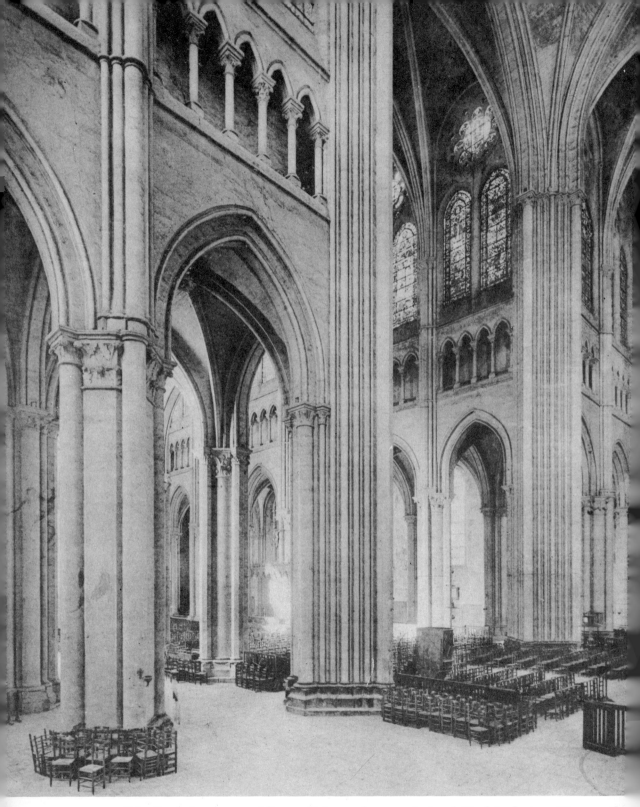

Rhythmic harmony of line and form characteristic of Gothic design. Nave and crossing of Chartres. Opposite, engineering requirements producing a similar rhythmic arrangement of line in modern design. George Washington Bridge.

Rhythmic line and form in Brunelleschi's Dome, Florence (1437) and in the Taj Mahal, Agra (1630).

76

Opposite, the enforced repetition of characteristic lines and forms in modern transport planes places them among the most successful of all our creative efforts

BOURKE-WHITE

77

A short parabolic curve and a long sweep, straight or almost straight—an extraordinarily vigorous line—is our characteristic "line of beauty". It recurs in all forms streamlined for speed, but in many static forms as well. Here it is seen in the tail of a Douglas transport plane.

This vigorous line frequently appears in modern structural
forms. The steel and wood bridge from the Administration
Building, New York World's Fair.

Beautifully rhythmic forms of purely functional origin.
"Hortonspheroids", or, in plain language, oil tanks.

are indicated. By means of these two lines a series of squares can be drawn, diminishing to infinity around a center and forming by their outline a square spiral. On this square spiral a true logarithmic spiral can be drawn. For this reason Mr. Hambidge calls our golden-section rectangle a "rectangle of the whirling squares." We too are whirling by

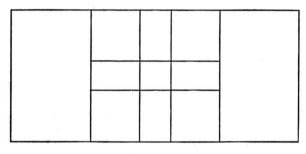

FIGURE 11

this time, but we have only been introduced to the ABC's of Dynamic Symmetry.

There are many other fascinating and significant arrangements to be made of squares and their golden sections, and others than those described undoubtedly can be utilized. But the basic principle of all is the golden section principle. Mr. Hambidge uses three rectangles in addition to the two we have discussed, principally, I think, because they lead in a logical progression from the square to the root-five rectangle. Thus, the diagonal of a square is the length of a root-two rectangle; the diagonal of a root-two is the length of a root-three; similarly a root-four can be formed from a root-three, and a root-five from a root-four (the height in all cases being assumed as unity). But while they may all be subdivided into reciprocals by means of the diagonal and the perpendicular to the diagonal, four of them lack the dynamic attributes inherent in the principle of extreme and mean proportion and found only in the golden-section rectangle and the root-five rectangle (Figure 13). There are no other quantities in this series of which one can say that the smaller is to the greater as the greater is to their sum.

Mr. Hambidge's root-two rectangle (in which the end is one and the side the square root of two, or in which the height is the height of a square and the length is the diagonal of that square) has the proportional ratio of the circle-and-square system of symmetry used by Roman, Renaissance and many modern artists. It is definitely static in character. (See Plates 70 and 71.) The root-three rectangle has the proportional ratio of the six-pointed star and hexagon, which also have been used frequently

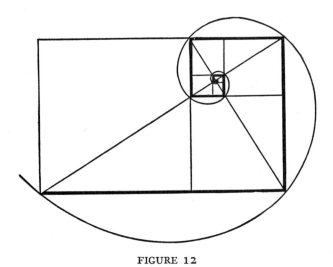

FIGURE 12

by architects to obtain the "regulating lines" [4] of their designs. It also is static. (See Plate 72.) The root-four rectangle is composed of two squares (its end is one and its side is two) and as such has little utility. The cross-

[4] Le Corbusier's phrase, in *Toward a New Architecture.*

lines of a five-pointed star are divided in golden sections, as shown in Plate 72.

Our brief summary of some of the properties of the golden-section and the root-five rectangle is sufficient to show that, given an area which

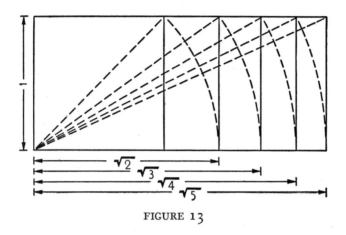

FIGURE 13

can be fitted as a whole into either one of these shapes, or a combination of them, the designer has almost unlimited scope for the creation of a framework or "design trellis" within it. Any number of these schemes of subdivision may be devised, but in every part of every one the same ratio can be recalled—the ratio of extreme and mean proportion. In this way a rhythm can be made to permeate every detail of the structure, so that as the eye passes over it there is an experience of fulfilled expectation, and we feel a serenity and rightness and completeness in the composition.

Great design has been achieved without any knowledge of Dynamic Symmetry, and without any conscious application of the golden section principle. Great design has been based on the square-and-circle scheme, or the hexagon scheme, neither of which is dynamic in the sense that it

159

embodies the vital, progressive principle of extreme and mean proportion. Although great design has been achieved without any mathematical aids, most designers in their really important work, which must stand the test of time and the critical analysis of generations, have felt the need of some sort of "regulating lines" with which to adjust their rhythmic relationships. But in every instance of great design, the designer's innate sense of right proportion has approximated the ratios he may not have known, and introduced them even when the system he consciously used did not call for them. The architect of the façade of Rheims Cathedral used an arrangement of equilateral triangles composing a mystical six-pointed star as his "design trellis," but nevertheless we find the approximate ratio of the golden section recurring again and again, and we find the lower numbers of the summation series recurring constantly. The same is true of the Arch of Titus at Rome, in which the designer used the square-and-circle system (Plate 71). There is no design in the world, however, which has the serene perfection of the design of the Parthenon, where the designer consciously and exactly applied the system of root-five rectangles and the golden section of areas. (See Appendix A.) That the perfection of his work was no accident we can see by comparing his façade with that of the Temple of Ceres at Paestum, built a century earlier when the Greek architects were still feeling their way toward a correct solution of their basic problem.

Mind you, the architect of the Parthenon did not create his basic scheme. This had been done for him, and generations of gifted men had worked to adjust its elements more and more accurately in relation to each other. He took the scheme as it came to him and made the ultimate and perfect harmonization of its parts, beyond which there was nothing better to be done with that scheme. His work was inspired and in no sense mechanical, for the geometry he used was a tool as inert in itself as a sculptor's chisel. As a matter of fact, it needs almost as much ability to use geometry in design as to get along without it, perhaps more.

Our problems today seldom come to us prepared by generations of predecessors: they are new, both in function and form, and often in materials and methods as well. It is more than ever necessary that we bring to bear on them a trained and accurate sense of proportions, and that we use whatever means are available for improving our vision and for testing it. Knowledge of the ratios of extreme and mean proportion, and experience in creating them, will refine and sharpen our sense of rightness in dealing with areas and dimensions, but the more nearly automatic we can make the exercise of this sense, the more vital our work will be. Our designs should shine in our minds, rhythmical and whole, as a composer's music sings itself to him before his ears have ever heard it. If later we will test our vision for the perfection of its harmonics, it may gain in clarity and purity; but the geometry of our work should be as innate and spontaneous as the geometry of growing forms.

The rhythmic relationships we create must be perceived by the unaided eye, without the assistance of dividers and slide rules, and when seen their rightness must be felt emotionally. Their origins, similarly, should be in our eyes and in our emotional responses. In this way the geometry of design will provide a basic system for the creation of order in whatever we make of our world.

CHAPTER ELEVEN: RHYTHM OF LINE AND FORM

"Rhythm is a movement that tends to come to rest, that is taken up and carried on despite partial assimilations, and which is concluded only when the vibrations are stilled by their diffusion through the whole." —LEO STEIN

There is a time when a design is merely an image in the designer's mind; there usually is a stage when it has become a network of lines on paper; and lastly with these lines as a guide some craftsman or some succession of craftsmen make it a reality. The mental image, seen only by the designer, and the finished object, look alike: the network of lines looks like neither.

We are in the habit of representing any three-dimensional object, a building, a machine, or a man, by drawing lines on paper to indicate its silhouette and principal subdivisions. If asked why we know that a particular arrangement of lines represents a man, we would answer, no doubt wearily, "Because it looks like a man." But actually it doesn't look in the least like a man: there is nothing whatever in our bodies that corresponds to these bent wires we map on our paper. We have merely made a symbol of a man, a symbol generally recognized and accepted, but corresponding to the actuality little more closely than the three letters which also mean "man" to us. In actuality an object has forms and areas, and these have contours: the forms and areas make silhouettes and patterns against the background, or against each other, and these are shifting and unstable:

162

they change as the object moves, as we move, as the light moves. But throughout all this variation in aspect the object does not lose its recognizable identity. We know our friend when he is walking away from us or when he is walking toward us. We recognize the Church of St. Martin de Boscherville if we look down on it first from the hilltop behind it or if we arrive from the other side at its front door. The contours of a plane as we see it flying over us bear almost no resemblance to the contours of the same plane as we stand beside it at the airport, yet we know it is the same plane. What we recognize in every instance are not the shifting outlines of an object, which we may never have seen before in quite that arrangement, but the component forms which these outlines define. A store of experiences derived from our sense of touch and our habit of viewing objects from various angles enables us to know forms in their three dimensional character, so that they retain their identity no matter how our viewpoint shifts. Our first interest is in form, the stable, rather than in contour, the inconstant.

So the designer, dealing with the problem of line in design, does not think of line as bent-wire maps on paper: he thinks of it as the contours of three dimensional forms or of the areas into which these forms may be divided. Line is important to him because of the volumes it defines, and the designer's first interest is in these volumes. If he is wise, he will refrain from any attempt at first to translate his mental image into drawn diagrams, but will give it immediate substance, however crudely, by means of plastic clay or easily carved wood or even constructions of paper and cardboard. Step by step he will develop his image into an object that can be handled and walked around and viewed from all possible angles. When this model gives him complete satisfaction, it is time for him to begin making the diagrams that will guide its final translation into reality.

In this whole process he will seek to create, in his design, forms that repeat or recall or harmonize with each other, and they will do this not only by their shape but by their stresses and thrusts and functional action. If this kind of rhythmic relationship between forms and areas is created, the lines that define them will also be rhythmical. According to the geometricians line has only direction, and it is as direction that it is important to us: the direction our eye and our hand follow as they move over forms, perceiving their character, sensing their volumes, feeling their strains, their reactions, their repose. If, in perceiving an object, these movements repeat themselves within a proportional scale, we sense a rhythmic recurrence that pleases us as do the rhythmic movements of a dance.

In Brunelleschi's dome at Florence, the upward leap of his eight vaulting ribs defines a beautifully proportioned octagonal mass: its eight curving surfaces express upward thrusts against the force of gravity that come to rest in serene equilibrium at their meeting point. Ribs and vaults among themselves create a varied rhythm, and their movement, and the form they define, are repeated in the four smaller domes that thrust like buttresses against the collar of the great dome. They are echoed again in the four still smaller semi-domes that crown the bays of the remaining sides. Similarly in the Taj Mahal, the great dome is repeated in the four smaller flanking domes, and in the lanterns of the free-standing minarets around it, while the contour of these domes is recalled in the shapes of many arched openings.

In a Douglas plane, the form of the fuselage is repeated in the form of the motor housing, and the horizontal fins of the tail recall in diminished size the contours of the wings. Everywhere in the plane we find a recurring contour-line, consisting of a forward thrust and a long back-

164

ward sweep: it begins with a relatively short parabolic arc that quickly straightens out into a long backward-streaming curve which gradually and gently descends to the level of its starting point. This line defines the form that bodies take when they have adapted themselves most perfectly to the flow of air or water currents, and it has become, as much by its own character as by association, expressive of forward-straining flight. We find this form and its expressive line recurring throughout the whole structure of the plane, as we find them in fish and birds and falling drops of water. I do not know where in modern design to look for an example of rhythm of line composed more perfectly than in these transport planes. Exigencies of function have forced every form to be modeled after the same pattern, a peculiarly significant pattern, until from any point of view we find in the whole a harmonious consonance approaching perfection.

This line, composed of a short parabolic curve and a long sweep, straight or almost straight, expresses force and grace in whatever form it defines. Its nervous tension gives an especially dramatic quality to the vertical fin of the tail of a Douglas plane: the line begins along the backbone of the body, to rise slowly in a gentle curve, then suddenly sweeps upward in a straight, steep leap to a startling height, arches backward as if its energy were spent, and drops straight down to the axial line of the fuselage. There surely is no more exciting form in modern design. But the line is significant wherever it occurs, and in forms that have nothing to do with flight or with "streamlining." It is in fact the ideal toward which the Doric capital was evolved (see Figure 22, page 271), and it recurs constantly in the profile of Greek vases, Greek ornament and Greek statues. In Gothic building, the long upward sweep terminating in a shorter parabolic curve is the most characteristic feature of the style, and from it we derive much of the emotional satisfaction we feel so strongly in Gothic interiors—a satisfaction that is based on a sense of competent and exquisite engineering almost as much as on noble proportions or spiritual uplift. In our design today we are exploring the possibilities of this peculiarly tense but gracefully adequate line, and we feel its appropriateness to our mood: which probably explains our tendency to create "streamlined" forms in objects that will never move or feel a flowing current. In reality we seek in forms a combination of tension, force and grace, and if we understand this we can get it without giving inappropriate air-foil sections to our objects. To appreciate our subconscious aim we need only contrast this powerful line with what Hogarth called the "Line of Beauty"—a sinusoidal curve that has grace and charm without strength or tension. Hogarth's beauty was a rococo beauty, and while he had anything but a rococo attitude toward life he could not help but derive his standards of taste from the preferences of his age. His line was appropriate to the graceful delicacy of the design of his time, but it is weak and inept in the stark primitivism of ours. Our "Line of Beauty" expresses a form that has much more energy, more power of resistance, than anything the rococo period found sympathetic.

Mansard's dome of Les Invalides in Paris is a fine flower of the rococo period in its more vigorous youth. It is a masterly design, rhythmical and complete, but what we find most satisfying in it today is its effect of balanced thrusts and stresses, its revelation of graceful but thoroughly adequate engineering. Its major lines express a delicate equilibrium of forces artfully and rightly achieved, and to this our sense of appreciation responds much more enthusiastically than to the charming ornament with which it has been embellished or to the sinuous forms in which some of its lines of force have been concealed. But this rhythmical balance of forces is more clearly revealed in Brunelleschi's dome in Florence, with less overlay of irrelevant material, and consequently we find Il Duomo more sympathetic to our modern mood and our more primitive taste than the later Invalides.

We ask that our modern forms be expressive of function, and that our materials and techniques be revealed with similar candor; we also ask that line in our design, in so far as it can be separated from the form it bounds and can be considered as directional movement, shall express the forces active in our forms. We respond to the revelation of structural efficiency. Our great modern bridges owe much of their beauty, and the popularity of their beauty, to this display of exquisite engineering. The public feels their rightness with gratifying unanimity, and its response has grown as the bridges have evolved toward this ideal of frankness. The Brooklyn Bridge set an extraordinarily high standard; pioneer efforts, the result of clear vision and great inspiration, often do just this. But the piers of the Brooklyn Bridge were of masonry and no more like them were built. It was necessary to find an equally satisfactory expression in steel. The designers of the Manhattan and Queensborough Bridges in New York felt an apologetic need to relieve the stark simplicity of their steel piers with ornamental elaborations; the result is unhappy and un-popular. It was originally planned—wonderful to relate—to draw a boiled shirt of masonry completely over the steel framework of the piers of the George Washington Bridge, but this calamity was averted by vigorous protest. The Triborough in New York and the great Bay and Golden Gate Bridges in San Francisco were planned in no spirit of apology or conceal-ment whatever, to reveal every member of every truss, every gusset plate and rivet head. But they were planned with a sensitive appreciation of the importance of proportion and line, and as a result they are thrillingly successful. The public response to their beauty is universal, deep, and unself-conscious.

These bridges are a training course in rhythmic line. The basis of the scheme is of course the vertical lines of the piers opposing and supporting the far-flung catenary curves of the cables, these in turn opposing and supporting the gentler upward curve of the roadway. But in the great piers themselves, on a heroic scale, every tension and compression member is seen in action, composing a positively vital harmony of thrusts and counterthrusts. The curve of the cable suggests complete adequacy: a catenary curve is the line naturally assumed by a flexible cord supported at two points, and hence there is no sense of uncompensated strain in its line. The delicate lines of the vertical cables to the roadway repeat the major supporting motif of the piers, diminishing rhythmically to nothing in the center and increasing again beyond. These few statements apply only to the direct elevations of the structures; as one approaches them and crosses them or sees them from various viewpoints at the side or below, there is ever-changing variety in their rhythmic composition. It is true that only God can make a tree, but men need not be ashamed of their bridges.

We have not been so successful with our buildings. As the fascinating patterns of their steel framework rise against the sky, we feel a deep regret that a sheath of far less interesting masonry must conceal them, and we are wondering actively if this is really necessary. Economy of space in our crowded cities, economy of maintenance, and the fire laws, have compelled us to put our screen against the weather outside rather than inside the frame. But there is a probability that all these deterrents may be removed in time. Then, as we have already said when we discussed steel as a building material, it will be possible to hang our weather-proof enclosure inside a supporting cage, leaving the exterior structural mechanism exposed to view. This will mean a vast enlargement of the designer's vocabulary and an enormous increase in interest and emotional stimulus. It will be possible to follow the lines that make our structures stand erect, observing the stresses and tensions at work in them as we observe the clearly revealed engineering of our modern bridges or of Gothic vaults and buttresses.

Our steel buildings will then be able to rival in variety of structural organization, in complex rhythmic integration, in emotional appeal, the masonry structures of earlier builders. In masonry construction as it was practised in the most vital periods, structural elements composed the design and were revealed perforce in their functional capacity. In our building to date, even the best, the structural elements have been concealed of necessity within a masonry envelope, and their functional existence indicated in the vaguest way only by emphasis on certain vertical or horizontal lines. The current severity of exterior is vastly preferable to elaboration by application of classical orders and ornament in which the earlier builders of steel buildings indulged, but it is not true simplicity. Simplicity and concealment are antipathetic, and concealment would seem permissible only in the case of those mechanisms where ease of operation and maintenance demand it.[1] A building is always more simple if we see clearly what makes it stand up and what holds it together, provided of course that the functional structure is organized in a unified rhythmic scheme of proportion and line, as the Gothic builders organized

[1] It is often desirable to enclose a mechanism when the operator would be confused or distracted by too many parts, when safety is involved, or when it is difficult to keep an intricate mechanism free of dust and dirt. But many domestic machines now enclosed in cabinets of one kind or another may be released to view, with great gain in interest and beauty, when our homes become entirely dust-free.

theirs. If the modern designer could leave his steel exposed, the material out of which he could construct his rhythmic relationships of area and line would be enormously enlarged, and it would all be essential and significant material: his design would gain thereby in unity, and hence in simplicity.

A world's fair justifies itself, in one sense, as an experimental field, where tentative essays in structural experiment are permissible simply because they are impermanent, and because the carnival spirit does not demand that every flight of invention be justified by utilitarian logic. One of the functions of world's fair architecture is to be amusing, and if it achieves this end it may be highly inconsequential and non-functional by more prosaic standards. Hence world's fairs have always provided a field-day for designers to try out, in form and building technique, all sorts of ideas that would not be tolerated if their permanent acceptability had to be guaranteed in advance. While there are many failures, there are usually a few successes indicating future lines of development. The world has been a long time catching up with Eiffel's tower of 1888, or Louis Sullivan's Transportation Building of 1893. The New York World's Fair made its own contribution, perhaps too tentatively, in experiments in new forms and in the external use of steel on enclosed buildings.

It is unfortunate that the great Perisphere of this Fair of 1939 was not planned as one of these latter experiments. Its steel frame had a thrilling beauty which the structure did not possess as a perfectly smooth sphere. The frame added an intricate rhythmic variety to the simple unity of the major form, and if its white skin had been placed inside this frame to accent its members the effect would have been startlingly beautiful. The United States Steel Building was a modest essay in revealed structure, and no one could fail to feel the effectiveness of its

170

curved trusses supporting the dome. At the risk of inviting an absurd comparison of this temporary building with Brunelleschi's masterpiece, it is fair to point out that these steel trusses indicated how our modern materials and techniques can be made to provide the same rhythmic accents to the major form, achieved by Brunelleschi with his vaulting ribs of masonry.

In the du Pont Building at the same Fair, a steel frame, originally designed to support a curved wall, was left exposed simply because one did not have the heart to hide it behind stucco. In a fair one can do this sort of thing, for the hell of it, such as would not be possible in more normal circumstances. As a lovely pattern against the sky, this curved framework fulfilled its exposition function of being interesting, novel and beautiful. But it also indicated what a great enlargement of his esthetic resources, particularly in rhythmic line, awaits the more sober builder who will develop the visual possibilities of his steel instead of hiding it away.

Louis Sullivan remarked that there are only three letters in the alphabet of architecture—the vertical line, the horizontal line, and the arch.[2] Modern architecture, so far, has gotten along with the A and B of this trio, but it hasn't benefited by the limitation. It is true that in the vernacular of steel, concrete and glass there is small place for the arched opening and little reason for the vaulted ceiling. Principally because it is easier to roll steel in straight sections, we have practised a rectangular style. Our low buildings emphasize horizontal lines, our tall buildings with few exceptions specialize in vertical lines. This is right and proper, and

[2] Sullivan, like the whole International School that flourishes today, ignored the canted line of a sloping roof. Sloping roofs have definite functional advantages in certain structures, and no architecture that eliminates them as a matter of dogma can be really functional.

can be extremely effective. Wright's Kaufmann house near Pittsburgh is a masterly arrangement in horizontals, and Le Corbusier, Mies van der Rohe and a number of others have shown the possibilities of this highly ascetic manner. The Daily News Building in New York is an equally severe exercise in verticals, which have become an accepted expression, almost a cliché, for skyscrapers. But the vocabulary is extremely meager, and we are bound in time to find it too restricted. It is easy to see that our bridges gain enormously through the opposition of straight and curved lines. As we grow easier, less self-conscious, in our handling of steel and concrete we are inevitably beginning to experiment with a wider range of forms and to seek greater subtlety and variety of line in our rhythmic arrangements.

We will not enlarge our alphabet merely by adding an arcuated form to our verticals and horizontals. What we seek is something more dynamic, more relevant to our own mood. The vertical line, the horizontal line, the arch, all are relatively static: the first has strength, stability, adequacy, and it may have of course an uplift which carries our spirits up with it; the horizontal line expresses successful opposition to the force of gravity, an achieved inertia, and if prolonged it may have a liberating breadth and scope; the arch represents an equilibrium of opposing forces, and it may have a fine serenity and dignity. But our spirit today seeks an expression of force, active energy, positive tension, embodied in forms peculiarly our own and significant to us as the forms of planes and automobiles and machine tools and bridges are ours. The rhythms we seek to create are vibrant and alive, not static—at least they must seem so to us, whatever they will seem to later times that go beyond us.

Again the New York World's Fair has served as a proving ground for new forms. The Perisphere and Trylon demonstrated that nothing

172

is impossible to our building art, and, together with the long sweep of
the ramp that married them, they achieved a dynamic opposition of
forces which neither would have expressed alone. Mr. Harrison and
Mr. Fouilhoux created here a symbol of a liberated architecture which
will find its variety in major forms and not in elaboration of details.
These particular forms may not be functional in any other context, but
they proved that the range of possible forms is unlimited.

The walls sloping inward at the top, in Mr. Geddes' General Motors
Building, created an interesting rhythmic pattern of vertical lines and
curves—a sort of Gothic turned inside out. The grouped masses of this
building, repeating or recalling the same motifs and the same groups of
motifs throughout, were finely rhythmical in a fresh vernacular. The
spiral ramp of the Ford Building, with its sweeping curves and its inward-
sloping, angular piers, was a logical expression, in reinforced concrete,
of a dynamic opposition of forces, and of lines expressing forces. This
ramp also demonstrated a type of highway construction which is dis-
tinctly prophetic of a world freed from many of the technical limitations
of the past. Throughout the Fair there were numerous experiments in
new forms, some successful, some merely bizarre, but all liberating in
their final effect. And it is interesting to see how often our favorite "line
of force" recurred—the long sweep, the sudden terminating curve. Here
we found an expression of active energy, of nervous tension, especially
stimulating to our responses. This line lent itself, and still does, to the
tense rhythms we prefer to create in buildings as in planes and automobiles, ships and machines.

Rhythms of line and form, like rhythms of proportion, are created by
a sensitive discrimination and a trained eye, and there is no mathematical
means of educating and testing our vision here, except as to proportional

relationships. The dynamic expressiveness of line and form, the directional value of line, the value of repetition and recall, the adequate balancing of masses and forces—all these must be felt and cannot be made subject to rule. We train our discrimination, as we train our bodies, by exercise, and the healthy, vigorous human body in action is the most productive field of study we can find. Balance of forces is the essential factor in any human action, and this self-contained balance is expressed in an inexhaustibly intricate interplay of line and form. Later we shall discuss the human body as the source of balance and symmetry in design, but its importance to any adequate appreciation of rhythmic line and form must be indicated here; and the value of similar study of many natural phenomena must not be overlooked—the branching of trees, the currents of flowing water, animal forms and movements, wind-eroded and waterworn sand, to pick a few at random. If we see how life and movement flow in inevitable and uninterrupted rhythmic patterns, and if we feel the infinite satisfaction of their perfect harmony, we can take up the problems of our steel, concrete and plastics with a competence at least somewhat enhanced. We may hope to inject some of the harmonics of nature into our own contributions to our environment, and eliminate some of the discordant production with which we are in the habit of defiling the world we must live in.

CHAPTER TWELVE: DOMINANCE, ACCENT AND SCALE

"The most absolute and the most important idea in the production of art is Principality, that one object or order shall be supreme." —H. R. POORE

A design in music marches across the field of our attention like a procession, with all its elements and intervals revealed in the precise order planned by its composer-marshal. Thus its melodic structure is clearly stated and may be clearly perceived in the manner its master desired. But a visual design is presented to our field of vision like a massed army, with all its commands, its banners and its *matériel* drawn up for simultaneous inspection. Neither an army nor a design can be inspected instantaneously, however. The little general must march up and down the lines of his troops if he is to view them all, and the little spotlight of our fovea centralis must play over a design point by point if the design is to be seen completely. The whole design may stand before us in our visual field, but we see it clearly only by feeling it over with the finger of our acute vision. It is this method of serialized seeing that makes it possible for us to feel the rhythmic relationships existing between areas, forms, lines, textures and colors: it supplies the time element without which rhythms could not be felt.

But it does not supply this time element in any clear-cut order. The general has an advantage, because he knows from experience just where to begin his inspection and how to conduct it if he is to come out right

175

without missing any of his ranks. The fovea centralis hasn't had this military training, and besides, the design it is to inspect may not be assembled in a familiar pattern. Our visual inspection may begin at the wrong end, it may read its rhythms backward, it may jump here and there like an agitated flea, and it may miss entirely large hunks of extremely pertinent matter. To sum up, the melodic structure of music is clearly stated in precise order, and may be read, as it were, from left to right. The melodic structure of design, on the other hand, is discharged at you in one blast, and unless you have the key to it and understand its order, it may strike you as having no order that you need bother about.

There are no fixed rules of procedure for the seeing of objects, and that no doubt is why so many of us see them so badly, and are so dull and inept in our esthetic responses. That is why the emotional response to music, even the intelligent appreciation of music, is so much more widespread than any active response, either emotional or intellectual, to design. Thus, many people who have an ardent and understanding love of music are satisfied to live in hideous houses amid appalling furniture, and never lead a revolt against the squalor that surrounds them in their home towns. I've known painters to do the same, but then it often happens that painters also have little or no sense of design.

Understanding is the prerequisite to appreciation in design, as in so many other fields. Whenever people have lived for a long time under healthy, happy but relatively static conditions, as in the case of a contented and prosperous peasantry, they have time to become thoroughly familiar with the conditions of their life, and to work out a satisfactory frame for it. They develop a picturesque costume, a native style of architecture that meets their needs in a practical way and is also delightful to behold, a type of furniture often gay, colorful, esthetically fine. They also develop folk music, folk song and folk dances of great charm: but the point is that their visual design is as good as their music, sometimes better. They have had time to understand their problems and solve them to their own satisfaction.

Similarly in our own time, we have fine discrimination in dealing with those things which we know thoroughly, as we noted near the beginning of this book. When we understand the function of an object, its manufacture and materials, and can assess the relative importance of its parts, and have not been confused or misled by false education, our judgment is accurate and our emotional responses profound. Also our production is highly creditable. We know *how* to look at our motors and airplanes, machine tools, bridges, kitchen ranges and all our indispensable mechanical gadgets. We know what is important in their design and we learn to read it as fluently "from left to right" as though it were a musical score.

All this repetition of what has been said before leads up to the fact that a designer must assist his audience, by every possible means, to read his rhythms aright. To create rhythmic relationships is not enough. If these are to be effective they must be bound together within a dominant scheme which controls all their elements and stamps them with a blood-bond. They must be presented in an orderly arrangement, with accents, emphases and suppressions which give a clue to their reading. And they must be held within a scale which makes it possible to grasp their ratios, and which at the same time relates them to our human proportions.

A competent designer instinctively chooses a theme, or leitmotif, for a given structure, and allows it to influence all his choice of form and

177

line within that structure.[1] His theme usually is suggested by the problem itself: he abstracts it from the object with which he must deal, from its most essential shapes, its structural necessities, or its functional purpose, and thus it has significance and authenticity. Often his selection is not made by a careful balancing of various possibilities, but by a quick instinctive perception of what is most vital, most characteristic among these possibilities. In many instances structural or functional necessity determines his choice of theme without his option, and his job is simply to refine and clarify and repeat the forms and lines that are offered him by his subject. In airplane and bridge design, as we have seen, form is strictly functional in the extreme sense that no other form would work— any other form in fact would be disastrous. But the designer still has scope, and we have been able to watch him at work as he perfected these forms, stripped them of confusing non-essentials, and gradually made them govern every element of his design. Within a few years we have seen this evolution toward perfection, from the crude transport planes of only ten years ago to the sleek silver swallows of today, from the Queensborough to the Triborough Bridge.

Since the automotive designer has been under no such helpful discipline as the airplane designer, he has defined his theme far more slowly, with many hesitations and fumblings. But here too we see it gradually emerge, the single simple form that all objects should assume if they are to move at high speed through air or water. We have seen the influence of this form slowly become evident, although not yet clearly defined, in the body of the car, and we have seen it mold the hood and the fenders

[1] "The form of the whole is therefore present in every member," Dewey, *Art as Experience*, page 56. And his phrase "the reciprocal interpretation of parts and whole" (page 171) is an accurate expression of the designer's aim.

178

in new shapes, with a progressive elimination of excrescences. We shall soon see hood and fender themselves eliminated by absorption into the body, and the emergence of a form that is encumbered by no barnacles of lamps or handles or trunks whatever. It will be a sleek projectile, but within its unity there will be a subtle variety of planes, lines, and accents; a satisfying variety, because they will all be controlled by the major theme and all contribute to the functional perfection of the whole.

In many less dramatic fields we find this clarifying process at work. We undertake to design an office appliance, a Mimeograph, let us say, and find that a certain major form is enforced by the operating mechanism itself. Within that form we find that a certain radius is required at vital points: we accept this radius as our norm, and repeat it wherever a radius is indicated. We have simplified our surfaces and our masses as much as possible, and reduced our scheme to vertical and horizontal lines, with one large accented radius, and one small radius many times repeated. With our few controls repeating the same form in different sizes, and our levers, handles and knobs likewise uniform, we complete the unification of what had previously been an exceedingly complex, even confusing mechanism.

We apply the same unifying process to gas ranges, refrigerators, X-ray apparatus, furnaces and machine tools: find the dominant form within the essential elements of the machine, and let that determine our choice of form and line throughout the whole. We have seen how Brunelleschi set us an august example of just this method of design when he built his dome, and likewise the builder of the Taj Mahal. The Gothic builders allowed every phase of their gigantic and infinitely complex schemes to be governed by the engineering principles of the pointed arch, the vaulting rib and the buttress. In our time we have seen our skyscrapers progress from the Woolworth Building and the Grand Central Building, their faces broken out with a rash of historic acne, to the smooth-cheeked masses of the RCA Building in Rockefeller Center and the vibrant verticality of the Daily News Building. Both these latter have been subjected to the control of a dominant theme inherent in their structure, and both have been vindicated by the profound response to their beauty among the mass of the people who must be moved if art is to have any deep-rooted vitality.

As we bring our scheme into subjection to a pervasive motif, we must arrange our rhythmic structure with major and minor accents related to each other within a logical scale, so that our pencil-point of vision may be led from accent to accent and feel the relationship between them. By means of these accents we provide starting points for the eye, and steps whereby it may pass progressively over the whole scheme. We direct the eye in its exploratory course, and we provide that variety within our unity which must save the scheme from too quick exhaustion. Every competent designer has felt this need for directional control of vision and his success must be conditional upon his skill in guiding our perception of his work.

As we approach the west front of Notre Dame de Rheims, the major accent of the façade is the three great shadowed porches over the three portals. They are functionally most important, they are nearest our eye level, and so they are most deeply modeled and most richly elaborated of all the elements of the façade. But they are not equal in their appeal: the central porch is highest and widest and is crowned by a dominant gable, piercing the circle of the great rose above it. This major rose is recalled in smaller roses above the other portals, and the three gables of the porches are recalled in minor gables on either side, so that we have an arrangement of five units ascending in scale toward the center. From the piers of the three porches, four buttresses lead the eye upward along the towers, but at each course these buttresses are united with the horizontal elements of the scheme by columns, niches, moldings, statues and turrets. There are three principal horizontal courses forming the whole façade, below the towers. First there are the three porches with the five steep gables above. In the second is the great burst of the rose, forty feet in diameter, occupying the exact center and focal point of the scheme, beneath a pointed arch which gives it added importance (the rose is the symbol of Our Lady, and its glory is placed directly in the line of her vision as she sits enthroned on the altar); the four buttresses flower here into their greatest elaboration, becoming columned tabernacles crowned with tall turrets and sheltering statues, and between the buttresses the rose is flanked by four tall, unglazed windows, two on either side, emphasizing the richness of the rose by their own dark and narrow voids. The third course is a band of statues of the kings of France, each in the niche of a tabernacle, beneath a pointed arch and a small steep gable. The towers grow tall and simply vertical, with central windows repeating the windows that flank the rose below. When these towers were crowned with spires, we had an arrangement of five elements again, this time horizontally emphasized, each distinct in character yet bound to the others in rhythms of lines and proportions and repetition of details, and each leading upward to the termination of the spires.

An arrangement of accents and directional lines as superb as this (we have mentioned only a few of the major elements, but the scheme is carried to almost incredible completeness), such masterly control of vision, could be achieved only because the basic scheme had been tried again and again and gradually perfected. Hundreds of churches comparable in importance to Rheims were built in France within a space of three centuries, and actually thousands of a scale smaller but still awesome by the standards of today. The master builders who did these jobs were working in a great experimental laboratory, where innumerable operations of a similar nature were going on around them. They had every facility for study and experiment, a great fund of accumulated knowledge and a body of highly skilled craftsmen, the stimulus of high standards, keen artistic rivalry and an enthusiastic, intelligently critical public. They progressed toward perfection: Rheims façade is as far beyond the façade [2] of St. Stephen's at Caen, fifty years earlier, as the Lincoln Zephyr of today surpasses a Model T Ford, and in very much the same way.

Threes and fives have been useful numbers in the stressing of accents. As we saw in Chapter Seven, the eye does not easily count beyond six, and six cannot be balanced on a central integer as we can balance three and five. We must soon take up this matter of balance and why it is essential, but for the present you may take for granted what every designer knows by instinct—that a design without balance makes us definitely uncomfortable. So wherever we can we use threes and fives of anything that must be arranged symmetrically (and three, five and eight are numbers of the Fibonacci series, be it noted).

Five hundred years separate the church built for Our Lady of Rheims from the Petit Trianon built by Louis XV for Madame du Barry, but the French have always done well by the women they honor, and the principles of design have no dates. The Petit Trianon is a slight but exquisite expression in the vernacular of its time, and a study in the delicate placing of accents. It is a small building of two stories and basement, and in the court façade all three are seen, with five windows in each. The base-

[2] Note the word "façade": certain features of St. Stephen's need not take second place to anything else in France.

182

ment windows are five panes high, the windows of the principal story eight panes high, and the attic windows three. In addition to their greater height, the windows of the principal story are given further emphasis by heavier frames and cornices. The basement story is demarked from the other two by rustication of its stone, creating a conspicuous difference of texture, while the two upper stories are united by tall Corinthian pilasters that run from basement to cornice. These pilasters are carried on a slightly projecting bay, and thus the three central windows of the upper stories are framed and given added importance: they are lifted out of the five and accented. In so compact a scheme there is no need for a single dominating feature, but the eye is exactly centered on a central panel of nine windows crossing in three horizontal and three vertical lines, and flanked on each side by a similar vertical line of three. From the center the eye is led outward through a graduated scale of accents, and a minimum of comprehension is needed to feel the rhythmic balance of the whole. As a final essential element, the walls of the basement court abut the house in re-entrant curves, pierced by small round windows. These gracious curves both stress and relieve the simple rectangularity of the façade, and at the same time extend a lateral dimension that might otherwise seem too short for the height and too little earth-bound.

The Petit Trianon is slight compared with Rheims Cathedral, but much of our time today is spent on work still slighter. As machines our liners and planes and transcontinental trains are as fabulous as Rheims, but when we build them we know they will last for a few years at most and we feel that they are still tentative. But on these and on our mechanical devices of every kind we can exercise the same creative ingenuity as if we were always building Rockefeller Centers: they call for the same skillful handling of rhythms, and of the accents that give the clue to these rhythms. It is probably an uneasy sense of the need of accents that has placed so much superfluous chrome plate, in moldings and ornaments, on our motor cars. But as our cars become more compactly designed, more completely functional and hence more significant in form, we will find that our accents can be stressed in the essential elements of the design itself, and we will realize that we have used chrome merely in an effort to dominate an unorganized scheme. We are not doing any such fumbling at the moment with our refrigerators and kitchen ranges: here we stick to essentials and have made some really superb arrangements of the few elements we find it necessary to retain. These enameled cabinets, inside and out, are as fine in design as any armoire, cupboard or cassone of other centuries, and far more chastely classical in their ascetic simplicity.

When we build today on the grand scale, the scope of our projects is as ambitious as anything the Egyptian or Roman builders attempted, and in our vaster structures the problem of preserving some relationship to our own human dimensions overshadows all others. Scale, it is true, is a fundamental consideration in all design, large or small: it is like the key in music—once established, it must be maintained. It is easy to see the relationship between quantities represented by, say, three, five and eight, but it is not easy to see any tie between eight and fifty-five, even when the intermediate steps in extreme and mean proportion are filled in; if these steps are omitted, the case is hopeless. Yet fifty-five bears to eighty-nine approximately the same relationship that five bears to eight, and if it is possible to see the greater quantities as wholes the proportional tie becomes apparent. So the scale of any design must be established in whatever register, upper or lower, the subject calls for, and its dominant proportions must be held there. Within the major elements it is possible to carry the proportional scheme downward as far as one likes, provided the minor elements always take their place within the major and lose themselves when one looks at the whole. In huge structures it is necessary to carry the proportional scheme down far enough to relate it to ourselves, if the full emotional impact of size is to be felt.

We walk into the dirigible hangar at Lakehurst, N. J., and find ourselves in a great unobstructed enclosure, the roof borne on arched trusses that spring from the ground and are supported only at their ends. It is large, but there is nothing to give us a sense of its really enormous size until we notice an automobile parked in a distant corner and realize with a shock that it appears to be the size of a housefly. So long as this automobile is held in the field of vision the truly vast dimensions of the enclosure can be appreciated, with some effort. The Lakehurst hangar is intended to house dirigibles, not people: there is no reason why the emotional values of its scale should be stressed, as would be worth while if it were planned as an auditorium or an arena. But most of our buildings are intended to house people, and most of our mechanical products are intended to be used by people: in these the human scale, within a dominant scale if necessary, is essential.

The Gothic builders were cunning in extracting the utmost possible emotional effect from their great structures, both inside and out. On the exterior of their church, which brooded among the low buildings of their city for all the world like a huge hen squatting among a flock of very tiny chickens, they used a controlled elaboration of detail to enhance the size and to retain the human scale. Five hundred statues lined the central porch alone, on the west front of Rheims. The statues on the west portals of Chartres, probably the most perfect adaptation of sculpture to architecture ever accomplished, are elongated but attenuated human figures, and their scale is repeated in slender columns that complete the porches. Means were found to compose practically every great mass in a Gothic cathedral out of smaller elements, humanized elements, without loss of major unity or any blurring of vertical direction. Inside, humanizing schemes less complex than the exterior devices (but just as effective) were adapted so as not to disturb the still solemnity of the church's mood. Every pier is compound, composed of many vaulting ribs gathered into a bundle, increasing in number at each course as they descend, until an adequate supporting mass is accumulated without any effect of too great size or depressing heaviness. These piers, multiplied many times with the light interlacing of vaulting ribs above, the tracery of the windows and the tracery of the arches diminishing in size as they ascend, give the visitor a deep and solemn sense of vastness without crushing his human dignity. We realize how cleverly the builders accomplished this effect without marring the peace and stillness of the interior when we encounter those baroque monstrosities of altarpieces and organ screens, writhing with angels, clouds and sunbursts, which were the contribution of the Seventeenth and Eighteenth Centuries to the Gothic scene. These latter people had no sense of scale, nor of decency.

What these centuries did to the churches of France is nothing to what they did to the scheme for St. Peter's at Rome conceived by Michelangelo —who may have sired baroque but knew how to control it. Even Le Corbusier's masterly invective is hardly equal to this calamity. Michelangelo planned a building which would have been, if built as planned, one of the greatest achievements of man. For Michelangelo, at seventy-two, had solved all the problems and had the answers clearly in his passionate young brain. He knew how to plan a house worthy to be the first House of God in Christendom, and how to give it perfect unity, faultless rhythms, sonorous accents, and such scale as few men have dared to attempt. His scheme can still be seen, almost intact, on the apsidal sides, with the curved cornice of the apses recalling the vast lines of the dome above, and such a piling up of mighty stylobate, pilasters, entabulature and attic as makes one gasp. Michelangelo made even moldings express power in a way that one can scarcely believe. If his portico with its great columns had been built, the geometry of the scheme in its basic simplicity would have stood revealed: a cube, surmounted by a dome and flanked on three sides by half-cylinders, on the fourth a square portico supporting a triangular pediment. All the relations of the parts would have been evident, and the penetrating rhythms which bound the fabric together would have been exposed to our perception. But the old man died, and Vignola added two cupolas at the front corners, and then Moderna hid the whole thing behind the screen of his prolonged nave and assertive portico, which has size (and what size!) but not scale. One is startled, but not impressed, by cherubs seven feet high. Perhaps some day a pope may arise who is rich, powerful and wise enough to tear down Moderna's work and build St. Peter's as fine as Michelangelo imagined it.

Assuming that we shall succeed in overcoming the destructive forces now active in the world, and are allowed to work out a rational destiny, we shall have this problem of scale to solve in the vast structures we probably shall build. We do not have the means that other periods have had: we do not have pilasters, moldings, cornices, because we are not working in masonry and we have learned that these details are ineffectual when plastered as a thin skin on our steel buildings. Besides, the proportions of our tall buildings have outgrown even Michelangelo's gigantic orders. Nothing but simple masses count when a building rises, slender and rectangular, to heights of a thousand feet or more. (Such buildings will be built again in the world of tomorrow, never fear.) We have learned to handle masses with great skill, as Rockefeller Center and the Empire State Building (except for its egregious "mooring mast," an impertinent priapic symbol, added as an afterthought) stand to prove. And fortunately we have windows, to give us a human factor of measurement. These windows were the headache of the earlier skyscraper architects, so long as they felt they must vary and accent the windows of a thirty-story building as they are varied and accented in the little three-story Trianon or the Roman palaces of the Renaissance. Came a day when windows were not individually stressed, but were banded together in simple vertical lines as in the Daily News and the Empire State Buildings, or less successfully in horizontal lines as in the McGraw-Hill Building. Louis Sullivan and some of the Chicago school had known how to do this years before, but their fine pioneer efforts were swamped in a tidal wave of Beaux-Arts preoccupation with details. Aligned windows were a notable relief from bracketed and pedimented windows, and often highly effective. But then came architects with enough self-control to keep their accents within bounds, allowing their windows to register principally as a texture of the wall, and we have the superior effect of the RCA Building. Here they perform their most useful esthetic service, and become mere familiar units of measurement creating texture on a surface. We know their dimensions from a lifetime of experience, and it is not necessary for us to count them—they become one body in the way soldiers in ranks become a regiment, but their multitude is sufficient evidence of the building's scale.

If our method of framing steel structures is altered, as seems possible, so that the frame is revealed to the eye just as Gothic piers and buttresses are in evidence, we shall have means to develop our scale and elaborate our rhythms: we shall be able to use our steel piers, girders and trusses to

An arrangement of accents and directional lines, controlled by a single dominating theme, in the façade of Notre Dame de Rheims (before bombardment).

82 The Petit Trianon (by Jacques-Ange Gabriel, Versailles, 1768) is a study in accents. Below, the present façade of St. Peter's, Rome, bearing no relation to Michelangelo's dome.

Michelangelo's dome and apse of St. Peter's, the order partly concealed but
revealing the splendid proportions and dominant theme of the whole.

83

A Gothic cathedral brooded over its city like a hen among its chicks (Amiens). The controlled proportions of the detail emphasized size while it retained the human scale. Opposite, West Portals of Chartres. See also Plates 73 and 74.

84

86   We have no ornament to assist us, but in the RCA Building, Rockefeller Center, windows simply organized as a texture of the wall form a human unit of measurement.

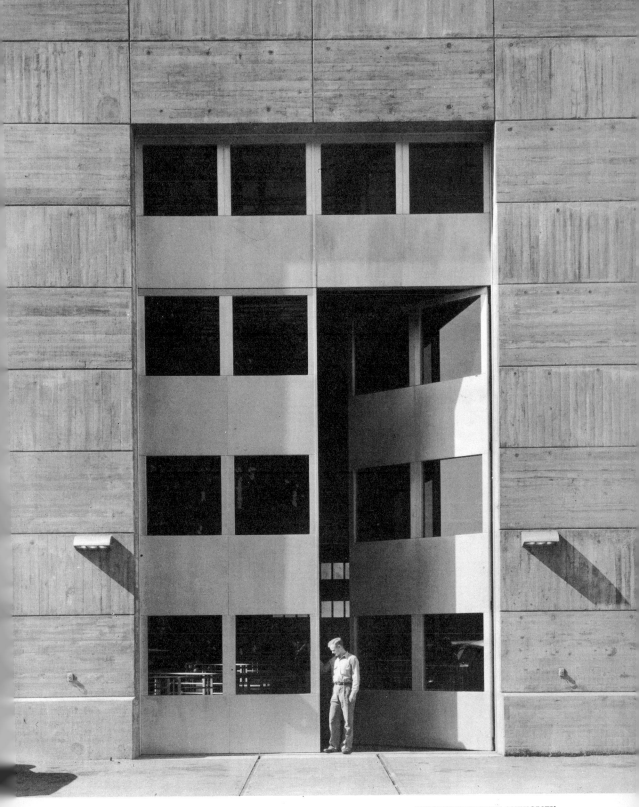

A magnificent simplicity serves to emphasize a really grand scale. Doors of Generator Hall, Norris Dam, for passing large pieces of machinery. R. A. Wank, Architect.

In steel construction we see members that are in tension as well as in compression,
as our bones and muscles are in both tension and compression. TVA power line.

Steel construction stirs us today because its system of thrusts and tensions is more human in principle than anything in past art. Pier of George Washington Bridge.

In the vertical direction we demand stability, adequacy, a firm resistance to the pull of the force of gravity. In the S. C. Johnson and Son office at Racine, Wis., Frank Lloyd Wright has obtained this satisfactory equilibrium by means of up-ward-thrusting forms.

The Erechtheion at Athens proves that classic designers understood the effectiveness of equilibrium created among unequal masses, and among forms and areas of unequal interest. A study in asymmetry, beside the severely symmetrical Parthenon.

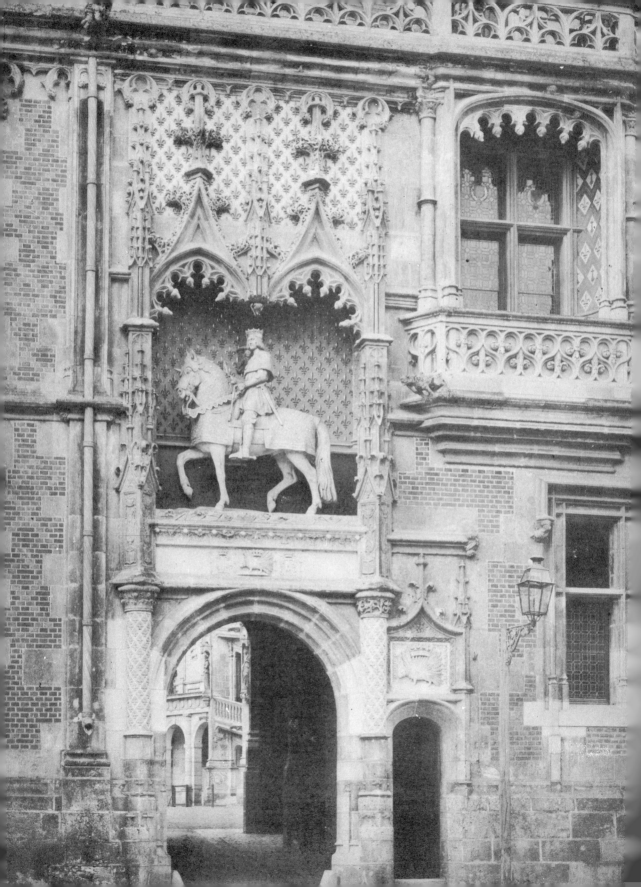

CHICAGO ARCHITECTURAL PHOTO. CO.

Two examples, four hundred years apart, of asymmetrical balance achieved by similar means.
Louis XII Wing of the Chateau de Blois, and Richardson's Glessner house, Chicago, 1886. 93

Today we prefer this dynamic quality of balance achieved between unequal forces. Above, residence at Miquon, Pa., designed by Kenneth Day, and below, the Wasserman house at Whitemarsh, Pa., by George Howe.

DAMORA

DOONER

The fluid character of the modern plan lends itself to a proper adjustment of stresses and forces. Court of apartment building, Palm Springs, Cal., by A. Lawrence Kocher and Albert Frey. See also Plate 107.

The Philadelphia Savings Fund Society Building, by Howe and Lescaze, an admirable multi-story study in asymmetry.

the same ends that Michelangelo sought when he distinguished his various masonry elements as pilasters and architrave. So long as all the structure of our buildings must be concealed beneath a thin skin of cut stone, we can design only in very large and simple masses and our means of carrying our rhythms inward and downward to the human scale will be limited. All this will be changed when we can show clearly how and why our buildings stand up: our architects must then all be engineers in fact as well as in theory, and they will construct as satisfying syntheses out of the necessities of the case as they are now doing with bridges and dams.

But the problems of design confronting us go far beyond the proportions of single structures, no matter how vast these may be. A complete disregard of dominance, accent and scale in the larger phases of our design schemes is one of the most harassing features of our chaotic world. In our minor products, and even in some individual undertakings of considerable size, we manage to enforce a dominating motif on the whole, and regulate the claims to attention of its various features, and subject them all to a controlling scale. But our cities and towns and communal enterprises in general are allowed to develop in anarchic disorder. Almost any street in any American city is a distracting and exacerbating mélange of completely unregulated elements, having no relation to each other and hence no serenity and no dignity; any main highway in any populous countryside is an array of signboards, roadside stands, service stations, unprofitable enterprises, and pathetically stranded dwellings, filling the traveler with dismay and discouragement. Whenever order is achieved, and the scene subjected to intelligent controls, as in our metropolitan parkways, our more successful expositions, a few residential communities, and a few relatively good urban developments of which Rockefeller Center is the prototype, we feel a vast sense of relief and gratitude. The

189

public appreciation of these efforts toward order is heartfelt beyond words.

Thousands today are studying the extension of this kind of organized design. In a few years we have learned to accept it as a *sine qua non* in our manufacturing operations. No intelligent industrialist today would dream of putting on the market a product which had not been studied with a view to perfecting its organization. Whatever it may be, an attempt is made to give it functional form, unity and a dominant motif, with an arrangement of accents and an adjustment of scale as skillful as the producer can devise. A few years have taught us the importance of these attributes in the things we take to the public markets. And now we are restlessly conscious of the lack of this consideration for our feelings in the market places themselves, and in the places where we work and live. Since we can do our kitchens and bathrooms so admirably, and even our parkways and some of our more progressive industrial and commercial centers, why not the whole of our environment? Why not eliminate the physical handicaps that thwart the lives of so many of us and that crowd our sanitoria with only a small portion of the pathological and neurotic cripples made by a world unadapted to human living? This is the problem that thousands are quietly studying.

The effect of our environment on our mental and physical well-being cannot be exaggerated. We are first of all animals, and we are bilateral, two-legged animals who have learned to walk upright. We translate the world around us into our own physical sensations, and we can be made cruelly uncomfortable, physically and mentally, by the influences that play upon our nerves. We have no firm grasp on serenity, and we lose our mental and physical equilibrium with fearsome ease. We need a world in which we can stand firmly and proudly, our mental balance unendangered.

CHAPTER THIRTEEN: BALANCE AND SYMMETRY

"A four-footed animal would never, in all probability, have developed the arts. His equilibrium is too stable." —LEO STEIN

Most of us have seen a championship tennis match, and known the tense hush that descends on the spectators during a critical rally. Our muscles are taut, we hold our breath, our eyes follow the ball in its swift flights to and fro; and we sigh with relief when the point is made. Or we have stood up and cheered during a long run for a touchdown, trying by our own muscular efforts of arms and legs and body to help the runner move more swiftly to his goal. And we have gone away from a boxing match with a definite feeling of fatigue because, although we may have seemed to sit quietly, our nerves and muscles have felt the impulse to mimic every feint and blow of the fighters. The entire battle has been emotionally re-enacted within our own mysterious nervous, muscular, and visceral systems.

Our pleasure in all kinds of athletic displays, ballets, and feats of physical skill is the pleasure of a vicarious participant. We feel within ourselves the exhilaration, excitement, fear and satisfaction of acts we see others perform. We project ourselves into the minds and bodies of the actors, and feel what our experience tells us we should feel if we were doing their routine. Not, mind you, what the actors do feel, because they may be too accustomed to their work to feel very deeply about it in any way at all.

The spectators usually are more excited than the players, either in a stadium or a circus; having no work to do, the spectators can give themselves up to the emotions aroused by an imaginary transplantation into the players' shoes.

This process of identifying ourselves with others whom we are observing is none the less real because it usually is subconscious. We may not be aware that we are playing the tennis match on our own nerves and muscles; it is only in moments of intense excitement that we find ourselves smashing the hat of the man in front of us, and only at particularly breath-taking feats that we find our stomachs behaving in a noticeably uncomfortable manner. But our emotional response to displays of strength and skill is none the less physical in its origin, the product of nervous impulses conveyed to our muscular systems, our viscera and our glands as we "feel ourselves into" the acts and the situations of those we are watching.

It is not surprising that we should have this habit of identifying ourselves with other people, and feeling an emotional response to their acts: we all belong to the same race, the experience of all of us runs parallel along its main lines, and all men generally respond emotionally in the same way to the same stimuli. What other men do is likely to be within the range of our comprehension, and self-identification is not too difficult. But a more curious fact is that we do not stop this procedure at the boundaries of our own race: we extend it to plants and hills, clouds and running water, and all the things made by men.

We are completely anthropomorphic, and hopelessly egocentric. We understand only in the light of our experience, and so we refer the whole visible world to ourselves as a yardstick, and interpret all the data it offers us in terms of our own past history. We are as prone to "feel ourselves into" a tree as into a ball player: we have stood in the presence of a great oak and felt the impulse to take our stance more firmly on the ground, lift our arms wide and flex our muscles as we sensed the tree's earth-gripping roots and the power of its far-spreading branches; if we did not actually complete these gestures, it was still by a kind of imagined mimicry that we made the tree's quality real to ourselves. We have soared gracefully in the summer sky as we watched a hawk above us, and something of ourselves flies swiftly with every plane followed by our eyes.

We have lifted stones, and we have put our shoulders against great weights: so when we see a masonry buttress resisting the downward and outward thrust of an arch, we have in our own muscles a gauge for measuring its strength. We imagine our own shoulder against the arch and we interpret the buttress, subconsciously it may be, in terms of the giant we should have to be to do its work. We have held steel in our hands, and tried to bend it; and so we have experience of its torsional strength. As a result there is an almost envious admiration in our attitude toward a light steel framework supporting a great weight, and something peculiarly sympathetic in the nervous tension of its members.

We constantly see and describe the forces operating in man-made things as though they were operating in bodies like ours. We speak of the upward thrust of columns and buttresses, the spring of arches, the soaring of a dome, when all we have are masses of masonry held in compression by the force of gravity as their weight is distributed along certain lines to the ground. Perhaps this is why steel construction and modern machines are so especially satisfying to us today. In steel frames we see members that are in tension as well as members that are in compression, just as the bones and muscles of our bodies are in both tension and compression when we stand upright or balance ourselves beneath a weight; here is stability achieved in a manner more like our own than anything we can see in piled-up masonry, and hence more easily and fully interpreted in terms of our own structure. In machines we see active forces moving, thrusting, resisting, overcoming, in a way we can understand perfectly from our own experience of motor activity; hence a greater range of our vital interests is aroused than could be stirred by any immobile structure. Steel construction, moving machinery, interest us and stir us today because they actually are more human than anything in the art of the past: they arouse a great mimetic activity within us, and hence we feel their values more intensely.

German psychologists invented a word that means exactly this "feeling oneself into"—*einfühlung*—and this has been less happily translated into English via Greek as *empathy*. Having named their prey, the psychologists at once were off into thickets of speculation as to how far we really physically mimic the things we see—that is, translate their seen forces into nervous impulses and motor sets of our own—and how far the whole thing happens on an ideal plane, where action exists only mentally. The argument is pointless, because it is an obvious fact that our empathic responses do often appear as overt reactions, and much oftener than we realize. We have all seen our friends under the stress of keen interest make movements of the head, hands or lips, of which they were completely unconscious, and we have every reason to suppose that we make the same betrayals ourselves. These are only surface indications of much greater activity within, affecting not only our nervous and muscular systems, but our circulatory and respiratory systems, our unstriped muscles and our ductless glands. Where mental imagery leaves off and bodily mimicry begins is of no consequence to design, if we realize that we do inevitably interpret all visual data in terms of our experience, and that our design structures must always stand translation into the familiar idiom of our own bodily activities.

The fear of falling, as we have already said, is one of the two fears we bring into the world with us. As we learn to stand on two legs, the preservation of our equilibrium becomes a vital matter: if it is disturbed, it must be instantly recovered, by whatever effort. Also strain of any kind is painful to us, and prolonged strain impossible. Therefore when we feel the tensions, the weights, the thrusts and counter-thrusts of a structure, we must feel that an equilibrium of forces has been attained and that no uncompensated stresses exist to create what would be, in human experience, a state of discomfort. If not, we too feel the discomfort, and the design makes us uneasy and dissatisfied. Unless an object contemplated has the serenity of balanced forces, our own serenity is disturbed.

"Equilibrium," to quote John Dewey, "comes about not mechanically and inertly, but out of, and because of, tension." [1] In other words, equilibrium is always attained by the opposition of equal forces. The oldest and simplest form of weighing device is the "balance," in which equal weights are suspended at equal distances from the fulcrum of a beam. But what we are balancing here is the pull of gravity on two masses, and not the masses themselves: a very small pound of lead will balance a very large pound of feathers. Unfortunately we cannot see the force of gravity doing its work, while we can see the masses: therefore, in design, the simplest method of attaining a satisfactory equilibrium is by the equal distribution of masses about a central axis. In design we need to have lead on both sides of the fulcrum, or feathers on both sides.

This type of balance we generally refer to as symmetrical—although the word "symmetry" should be restored to its older and richer meaning of

[1] Art as Experience, page 14.

195

"analogy," the measuring of one thing in terms of another. By symmetry we commonly mean, today, a mirror-like reversal of masses, forms, energies, about a center. Our human bodies, viewed directly from the front or back, have or should have this kind of symmetry when we stand erect in complete passivity. It is the symmetry of snow crystals, and of many flowers; it is the kind of symmetry children and very simple peoples always seek in their designs.

It is not for that reason negligible. Some of the finest design schemes ever conceived, including many discussed in this text, have been symmetrically balanced. Symmetry may have the dignity and serenity of complete repose, even when the forces composed are themselves gigantic. But it is necessary that the elements of a symmetrical design should have value in themselves, and form an impressive whole, or we have little besides repose and not always that. When the composition is as perfect as the Parthenon, as magnificent as Rheims, as noble as St. Peter's, as graceful as the Petit Trianon, we are satisfied. Give our design elements sufficient interest, adjust their balance with exquisite exactness, and we can bear to see them duplicated. But, except in masterly hands, there is apt to be a certain dryness, an excess of inertia, in a purely symmetrical scheme. Symmetry is not the only method of attaining equilibrium, and to our modern mood it is not as a rule the most attractive. We are inclined to prefer a less static scheme, a more dynamic opposition of forces, the greater interest and variety of an asymmetrical balance of obvious tensions.

It is true that when we stand erect and passive, eyes front, arms at the sides—the position of "Attention" in the military Manual of Arms—our bodies present a symmetrical pattern. But we find it tiresome to stand long in this position and seldom do so. We are much more apt to stand on one leg, relax the other, and counteract this disequilibrium by throwing out one hip and inclining our shoulders. Immediately symmetry is destroyed, but balance is preserved and the grace of our posture is probably enhanced. As a matter of fact, we find it tiresome to stand still for very long in any position whatever, and no matter what our action may be it inevitably involves a disturbance of our equilibrium and demands an asymmetrical readjustment. Symmetry in our bodies stands for inertia, immobility, and tediousness. Asymmetry of pose and asymmetrical balance are associated with action, play, work, and all that makes us aware of our vitality.

Our skeletal and muscular systems consist of a multitude of levers. If, on a steelyard, we place a pound weight two feet from the fulcrum, it will balance a two-pound weight one foot away from the fulcrum on the other side. This is the basic principle of the lever—Force × Distance—and it is the application of this principle in a thousand subtle mechanisms within our bodies that keeps us from falling on our faces whenever we move out of a rigid perpendicular. It works as satisfactorily in design, and in as many curious ways, as in our bodies. It is the principle of asymmetrical balance in art as in ourselves.

We cannot see the force of gravity, but we can see distances; and we are familiar from childhood with the effect of distance in multiplying forces, both inside and outside our bodies. So by judicious spacing we are able to effect an asymmetrical balance between very unequal masses. By this means the scope of design is enormously broadened and we escape from the monotonous necessity of always making our right hand do exactly what our left hand does. Our rhythms gain in variety and unexpectedness without losing any of their binding force, and our designs acquire the repose, not of inertia, not of equally distributed dead weight, but of evident, counterbalanced forces. The possibilities of arrangement, when balance is achieved by the interplay of unequal forces at varying distances, are infinite: we cannot read half of such a design, and know that all we have seen is to be seen in reverse beyond the axis. We cannot be sure, in fact, what is to be found in any part of the whole until we have explored it all. Only when we have read an asymmetrical design in all its details can we fully realize its unity, and by this active assimilation our interest is increased and held, and our pleasure enhanced.

In all this use of words there is a good deal of symbolism: we talk of this phase of design largely in metaphors. It is true that we may balance actual weights or masses, as in a building. And we may also balance actual forces whose actions are evident to the eye, as in a bridge. But we may also balance directional lines and the tensions or movements they express. Necessity compels us to do this in airplanes and motor cars and many kinds of machinery, and painters and sculptors have always done it in their compositions. We may also balance the factors that compel interest, and this is a common device for restoring stability in unequal masses, as we shall see: the grouping of elements in a small area may balance the comparative blankness of a large one, as a small spot of vermilion may balance a large expanse of dull maroon, an accent of chromium may balance a large non-reflective surface, a piece of intricate pattern may balance a much greater unbroken area. We deal both in tangibles and intangibles, and the latter have as much effect on equilibrium as the former, sometimes more.

Our own special bent today is toward asymmetrical design, but other ages have used it with superlative skill even though they did not make it their habit. Classical design was predominantly symmetrical, because the Greeks were content to carry basically simple schemes to ultimate perfection. The Romans were essentially unimaginative but addicted to grandiosity to which symmetry especially lends itself, as public buildings of Roman inspiration everywhere testify. But the Greeks could handle asymmetry as prettily as you please. Next door to the Parthenon they constructed an exercise in asymmetry that can scarcely be surpassed. In the Erechtheion we have a plan and four elevations that demonstrate the effectiveness of equilibrium created among unequal masses, and among forms and areas of unequal interest.

The motto of the Greeks was "Nothing too much," but also they did nothing by halves. The Erechtheion housed three shrines and it was built on a steeply sloping site: so it has three porches on three levels, and of three sizes, and including the western colonnade it has four types of treatment on its faces. The smallest of its three porches was the lovely Porch of the Caryatids, like nothing else on the Acropolis. Because this was a mere open-air tribune, placed at the west end of a long façade and balancing a tall porch which showed its lateral columns at the east end, the architect relied on his six maidens and his exquisitely elaborated detail to restore the equilibrium of his scheme. Because his north porch was even taller than the principal eastern porch of six columns, its stylobate ten feet lower, he made it only four columns wide, widely spaced, and let it project even beyond the western end of the building so that it would not overbalance his scheme. The result must have been, from any point of view, a fascinating composition of scale, masses, lines and treatments, and a delightful variation from the chaste symmetry of the typical Attic temple.

We are blood brothers to the Gothic builders who were, like us, engineers and designers in equal parts. Like us they loved asymmetry and knew how to play with it. The west front of a Gothic cathedral started as a symmetrical design, because this was the principal façade of the palace of the Queen of Heaven, whose majesty could only be expressed in a grandeur and dignity that demand symmetry. But by the time the towers had detached themselves from the façade, symmetry usually was forgotten, and the spires were completed, if ever, with little regard for each other. In fact the most important cathedral that stands complete today, with identical spires, the Cathedral of Cologne, leaves us singularly cold in comparison with the happily fortuitous inspiration of Chartres or Rouen or Amiens. And when the late Gothic or early Renaissance designers of France deliberately went in for asymmetrical design they were as skillful as so many inspired jugglers. The entrance façade of the Château of Blois, for instance, built in the Fifteenth Century when palaces were becoming lovely as churches were becoming trivial, is a masterly balancing act—almost a conscious display of virtuosity.

The portal of Louis XII's dwelling is placed well off-center in what is basically a formal façade: a stately arrangement of five panels separated by engaged shafts, each panel designed for a single window in each story with an ornate dormer in the roof above. The last panel on the right is widened, and filled by an intricate pattern of doors and windows and enrichment. It is demurely balanced by an irregular treatment of the last panel but one to the left: an extra window on the first floor, a larger window with a balcony and enriched cornice on the second, these two windows with the dormer above not centered but moved to the extreme left of the panel. The result is a serene equilibrium restored to the whole.

Now look at the arrangement of the entrance panel, with its deeply shadowed doorway, and the king on his horse elaborately canopied in a niche above. The little postern gate buries its shoulder in the engaged column beside the big portal, and the entablature above it, topped by an arbitrary horizontal molding, seems to have nothing whatever to do

200

with its neighbors—except that the whole arrangement works. Then note the first-story window and the large second-story window placed above it, not on axis, but aligning at the right. Here we have space filled with elements of different sizes and unrelated character, their placing determined by functional needs without regard for horizontal or vertical symmetry, but adjusted carefully to effect a perfect if unconventional balance. In this scheme, even the apparently accidental way in which the carved jamb-stones are engaged in the brickwork plays its part. The result is a beautifully serene and dignified, but amazingly animate, composition.

When Richardson built the Glessner house in Chicago in 1885 he created an example of craftsmanship in masonry that is almost perfect, and he also anticipated later trends in planning by turning the back of his house on the street and opening his rooms in wide glass expanses on an interior garden. But in the long façade on the side street, he balanced his scheme by means almost identical with the methods of the architect of Blois. The internal plan dictated a number of window and door openings at the service end, and he concentrated these, in different sizes and shapes and at different levels, in such a way that the group balances a much larger gable with its small engaged tower, at the other end of a long, simple wall. This balance would not have been effected if the large gable-end and the long wall had not been very formally treated, with approximately regular placing of openings. Richardson had seen the Blois façade, undoubtedly, and its precedent may have affected his thinking, but hardly consciously so. Certainly there is no trace of imitation. We see however the minds of two master builders instinctively adopting the same means to solve the same technical problem.

We find too the same processes of thought in operation, the same attainment of asymmetrical balance through the varied grouping of openings, in the work of Wright, Le Corbusier, Gropius, Mies van der Rohe—every designer who is sensitive to the empathic qualities of equilibrium. There are extremists who maintain that plan alone should determine the exteriors of structures and that the designer who adjusts his elements in the interest of serenity and balance is a traitor to functionalism even when his plan suffers no perceptible impairment thereby. They are going counter to the practice of every real designer, of course, but they are also offending the instinctive preferences of every man who has to stand on two legs.

Horizontal balance is important to us, but vertical balance—or vertical symmetry—is so completely foreign to our natures that it seems absurd to mention it. Yet it is a revealing fact that balance in one direction should be essential to us while in another direction it is difficult to imagine. Vertically we demand quite another attribute than symmetry, although it is still the need of equilibrium that controls us: vertically we demand stability, adequate support, a firm resistance to the pull of gravity that would level everything like water. We like things firmly rooted, broadening at the base, as we stand with legs apart to increase our own stability. This is why we instinctively make our columns wider at the base, like tree trunks, and spread our foundations. The Greeks set their temples on stylobates of spreading steps, marrying them to the earth, and the Egyptians habitually gave their walls an inward slope, or batter, toward the top. Permanence dominated the Egyptian ideal of building, as much as any other factor, and an inward sloping wall gives us an enhanced sense of security. The piled-up castles of the Middle Ages owe much of their mighty impressiveness to the lines receding upward which engineering necessities dictated, and no concrete pill-box fortifications of today can ever appear half so formidable to our eyes.

We want to be reassured as to the structural soundness of anything built, and if we can see what holds it up and can see that the supports are adequate, we are pleased. This preference of ours for the revealed adequacy of structure is the reason why the columnar styles were so satisfactory to so many generations and races of men. It is another reason why the intricate engineering of Gothic builders, all in the light of day to be seen and appreciated, fills us with such delight. And it is also why our steel-framed buildings can never be wholly satisfactory so long as their supporting members are completely hidden and not even hinted at beneath their masonry envelopes. The first skyscraper builders of the Chicago school were guided by a sure instinct when they felt a need to indicate the presence and the character of their steel frames beneath the masonry screens which could not be dispensed with. It is unfortunate that their early efforts were completely overshadowed by the Beaux-Arts exuberances of the New York builders who followed them in time but not in sensibility. We await the creation of a more candid and more effective technique in steel building.

There is a healthy spirit of experiment in both steel and concrete construction today, starting with a study of the physical nature of the two materials and leading to new forms of great practical use and great expressiveness. But we need to be mindful, in our use of cantilevered construction particularly, that we are still rather small animals with an extreme distaste for being crushed by falling weights, and for having supports give way beneath us. There is no need to make us uncomfortable by ignoring this human weakness. We should build structures that will stand up, and that will *look* as if they would stand up. It should be possible to use the cantilever principle in such a way that the counter-balancing tension or weight—which must of course be there—is evident. Otherwise the cantilever principle should remain a principle. The Philadelphia Savings Fund Society Building is a fine achievement, with many admirable features: but at least one observer has an uneasy feeling that the stories of the cantilevered corner, with no visible means of support, may at any moment close up like the pages of a book. For the same reasons the legendary piano leg was not the result of a mere Victorian preference for embonpoint: the substitutes of spindly chromium or glass occasionally seen today evoke a disturbing picture of the instrument collapsing in the player's lap. Structures and supports, in buildings, machines, furniture, what not, should not only be adequate but they should convince us at a glance that they really *are* adequate.

We have shown that we are capable of obtaining these gratifying qualities in single products or structures. But a balance of forces, a reassuring stability, must be evident in the whole of any scene we can inhabit with peace of mind. We cannot be happy in an environment which constantly outrages our sense of equilibrium, and excites uncomfortable reactions in our sensory, muscular and glandular systems. The world as we see it today disturbs our peace, allows us no repose. An orderly adjustment of forces around us must be effected, not only in the isolated instances with which we have shown ourselves competent to deal, but in the larger elements of the scene as a whole.

Here we have the last of the principles of design that may be consciously studied and consciously applied in the extension of order throughout the world. When we have analyzed the function and materials of a product or a city, and the methods by which it must be built, and have let these factors determine the form we give it; when this form has been simplified and clarified, and knitted into an indestructible unity by creating rhythmic relations between its parts, lines and areas; when these rhythms have been subjected to a dominant theme within a consistent scale, and given order and continuity by means of graduated accents; when the whole structure has equilibrium and stability, and that balance of tensions which reflects itself in our own physical satisfaction as we contemplate it—when all these things are done, the designer has used the tools that may be mastered and handled with planned intent. What must still be done to lift the work out of a pedestrian mediocrity can be discussed and defined, but is not subject to the designer's will. The spirit of a time cannot be consciously evoked, and inspiration that goes beyond planning cannot be turned on and off like a water-tap.

CHAPTER FOURTEEN: STYLE

"We know so much about past schools of art that we have divided what was a fast-flowing stream into sections to which the names of 'styles' have been given, but the names are ours, and when the works were being done it was thought that each one in turn was the natural way of building."

—W. R. LETHABY

"For no people can create except in its own subjective image."

—LOUIS SULLIVAN

When Marie Antoinette found the great open spaces of Versailles' salons no longer endurable, she caused a little apartment to be built for herself in a cranny of the palace wall. Instructing her architect, she had only to tell him that she would have her little boudoir in white and gold, that one of her book rooms should be blue and the other rose, the tiny bedroom yellow.

She was not confronted, as so many American housewives have been in the past generation, with the problem of deciding whether her rooms should be Georgian or Directoire in style; she did not have to weigh the merits of Early American as against white-washed Victorian. It would not have occurred to any lady of Marie Antoinette's time to do her house—or for that matter, her carriage, her gown or her park—in any style but the one then current, which they no doubt called something equivalent to Modern but which we call the Style of Louis XVI.

206

That is what it means to have a living style: a single character of design gets itself expressed in whatever is made at the time, and not a chair, a teapot, a necklace or a summerhouse comes into existence except in a form which harmonizes with everything else being made at that time. The people's costumes accord with their houses, the houses with their furnishings, and all with the accouterments and utensils of daily living. A very satisfactory picture they make, too, as you view the period in retrospect, whether you happen to like the prevailing style a great deal or very little. The scene has unity, harmony, repose, and at least one irritant is absent from the social organism.

Throughout the painful confusion of the Industrial Revolution we have had no living style and no dominant style. Our germinal stream was sterilized, for the time being, by the distractions and upheavals of the vast transformation that was taking place, and there was no creative force strong enough to ride the storm. The great economic and political readjustments which swept away Marie Antoinette, her phlegmatic husband and all they represented, also interrupted the age-old stream of evolution in design.

For many centuries a gradual but continuous process of change had kept the dominant design of western Europe adjusted to the changing tastes and interests of the people. As intellectual horizons widened or contracted, as new orientations were given to human thought by veering religious or secular absorptions, we see the prevailing mood adapting to itself whatever came from the hands of the builders and makers of things. Even the development of new engineering principles was stimulated by the need to express a current enthusiasm, as the pointed arch and flying buttress were evolved to satisfy the urge to build vaster and lighter palaces for the Queen of Heaven. But throughout the whole course of French

history—and France from the Eighth Century has been almost unin-
terruptedly the arbiter of style for the western world—throughout the history that led from Romanesque to the Neo-classicism of Louis XVI, we
find a steady and gradual development resolving one style into another
without violence or retrogressions. We see the developed Romanesque
taking on Gothic characteristics, as in St. Stephen's at Caen. Speedily
the pointed arch and the flying buttress emerged so completely that all
trace of Romanesque was eliminated, and we see this Gothic style evolve
in a few centuries from the chaste severity of the South Tower of Chartres
to the flamboyant intricacy of the North Tower. Then the Revival of
Learning in Italy began to divert men's thoughts from heaven to history,
and we see the classic influence of the Renaissance beginning to appear in
what are still essentially Gothic schemes, as in Louis XII's wing at Blois.
Soon the pointed arches and the Gothic finials disappear entirely before
an outburst of Florentine garlands and pilasters, and these fatten and
swell into Baroque. Baroque in French hands becomes refined and attenuated into Rococo, and when the ogee curves of everything in sight had
been carried as far as was structurally possible, they began to be tightened
up, straightened out and rectified into the comparatively severe Neo-
classicism of Louis XVI.

Here comes to an end the long and relatively placid process of orderly
adjustment, the result of a natural subjection of designers and workers to
the dominant influences of their times, so that their work was deep-rooted
in the popular mood and nourished by the vitality of popular taste. From
here on all is confusion: with no unanimity of thought and no stability of
conditions around them, the designers and workers became more and
more rootless, starved, distracted. The beautiful consistency of the Louis
XVI style was jolted into the inconsequences of the Directoire and these

into the utter banalities of the Empire. From Napoleon's wreaths and bees it was only a step to the indigestible plum-pudding concoctions of Louis Philippe and Prince Albert and the horrors of Neuschwanstein. Nowhere any more is there vitality, discipline, direction. In the past century and a half design as always has reflected the mood of the times, and that mood has been one of confusion.

No matter what the circumstances, men must continue to make things and these things must have some kind of form. If there is not a strong, living impulse shared by everyone and deciding for us what this form shall be, we cast about in frantic search for some discipline to which we can subject our work. So the past century saw a succession of "revivals" of this and that, as men explored the past and said from time to time, "Now *that* was good; those fellows knew how to do things. Let's make our things like theirs." We had a Gothic Revival, and a Greek Revival. The mid-Nineteenth Century rediscovered Louis XV and fancied a version of his furniture in black walnut, and the "opulent eighties" gave their allegiance indiscriminately to all the Louis's with the result that we had a crop of offspring of Blois and Versailles. Esthetes discovered the Japanese, and there was a rash of coromandel screens and lacquered chests, not to mention prints and brocades. William Morris in desperation raided the Middle Ages and revived everything but chain mail and torture chambers. Here in America, about the turn of the century, we had a "Colonial Revival" and our suburbs blossomed with yellow clapboards and white-columned porticoes. This was one of the minor consequences of the Columbian Exposition of 1893, which showed America for the first time how superbly lovely a consistently planned arrangement of buildings, landscape and water can be; with the result that America put its neck enthusiastically into the Beaux-Arts yoke and kept it there for forty years.

Of course, in every period there are people of good taste who manage to extract something charming from the most unpromising material, and there are able, conscientious workmen who are morally incapable of succumbing to any demoralizing influences however prevalent these may be. Beautifully simple Empire furniture was produced in the minor workshops of France by men who had been trained in the old tradition of French craftsmanship, and whose customers could not afford to pay for the quantities of gilt-bronze ornament that were fashionable. Honest builders in this country produced a number of stately and beautifully proportioned houses under the influence of the Greek Revival. At the very worst of the General Grant period there were women who succeeded in furnishing lovely rooms with their black walnut, horse-hair-covered "parlor suits," their marble-topped tables and their oval photograph frames. At the same time, H. H. Richardson was winning his way back to a fine and honest craftsmanship in the use of stone, brick and wood. Louis Sullivan and his confreres in Chicago were indicating the ultimate development of steel-frame architecture while the plaster columns and cornices of the 1893 World's Fair were being erected. And Frank Lloyd Wright was laying the foundations of modern house planning at the same time that the country was losing its heart to Colonial reproductions. There were exceptions always throughout the Nineteenth Century collapse of taste.

But exceptions were survivals from a better day, or heralds of a new spring, as the case might be. They were the plants that managed to bloom and bear fruit in a garden overrun by weeds. It was not until recent years, within the life of the present generation, that a dynamic polarizing force began to reappear in design, bending the efforts of men in one direction, so that a growing harmony began to appear in certain phases of our environment. Houses began to be built in forms that had a striking kinship with our planes and automobiles and ocean liners; there appeared furniture that fitted naturally into this new type of house; people began to dress in a manner suitable to their vehicles, their houses and furniture. It became possible again for a man to build and equip a dwelling in which every item, from ash-trays to heating plant, bore a distinct, unmistakable similarity to all the others and all were obviously controlled by the same intention. A vital style, of and for the period, began to emerge once more, and the possibility of order restored to our scene became something more than a dream.

It is impossible for anything made by man to escape the impress of its time. No matter how banal the furniture or buildings of Louis Philippe or General Grant, they obviously express their day and could not have been made at any other time. A Colonial Revival house is definitely dated 1900 or whatever and could never be mistaken for 1770. But there is a great difference between things produced *at* a time and things produced *by* a time. The Nineteenth Century dated its products as accurately and as unconsciously as any other period has done, but these things were given their form by changing whims of fashion which sought some safe resting-place as hysterically as a frightened bird. The work of these times was not controlled and directed by any deep-rooted preference in the minds of the people. It was not governed by necessities of function, material or techniques (imitations and substitutions were more general than in any period the world has ever known) and it was not consistent with itself. So, while the work dates itself, it is not an expression of any dominant contemporary mood.

But when men began actually to study the needs of their time, and at the same time began to look objectively at the tools and materials they held in their hands for the satisfying of these needs; when they began to discard precedent, and let these present factors determine the forms of what they made, then style and order reappeared. A co-ordination of design in any number of fields took place, quietly, almost unconsciously, certainly without any prearranged concert of designers. A surprising harmony was discoverable in many categories and from apparently unrelated sources.

For instance, since the first World War women have quit wearing whalebone stays, petticoats and high-topped shoes. At the same time men have abandoned starched shirts, high collars, cylindrical hats (except on occasions of such formality that discomfort seems definitely demanded). At the same time, whether as cause, effect, or mere coincidence, automobiles have developed into a form which would make stays, stiff shirts and high collars cruelly uncomfortable. Simultaneously, chairs and couches have become wider, lower, deeper, so that one reclines rather than sits in them. A generation as rigidly shored-up as our immediate ancestors would find our present type of furniture impossible. We have progressively reduced our clothing in quantity and increased its loose comforts, until many of us spend a large part of the hot months in a mere surcingle. At the same time we—or what we are pleased to call the progressive-minded portion of us, and all of us to some extent—have been stripping and simplifying the scenes in which we live. Observe the bulging and dripping interiors that Madame Sarah Bernhardt or any other cultivated person thought suitable some fifty years ago, and the efforts of even our most flamboyant decorators will seem chaste by comparison; while those designers who are really creative in expressing the mood of today produce rooms that seem positively monastic. While we cleaned out plush and fringe and nicknacks indoors, we reduced moldings, cornices and pilasters outdoors. Our architecture became as clean-shaven as our chins, both as a result of the same change in taste.[1] And this change in taste cannot be credited to the progressive schools of architecture and design, which may be in advance of the current taste but do not necessarily lead it.

There is a distinct similarity in the work of Le Corbusier, Mies van der Rohe, Gropius, Frank Lloyd Wright in his later years, and a considerable number of other designers in Europe and America—a similarity so evident that it is possible to group them all in an International School. Their work is avowedly functional, professing to be formed by the needs of modern living and by a fresh study of the materials and techniques at hand. They turn their back aggressively—if aggressive back-turning is conceivable, and here it seems to be—on the past, its traditions, practices and habits, and the fact that a thing has always been done is their most decisive reason for not doing it now. They have in fact produced a great body of thrillingly fresh work, demonstrating new possibilities of gracious living and new applications of materials in the interest of our comfort and pleasure. They are acknowledged prophets of our time, and some are as vocal as prophets are traditionally supposed to be. The weakness of the whole school has been a tendency to develop clichés into dogmas, and to allow dogmas to control with their usual rigidity and intolerance; so that forms many times have been mistaken for functions, and plans are often determined by stylistic principles instead of by life, just as in older schools of design. The actual functionalism, under given circumstances, of flat roofs, plate glass walls, no partitions and cantilevered floors is not always investigated with an unbiased mind. The desire to avoid

---

[1] Two or three years ago a Fifth Avenue department store spent a large sum of money (by report a half-million dollars) scraping off its façades a quantity of carved stone ornament which, a quarter-century before, had cost a comparable sum to put on. Such operations, very common today, are known as "modernizations."

the obvious or the usual has often been so strong that it has succeeded also in avoiding the convenient and the sensible, and resulted in setting up a new group of characteristics that have become obvious and usual in the International School.[2]

These faults, however, are inherent in human nature, which can scarcely ever resist the impulse to rally round a flag and proclaim a doctrine. In spite of the new crop of clichés and the assertive nose-thumbing, the new study of design problems within the past generation has resulted in the polarization of a new and living trend in design. For we can detect the emergence once more of a style rooted deeply in the mood and spirit of this time. The men of the International School, mind you, have not made this style, which is a product of the mass mind as it once more crystallizes its opinions and, resolving its confusions, attains again a kind of unanimity of wants. The work of these men is but one phase of the

[2] In his *Modern Building*, W. C. Behrendt, a friendly critic of the International School, stresses the influence of the cubist movement in determining the characteristic forms of the new style, and says: "To characterize in brief the attributes of this new form-type, the bulk of the building is broken up in parts, following cubistic principles, and the various parts by skillful grouping of the masses are then composed into a whole, in its aspect 'still revealing the elements of the original analysis.' To such a simplified form of geometrical character belongs the flat roof: *it is the logical consequence of the esthetic principle of the style* [italics mine]: the cubic blocks of the building mass and the even planes of its walls need a clear and sharp-edged contour." Again: "Endowed with inner control and outer coldness, filled with renunciation, the new form convinces through the ethic force of the style idea more than the sensuous effects of its artistic substance. [Whatever that means.] *The style idea always prevails.*" Of J. J. P. Oud, Behrendt says, "He truly adheres to the principles of cubism, using no other form elements than cube, sphere and cylinder." Behrendt maintains that van der Rohe's design, "reduced to elemental geometric forms, clearly demonstrates the doctrine of cubism." All this indicates as purely stylistic an approach to design as any practice of the Beaux-Arts. Fortunately function also has claimed attention from the International School, as well as modern materials and building techniques: sometimes, in fact, these men were even better functionalists than stylists. But Le Corbusier is definitely too emotional and stylistic for Behrendt (there may be a certain Teutonic-Gallic defect of sympathy raising its head here): "Le Corbusier, however, the Picasso of modern architecture, deals not with the structural problem of building, but with the esthetic problem of an architectural style, and he uses modern construction mainly for its emotional power of expression." Mr. Behrendt clearly appreciates the danger of the International movement developing into a new academicism.

214

style trend: they are the focal points at which the "spirit of the times" finds itself a voice, and hears its inarticulate and generally inattentive self told what it is really coming to. The realization is something of a shock and has not been readily accepted: the prophets have been slow in acquiring honor among the masses, as always. They stand on levels toward which the mass mind is moving, but which it has not reached as yet; and the advance of the mass mind is not due to the exhortations or the object-lessons of the prophets, but to its own slow clarifying of its own preferences.

The Modern Style is seen crystallized in the work of Le Corbusier, Gropius, Wright; or of Dreyfus, Rohde, Geddes, Teague. But its sanction, its justification, the proof of its vitality, is to be found in the general cleaning up and rectification that has been going on all around us everywhere in circles that know little or nothing about modern art and cordially dislike what they think it is. Functionalism and simplification are mighty forces in the world, energetically supported by millions who never use those words, and they have worked an enormous revolution in the past third of a century. They are motivated in a sound earthy way by an urge toward greater comfort of body and repose of mind, and they make war on inconvenience, rigidity, stuffiness and fussiness. They have altered our habits of dressing, sitting, riding, and building, and their influence is as inevitable on the Beaux-Arts as it was on the Bauhaus, if not quite so sweepingly effective. They give direction and character to all we do: the same impulse that abolished whalebone stays at one phase of the design-scale produced Le Corbusier at another.

It is fatal for a designer today to concern himself consciously with style. That is what the world has been doing during the past Age of Confusion—desperately striving by thought, research, experiment, to give some kind of significant form to its work, and all because there was no unself-conscious force impelling us toward a result which had its justification solely in one's sense that it was right. Such a force is active in the world today, and unless we are completely insensible, intellectual hermits, or deliberately perverse, we cannot help but feel it and be guided by it. There is no longer any justification for looking beyond our horizons, or back into history, to discover a form for the thing we are making: we feel a compulsion to look within the thing itself for the form it should have, and we are the midwives of what we find there. If we succeed in evoking this right form—right for the use that is to be made of the thing —we need not worry about the way it dates itself. The pervasive spirit of the time that is active around us will turn us naturally against fuss and feathers, circumlocutions, indirections, disguises and elaborations; the form will issue in a chaste simplicity easily endowable with grace and charm but incompatible with any sort of pretentiousness or lack of candor. If we have made successful adjustments among its essential parts, so that they are bound together in a rhythmic unity, the thing will have style. It will bear the authenticating stamp of the day it was made, since the combination of circumstances that produced it could not have occurred on any other day. It will be "modern," in the only creditable sense of the term.

We are in the habit of applying the familiar name of "modern" to a multitude of ill-begotten bastards, simply because they have certain characteristics that originally appeared in legitimate modern work. Individual characteristics of any kind are no proof of legitimacy, and if we mean by the word "modern" to designate products shaped by a deep-rooted, pervasive spirit or mood peculiar to our times and as vital as the impulses that gave character to the great styles of the past, we must look much deeper than surface traits. We hope the style we are creating today marks a resurgence of order, a strong upwelling of the creative stream that flowed so mightily for hundreds of years until the violence of the Industrial Revolution drove it underground or dissipated it over marshy fenlands; if so, our conception of the problem of design, and the method of gestation and delivery it enforces, is the only authentication our work can have. "Modernism" is not indicated by cubical masses or cantilevered construction, nor by interpenetration of forms or unconventionality of plan. It is not proven by the use of steel, plate glass, aluminum, chrome plate, reinforced concrete, plastics or other synthetic materials. In fact it does not depend on any clichés or tags whatever, and if it is developing a vernacular it is only because certain forms and materials recur again and again as factors in the right solutions of our peculiar modern problems. The style may from time to time exhibit certain characteristics that become familiar: but it should never be forgotten that while the style produces these characteristics, they do not make the style.

Assuming that we mean by the word "modern" to designate an authentic style, an unconventional plan is entitled to be called modern when it is the best of all arrangements for a specific scheme of living and working. Flat roofs and plate-glass walls are modern when, all the factors of comfort, convenience, practicality and esthetics being weighed together, they are more desirable than sloping roofs and solid walls. The materials we have created and exploited are modern if they are chosen because they are superior to other materials for specific uses, and if they are used and worked according to their natures. Even our machine-tool processes are modern only if they are employed because they are the best methods of fabrication available, and if they too are applied according to their natures. None of these methods, materials, processes are

217

universally right: they must justify themselves in each instance as fully as if they had never been used before.

In short, the only factors in modern design that should always be assumed to be right, determined in advance of each problem and never varying in character, are the designer's intention and his approach to his problem. If these are not sound, nothing else can be right and no repertoire of tricks will save the work from futility. But even if they are right, the designer is still human and fallible: his work can fail merely from his lack of strength to realize his intention, however honest that may be. For success he must not only be sincere and do the expected, he must go further and surprise us with something more of interest and value than by all the rules we had any right to expect. And this illumination that by some curious access of vitality he is able to give his work at times will surprise himself as much as it surprises us. It is another factor in design that cannot be turned on at will.

CHAPTER FIFTEEN: BEYOND THE RULES

"Admiration always includes an element of wonder. As a Renaissance writer said: 'There is no excellent beauty that hath not some strangeness in the proportion.' "
—JOHN DEWEY

The popular conception of a scientist is that of a coldly rational thinking-machine. He is supposed to carry on his research as a series of deliberate and logically related steps, as if he opened a door leading to another door and that to another, and so on until at last he stands in the presence of a bright, shining and hitherto unsuspected truth. As a matter of fact, the most fruitful scientific thought does not advance in any such hay-foot, straw-foot manner. It is borne forward by creative imagination as much as by reason, and it surprises the truth by flashes of brilliant insight long before the structure of supporting proof can be built up. The scientist himself is keenly aware of how much he depends on intuition, and is put off his stride if he is asked to give an account of his mental operations before his goal is reached. In a delightful and too little known book [1] by a gifted English scientist, the method of scientific research is described in this way:

"The fact that the scientific investigator works 50 per cent of his time by non-rational means is, it seems, too little recognized. There is without the least doubt an instinct for research, and often the most successful

---

[1] *The Skeptical Biologist*, Joseph Needham, New York, 1930.

investigators of nature are quite unable to give an account of their reasons for doing such and such an experiment, or for placing side by side two apparently unrelated facts. . . . And not only by this partial replacing of reason by intuition does the work of science go on, but also to the born scientific worker—and emphatically they cannot be made—the structure of the method of research is as it were given, he cannot explain it to you, though he may be brought to agree *a postiori* to a formal logical presentation of the way the method works. He is no doctrinaire. A tendency is easily noticed in him to prefer not to discuss the working of the method, out of an unexpressed fear, perhaps, that if he knew exactly what he was doing he might not be able to do it. . . . Out of impulses which the investigator cannot understand and does not bother to examine introspectively, new experiments are born; facts which to all appearances have no connection are set side by side, the investigator cannot tell why, and illumination results; the mazes of technique are threaded by a sure instinct so that unisolatable substances are isolated and insuperable difficulties are overcome."

Here is drawn a conscious parallel between the method of scientific research and the method of artistic creation, but in emphasizing the importance of instinct and intuition in science, Dr. Needham underscores even more heavily their importance as factors in art. For if the work of science depends so much on the subconscious resources of the investigator's mind, the far less tangible and less measurable quantities of design must be still more subject to instinctive rather than rational control.

It is high time we got around to discussing these imponderable factors in design, because up to this time we have dealt almost exclusively with the designer's rational and consciously controlled tools: we have discussed methods and techniques to the neglect of insight and inspiration. It

The Nineteenth Century was an age of confusion which
attempted to overcome its uncertainty by self-assertion.

WILLARD VAN DYKE

A catholic taste in the Nineteenth Century felt compelled to prove its breadth beyond a doubt. Madame Sarah Bernhardt's drawing room, Paris. Today we are emerging into a new self-confidence and restraint. Opposite, detail of an apartment in River House, New York.

No trace of Nineteenth Century confusion, uncertainty, eclecticism survived in Frank Lloyd Wright's work when he designed the Robie house, Chicago, 1908. The genesis of a new style is seen.

This style was matured thirty years later in Wright's Kaufmann house, Bear Run, Pa., 1937. A clear statement of certain functional and structural facts, shaped by no precedent but by the site and the use to be made of it.

We seek our satisfaction today in form, line, proportion, texture, color—

—not in historical reminiscence. Executive Lounge, Ford Exposition.

In this commercial interior, much carved paneling and an ornate marble and bronze staircase gave place to this simple arrangement of unornamented forms and surfaces—a candid functional scheme, carefully arranged, emphasizing interesting materials, but eliminating all irrelevant detail.

This is typical of much reconstruction today, expressive of a new mood which rejects inconvenience, stuffiness, fussiness in favor of more directness and less distraction. Detail of stairs in interior shown on opposite page. Ford Salesroom, 1710 Broadway, New York.

Formality and dignity can be expressed in current terms of line and mass, without elaboration or pretentiousness. Furniture group in the State Reception Room, United States Government Building, New York World's Fair. Designed by the author.

The best domestic design today is motivated solely by the convenience, comfort, and pleasure of living. A common tendency to break down the separation between indoors and outdoors is here assisted by a favorable climate. Residence of H. V. Manor, Monte Vista, Cal., designed by Clarence W. W. Mayhew. See also Plates 94 and 95. ROGER STURTEVANT ⫸→

ALBERT KAHN, ARCHITECT   JOHN MILLS, JR.

Because of its impermanence and legitimately bizarre character, exposition design has served as an experimental field
for new structural forms and expressions. Today it obtains its
striking effects through purely functional treatment of the
given problem, without ornament or elaboration. Opposite,
the Texaco Exhibit, Dallas, 1936. Above, model of Ford
Exposition, New York, 1939. The author's designs.

110

Progress from right to left, in American Can Company's Building, Jersey City. Albert Kahn, Architect. Below, Sewage Disposal Plant. Alfred Kastner, Architect. See also Plates 16 and 61.

Essential in the modern scene, the rapid advance of service stations illustrates the crystallization of our style. Versions of a standardized station designed by the author. Five hundred have been built to date.

Having no ornament whatever, our style today deals in large and simple elements. Observation terrace, Ford Exhibit, San Diego, 1935. Designed by the author.

112

would be unfortunate if anyone should be left with the impression that a problem in design can be worked out, like a problem in mathematics, by the application of known rules; or that a design can be assembled from prefabricated parts, like an automobile. Design is not the product of any assembly line, no matter how well organized, and it is not evolved in any laboratory, no matter how well equipped. There is a non-rational, non-predictable, non-volitional element in design, and this element is the vital one. It is the spermatic force contributed by the designer himself out of his own vitality, and without it the work, however intelligently planned, never comes to life.

We have not discussed this creative element in design until now, because, like any other life principle, it cannot be analyzed and logically explained. There is no use writing books about the creative faculty: it cannot be imparted by explanation and it cannot be acquired by study. It exists in a man or it is absent, it may exist to a greater or less degree, it may exist in a man at a certain period of his life and not at another, it may be favored or discouraged by circumstances. But there it is, and it cannot be handed from one man to another in any known formula or by any kind of precept. The designer, like the scientific worker, emphatically is born and not made. The best we can do for him is to give him tools to work with and a salubrious social climate in which to work. These he must have—he cannot function without them—and his tools are perfectly rational implements about which a book like this can be written, and usefully written, too; and perhaps if the designer's technique is more generally understood his job of remaking our environment can progress in a more favorable atmosphere.

Dr. Needham's born scientific worker "threads the mazes of technique with a sure instinct." It is a safe bet that these investigators who prefer not to discuss their method for fear they will know too much about it have spent a great many years in directed study; they have performed innumerable sequences of experiments and acquired a habit of logical deduction so ingrained as to be practically subconscious. In the "mazes of technique" they are on their own home grounds, as familiar as the palms of their hands. Their distinction lies in the fact that their imaginations have not been crippled by this training but have survived it in full strength. Now they can use their acquired skill so easily that it does not distract them; their intuitive faculty is able to function in a sphere so familiar that its routine can be disregarded. It is of course only the exceptional man whose creative instinct is strong enough to survive the ordeal of training and arrive at this happy state of freedom to function.

Before Newton lay under the apple tree and watched the apple fall, millions of men had had the same experience without deducing from it the law of gravity. But Newton had spent years in the study of natural phenomena, and the operations of natural law were the common subject of his thought: a powerful catapult was all set to launch his intuition that day when he lay down in the orchard, the better to think. Innumerable men had seen weights swinging at the ends of ropes and chains, without perceiving the law that governs the movements of pendulums, but Galileo took to church a mind prepared to grasp the significance of the swinging lamp. Wherever there has been a conspicuous revelation, it has come to a mind prepared for it. If there are mute inglorious Miltons, it is because they never learned to read and write or never learned to sing.

In design, as in Needham's scientific research, the vision precedes the proof. A fine steel building is never designed by starting to figure the stresses and strains of the steel. We must get off the ground with an

222

impulse strong enough to make our building stand up, high and shining and definite, in our mind's eye, before we ever put pencil to paper in the matter. When we see it standing whole, it will be time enough to put its form on paper and begin to think about the steel that will hold it up. But the vision itself has a preliminary condition, not of specific calculations, but of generalized knowledge and experience: there is in the background of our mind a complete familiarity with steel, so that the building we see is one that steel will naturally support without asking it to do anything impractical or abnormal. We think easily in the terms of our medium without being preoccupied with the peculiarities of the medium —we speak the language fluently without fumbling with a dictionary.

Preoccupation with specialized techniques of any kind acts as a ground anchor on the creative imagination, holding it from flight. And yet a familiarity with techniques is essential to free and sure creative effort. These are the horns of a dilemma that confronts all training in design, and wrecks so very much of it. There are schools of architecture and schools of engineering, and these undertake to prepare their students for creative work. But creative minds among these students are relatively few, and since creative ability cannot be imparted, while techniques are teachable, the schools of design like the scientific schools suffer an inevitable tendency to deal with the technical minutiae of their subjects. This is not wholly an evil, for the schools in this way manage to turn out a great many sound journeymen technicians; and a great many sound journeymen technicians are needed to carry out and carry on the projects initiated by a few creative minds. These latter, however, must take the training as something to be subjugated, survived, and relegated to the background of consciousness.

Too many schools of engineering, especially, have been notoriously limited in the range of their outlook. They go deep but not far; and if these times, outside the schools, were not so stimulating to minds gifted in dealing with mechanical problems we should have a crop of minute specialists with too few to synthesize their specialties. Even in the more liberal schools there is an insufficient effort to train the imagination or the esthetic sensibilities of the students, although in determining right form in mechanical or structural engineering imagination and esthetic sense are certainly more valuable than a slide rule or a whole set of French curves.

The schools of architecture, on the other hand, have in the recent past divided their attention between the technical detail of construction, not in itself excessive, and an intensive but superficial devotion to the history of architectural forms. In the latter field there has been an enormous amount of time spent on columns, capitals, cornices and moldings, and their delineation with startling realism; there has been a widespread, glib familiarity with the surface characteristics of many buildings regarded as important landmarks, and it has even been considered of value to know the names of the master masons who built Amiens Cathedral and the Sainte Chapelle. As a reaction from this fiddling with period styles, there are "modern" schools of architecture that regard the past as an unmitigatedly evil influence to be avoided at all costs. They attempt to teach the "art of building well" as though it were something first practised, like flying, within the present century. Architecture, in their definition, becomes a filly by Frank Lloyd Wright out of the Bauhaus.

One thing the world needs desperately now is a synthesis of education in the arts that have to do with the making of things. And a thing it needs even more is a synthesis of these arts in the minds of their practitioners, so that they will be conscious of the kinship and the interdependence of all making. There is, in reality, no compartmentalism in design. A problem in design is a problem in design, whether it has to do with a train, a skyscraper, a national capital, a grinding machine, a housing project or a fountain pen: if the right form is evoked, the same principles and the same approach will obtain in every instance. The only difference is in the specialized techniques involved, and it is far easier to master these techniques than to acquire creative facility.

There was a time, in the Renaissance, when this truth was quite generally recognized and acted upon, and it was thought entirely reasonable that Michelangelo, being creatively gifted, should be equally successful at carving the Medici tombs, painting the Sistine ceiling, and building St. Peter's, not to mention the practice of a dozen less difficult crafts. The ultimate example of a synthesis of the arts occurred, of course, in the mind of Leonardo da Vinci, but there were a number of masters presiding over shops where they would undertake to execute any commission brought to them: they would build you a palace, paint you an altarpiece, devise for you a cunning strong box, beat out a silver service for your table or invent an intricate little machine that would do strange things for your amusement. In these shops a group of craftsmen and artists worked together, supplementing one another's skills and pooling their varied knowledge, under the direction of one creative mind. Nothing has ever existed so like these ateliers as the shops of certain industrial designers of today: the modern men serve a different kind of client, they work on a different set of problems, but similar working conditions prevail and there exists the same readiness—and ability—to tackle any commission that may be brought to them.

Enough has been accomplished along these protean lines to prove the fallacy of building dividing walls between the professions of architect, engineer, painter, sculptor, and designer of this and that. And to prove too the evil of attempting to educate youth in any of these fields without regard for all the others. A man's practice in any field need be limited only by his creative ability, and by his ability to master the specialized techniques involved to the point where he can think easily and fluently in these techniques. A man's education can easily give him too limited a set of tools: if he is to do creative work he needs the theory of techniques and the basic principles of techniques, but most of all he needs the habit of dealing in the fundamental and universal conditions that exist in all design problems; he needs only one set of principles, and skill in penetrating through superficialities to apply them. With this equipment, his achievement will depend on the intuitive gift that leads him through the "mazes of technique with a sure instinct," to results beyond the normal vision.

No maker of things today, unless he makes easel paintings or carves statuettes or practises some other small-scale art, works alone. He is part of a group activity, and even though he is the directing force he is still dependent on his collaborators. This has always been true in any large-scale production—"Architecture is the art of bossing a gang of workmen" —and it is increasingly true, now that machines and mass production are so completely superseding all other types of making. No man today could do with his own hands a tiny fraction of the vast number of operations involved in making even a simple manufactured product, or building a simple modern dwelling. But he has at his command a great, disciplined organization of men who, among them, are capable of doing all these things. Their techniques are too numerous to be learned and practised by one person; but the theories and the basic principles of their techniques are not too numerous to be thoroughly understood, and it is perfectly possible for a man today to think intelligently in steel construction, let us say, while other men figure the sections of his columns and beams, roll, fabricate and assemble them; and he can plan for economical machine production without himself designing any of the tools, fixtures and jigs necessary to make the thing he designs. Thus the modern specialization of knowledge and skill is actually working toward a new synthesis of design, by freeing the designer himself from the necessity of specializing in anything but design.

The circle is closing, and we find ourselves arriving once more at the point from which this modern movement departed some four or five generations ago: a point where the crafts are developed and organized so efficiently, each within itself, that a creative genius can direct many of them successfully in the carrying out of his projects. Our industrial age has advanced so far that its tools are beginning to be understood and controlled as well as in the days of the handicrafts. As a result, we see the re-emergence of pride in skill, and delight in things skillfully made; but we see, also, evident in many men of creative gifts, a stirring of impatience with restrictions, a restlessness at the confinements of specialization. There are engineers who feel an urge to experiment with the building of houses as well as automobiles, or try their hand at a mechanical solution of the farm problem; and architects who find building construction too narrow a field for their activities and are bold enough to want to plan the communities in which their houses are to be built and the equipment that goes inside the houses. Most striking of all is the rise, within half a generation, of this new profession of industrial design, in which one man of restless mind and many interests assembles around him a group of variously trained co-workers—architects, structural and mechanical engineers, painters, sculptors, craftsmen, investigators and writers—and directs their group efforts in an astonishingly wide range of activities. These ateliers in a few years have drawn within their scope practically every kind of making, and we find the same group at work on vast building projects, trains, ships, airplanes, machinery and mechanical products, manufactured articles of all kinds, the furnishing of simple or sumptuous interiors, projects of a purely esthetic intention, and the solution of difficult problems of modern group living. The success of these group activities, and the enthusiastic relief with which all sorts of projects have been entrusted to them, prove that the times were ready for them; they are, in fact, a product of the times, and the fruits of a trend quite as definitely as they are leaders of that trend.

There are, of course, resistance to the synthesizing forces, and efforts to maintain strict professional boundary lines. But these are rear-guard actions, the lingering spirit of a day that is very nearly done. The youths of today especially are filled with a spirit of exploration and an impatience with artificial limitations defining the field of their future activities. They want to range over the whole field of productive labor and make what they are interested in making, rather than accept a cell-like classification as a professional specialist. Every active industrial designer today has a stream of these eager youths seeking his advice as to how they can prepare themselves to escape professional confinement. He tells them—or should tell them—"Take your technical training as architect or engineer, and get the franchise that is necessary, still, to practise in these fields. But keep your mind on general principles rather than on minute details, and keep your eyes on everything that is going on around you in the world of creative effort. If you are studying engineering, pay special attention to architecture; and if you are studying architecture, pay special attention to engineering. In either case study drawing, and cultivate your appreciation of beautiful—significant—form. Go into factories, work in modern industrial plants, study machines, and learn how things are made today. And for God's sake, remember that slide rules and handbooks are tools and not vocations."

There are many schools that are endeavoring to adjust themselves to the expanding times, but they work against a time-lag that seems inevitably to act as a brake on educational advance. Wells, I think it was, remarked once that education represents the best ideals of the last preceding generation; and swiftly changing demands of these days are especially difficult to follow. The saving factor is that the young will take what they need: hungry minds will find their food if they have to go on a lone hunt for it, and what they get that way will be especially nourishing.

The schools of architecture, however, can save their students an enormous amount of time by giving them what they need for working in these times, and some schools are taking steps to do just that. They may, of course, make the mistake of throwing the past overboard entirely and in reaction against teaching all styles, confine themselves to teaching one style—that loosely known as International. This is the popular form of fanaticism at the moment. What is needed in dealing with the past is not amputation but a shifting of attention from external forms to vital processes. Architecture is not the art of assembling shapes, whether these shapes are Corinthian columns and molded cornices, as in one school, or flat roofs, ribbon windows and cantilevered decks, as in another. Architecture is the art of building well, and well building can be studied rather more successfully in Gothic cathedrals—or any other sound buildings of the past—than in the much less copious work of Le Corbusier or Wright. It all depends on whether we give our attention to the way the problem was solved, or to the problem's answer: the solution of any problem is good only for that problem, but the method of working out the solution may have a lot to teach us. The practice of looking at a Gothic cathedral as a collection of carved and molded forms of a special kind may not be helpful and may even handicap us with a set of sterile clichés. But we can look at the same structure as an orderly synthesis of masses and forces, carefully arranged in equilibrium so that a vast cubage is enclosed in a mere skeleton of masonry; and then we can observe how the designer has created dominating rhythms that are carried through every detail of form and proportion within the structure, binding it all together in a unified and vital whole. In this way the building becomes a study in function, materials and techniques, successfully integrated; and if we half-way understand it, we can turn from it far more competent to design a modern beach-house in steel, concrete and glass.

Historical design can be taught in this way, as the operation of unchanging laws which in dealing with varying factors naturally produce varying forms: the laws are vital to us, the forms are not. There is no better way to study the basic principles of design and make them our own habit of thought. But any adequate training today must deal not only with unchanging laws but also with the changing factors influencing form *as they exist in our day*. Our way of life is peculiar to us, and has created a vast list of functional requirements which designers of the past were never called on to consider. Our times, too, have produced a huge equipment of materials, tools, and processes unknown to our ancestors. And all these new factors have resulted in an organization for production that is unprecedented in the history of the world. No one who is not thoroughly conversant with these prevailing conditions influencing form can hope to apply the age-old laws successfully, no matter how well he knows them. A designer today must share this qualification of the great designers of the past: he must have a keen zest for the life of his times, live it, understand it, and share the hopes and ideals of his contemporaries; have a sympathetic knowledge of their problems, social and economic; and understand intimately how they do their work—which today means that machines must have no mysteries and factories must be familiar ground to him.

So equipped a designer moves in an atmosphere propitious to creative work. The flash of insight, the sudden illumination that may occur when he has all the factors in hand, revealing to him a solution that surprises him with its rightness, this creative intuition comes to him in the chromosomes transmitted to him by his ancestors. There is no school where he can acquire even a trace of talent, and certainly not any genius at all. But if he has a spark in him, the world today is full of many winds that will make it blaze. Surely there never was a more stimulating time than this, one that had more need of creative work or gave it more scope. It is a time of sweeping change, with gigantic forces loose in the world; evil and good, both are active on a vast scale. We walk between catastrophe and apotheosis. In spite of the mighty destructive powers that threaten us, our vision of a desirable life was never so clear and our means of realizing it never so ample. There is a world around us to be rebuilt and the man who does not take fire at the prospect of a share in the job had better realize at once that he has no creative gift and take employment under someone who has: then at least he will be in the fight and share its excitement.

CHAPTER SIXTEEN: PROSPECT

"While hate and conflict fill the air with discordance, and vast masses risk the fate of civilization itself for the sake of some falsehood, or some half truth embodied in a credo to which millions give fanatical allegiance, others, in all countries of the earth, are, step by step, stone on stone, discovery upon discovery, creating a new world in which the issues so loudly discussed are totally irrelevant." —DOROTHY THOMPSON

We are unique among animals—and this will bear repeating, although it has been said before—in that we have undertaken to adapt our environment to us instead of adapting ourselves to our environment. All other species of animals have managed to bring their powers and equipment into some sort of equilibrium with the conditions under which they live. Their lives are seldom easy, and casualties are frequent; but they have developed a set of offensive and defensive mechanisms which, under a given set of conditions, enables them to feed and propagate in sufficient numbers to keep their species alive. If conditions change, the results are serious: the advance of an ice age, or the advance of a wave of human population, both about equally fatal to wild life, will force them to change their habitat or give up the struggle for existence. They do not attempt to fight back against environmental conditions.

Our own species, on the other hand, has never accepted its natural surroundings with any docility whatever. It is true there are a few spots

232

on the earth's surface where the weather is always endurable to a naked human being, and where food is abundant without effort. But instead of being content to stay in these favored places and limit our racial size to theirs, we have pushed off into regions where naked human beings would freeze in a short time, and where we can keep from starving only by strenuous and ingenious efforts. We have developed none of the equipment that has enabled other creatures to survive—great strength, speed, fur, shells, fangs, poison, protective coloration, and still more surprising devices—but we have concentrated on two endowments that no other possessed: our hands and our rational brains. These interacting in mutual education have been able to reconstruct the world so successfully that we are able to ignore natural conditions almost entirely, and live where and as we please.

We are able to do so. If we do not, the fault lies in our intention and not in our ability to control the conditions of life. There is almost no *natural* obstacle to complete well-being of the human race today. Certainly in such advanced parts of the world as Western Europe and America, where we have effected a great concentration of knowledge and technological equipment to supplement abundant natural resources, there is no *a priori* reason why any human being should be ill fed, ill clothed or ill housed; live in ignorance or ugliness or be overworked; and there are only a few causes of physical pain which cannot yet be controlled. In fact, the small portion of the race which has arranged satisfactory social and economic circumstances for itself already is able to ignore climate and topography and, to a very large extent, time and space. It has achieved so much safety and comfort that our racial need to overcome obstacles is unsatisfied and the more restless spirits go out deliberately to seek the thrill of danger and adventure in all sorts of unnecessary

233

ways. Nature has been so completely subdued that it can be played with like a tame cheetah.

But these fortunate ones are only a few of the whole race. They prove that we have in our hands and in our minds the means to build Utopia tomorrow. We can at once set about the job of creating that race of fair, god-like men who have been dreamed about and talked about for ages. Also, this vision of a happy world and a serene people was never clearer, or shared by more men, than it is today. Conditions would seem to be all set for the dawn of that well-known new day.

But Utopia is not built, and the world is filled with unhappiness not by nature but by the stupidity of men. Ill will and truculence are dominant in many parts of the world, breeding insane wars, and causing the mass destruction of helpless peoples by invading armies, or by simple intolerance. There are millions upon millions of ill-nourished people who suffer from cold, hunger and preventable disease; millions who are overworked and even more millions who can find no work at all to do; a vast proportion of the population who live under conditions degrading to human dignity and inimical to all nobility of spirit; and uncounted hordes who grow up with little light in their minds, little health in their bodies and less peace and good will in their hearts.

A great many people are busy with the problem of changing these unhappy facts, and we may have confidence that sanity ultimately will be restored. But even more than war we need to fear our own strong racial tendency to find the solution of our difficulties in very simple devices external to ourselves. There are several schools of thought that start from different premises but arrive at the same conclusion: the relatively small group of harassed men known as "government" is not able to run the affairs of government satisfactorily, and so we should turn *all* our affairs over to it and then, by some miraculous extension of human power, all our affairs will be run satisfactorily.

There are beliefs in high places that by raising less food the ill fed will be better fed, and that by making fewer goods there will be more wealth to share. There is a contention by many envious but some surprisingly kindly spirits that, since scarcely a quarter of our people have been able to make life reasonably agreeable for themselves, the condition of the other three-quarters would be improved if the fortunate quarter were ironed down to the common level of discomfort.

There is a very general overlooking of the facts that abundance is the result of abundant production; that widespread distribution is the result of widespread good will; that "masses" are a fiction—only individuals exist, suffer and enjoy; that we have been diverted from our natural warfare with our environment to fight among ourselves, and that we will achieve racial happiness only when we concentrate in a spirit of unity on the task of remaking the world into a pleasant, comfortable, delightful dwelling-place for all human beings.

Instead of any such constructive effort, there is no denying the fact that we have made a deplorable mess of things in the past century and a half, and at the moment are engaged in a climactic exhibition of racial asininity. While we have made vast achievements in science and technology, and equipped ourselves with a great armory of tools which could be turned to the better shaping of our environment, large numbers of us are now busy using these facilities for purposes of mutual destruction. But even in times of peace we have devastated our lands by building any number of hideous factories and towns and reducing great stretches of lovely country to a state of blight in which hordes of our fellows are condemned to live under conditions inimical to health, happiness and dignity. Instead of improving our environment we have degraded it. We not only bear the guilt of war, but we must also take the responsibility for a degree of man-made peace-time ugliness unparalleled in history, and this ugliness is not merely visual but attacks the physical and spiritual well-being of those who endure it.

On the one side we have had a great busyness with test tubes, microscopes and reagents, the accumulation of knowledge and skills on an unprecedented scale; and we have had the building of a great industrial complex of machines and power sources for the production of better goods in bigger quantities at lower costs. On the other side we have had a simultaneous degradation of our actual living conditions and the condemnation of a large part of the race, even under normal conditions, to a thwarted and unhappy life. The anomaly can only be explained if we see this time we have been going through as the confused preliminary period of reorganization for a fresh attack on our environment. It acquires a shadow of reasonableness only if we see it as a time of discarding old tools and old ways and equipping ourselves with new. In that case the confusion we have lived through is the confusion of an army being retrained and learning new tactics with new weapons; so the technological advances acquire a meaningful pattern, and the constructive application of our powers waits on easy familiarity with their use.

If we find that we have only been training and equipping armies of the older type so that we can accomplish the racial destruction which nature itself is now powerless to effect, we can prepare to close the book of our history. But we cannot accept this end. We have reason to believe that the present upheaval is a final, violent crisis in the process of readjustment which has been under way since the Industrial Revolution began; and that its very irrationality has a quality of reassurance. We can see that as a matter of fact a constructive attack on our environment is already under way. As the old world goes up in flames, the building of a new world begins. It begins as we acquire mastery over our tools and adjust ourselves to an habitual consciousness of their potentialities. It begins as we tentatively, experimentally try them out on the physical betterment of the world around us, and see in flashes a vision of what we can make of it as more and more of us go to work on it. In this attack on our environment, as in all other wars, numbers count; and the sharing of skill, but most of all the sharing of intention, is essential to achievement.

A common motive, shared ideals, inclinations and preferences held by many men alike, with the means to give them effect—these are the necessary preliminaries to the reconstruction of a satisfactory scheme of living. Without this unity, we must inevitably have confusion and frustration of the kind we have experienced. A design for living must have a dominant motif, unifying rhythms, an acceptable functional form—just like a visual design. It must be orderly, closely knit, and directed to achieve definite ends. Ages far more meagerly equipped than ours have had this advantage of a controlling spirit and generally controlling conditions, and, in spite of a poverty of means we do not share, they produced schemes for living we still look on with nostalgic admiration. Against all sorts of handicaps we do not have, they managed to create a beautiful setting for their existence and give it a dignity, serenity and stability we cannot find in our jerry-built world in the best of times.

Life on New England farms and in New England villages, before the Industrial Revolution touched them, was bleak and narrow, full of privations and lacking in graces. But because these people were united and definite in their aims they produced a machine for living that was com-

237

pact, orderly, adequate; so sufficient that we are apt to mistake their solution of their living problem for a solution of our living problem, and consider that happiness is an affair of elm trees and white clapboards. Their success entices us to a defeatist retreat from our own struggle.

Western Europe, naturally, has a much richer inheritance from a far longer past than ours. It is dotted with tightly-built old farms that can still be locked up into minor fortresses at night, and each a beautifully composed picture. It has a multitude of towns and villages—Rothenburg-am-Tauber is the perfect type—that exist almost unchanged from the Middle Ages. The times that produced these lovely farms and towns were not happier times than ours. They were filled with poverty, famine, disease and injustice that make our efforts along these lines seem amateurish. Wars are on a larger scale today, but the records and pictures—particularly the more obscure popular prints—of old wars show that within their narrower range they were "totalitarian" beyond anything we have achieved. Whole populations were blithely and expertly exterminated, and there was an addiction to intimate cruelties that make our civilian air-raids, barbarous as they are, seem unimaginative by comparison. Wars may have been less extensive in dimensions, but they were shifting and persistent and sooner or later reached every nook and corner of the land.

A citizen of Rothenburg-am-Tauber, for instance, knew that at almost any time his town might be attacked. If it should be taken by the sword he knew that he and his family would probably be put to death in excessively disagreeable fashions and after most repulsive indignities. He knew that if it should be besieged long enough, he and his fellow citizens would starve; but he knew that if the crops failed in time of peace they would starve just the same. He knew that any householder might be the prey of evil-minded marauders who were not restrained by the most ingeniously unpleasant legal penalties. He knew that in winter he could not hope to be warm except for brief intervals, and he knew that if he got really sick he probably would die; in that case, only the protection of the church could prevent his spending eternity in even greater discomfort than he had known in life. If he were rich he might be less subject to these disadvantages than the poor, but no matter how rich he was he could not escape them entirely. His father and grandfather had lived under the same conditions and so would his children. And so he planned his living and built his house and his town to meet all these exigencies as adequately as possible.

These considerations were the force that compressed the medieval towns into a pattern we admire so enviously today. It placed them on a hill, easily defensible, within walls planned strictly by military engineers. It packed them tightly within these walls, wasting not an inch of space. There was no room and no need for wide streets or for an arbitrary, geometrical plan. Each house was in itself a little stronghold, and its charm was what the designer gave it—there was little help from lawns and trees. What seems to us today to be mere picturesqueness was in reality stark functionalism. The design of the whole town was controlled by a single group of motives which gave it order, coherence and a well-nigh perfect composition.

These are the qualities we find so profoundly lacking in our frame of life today, particularly here in America where most of our building has been done under the influence of the Industrial Revolution. With far greater security than the burghers of Rothenburg ever hoped for, with comforts and assurances they never dreamed of, with means they would have considered magical, we produce sprawling, ungraceful towns devoid of charm and stupidly extravagant. They are not even practical—our traffic cannot move in them and the waste of life, time and values due to infantile planning would be incredible if it were not constantly before our eyes. If our towns are so fortunate as to possess a presentable park, or a partly finished "civic center," or a group of attractive homes in a carefully isolated "residential section," we show them with pathetic pride. And we accept as inevitable the disorder of most of our streets, where poorly built buildings, weed-grown vacant lots, broken fences and signboards, squalid houses and hopelessly ineffective commercial enterprises are mingled in depressing confusion. There is no American town which is not given over in large part to this kind of evil mélange, but our faults while widespread are not unique. Wherever industry has spread in the western world we see the same ugliness and disorder. The industrial towns of England are as incredibly atrocious as ours, if not worse; and the modern suburbs of Paris reveal a degradation of taste we seldom descend to. The curse of confused ideals and unfocused impulses is on all the modern world. Our Hamtramcks, Ciceros and Long Island Cities stem from the same sources, that, in another phase, have produced Nazi and Fascist ideologies and Communist autocracies.

And yet, when ugliness is most ubiquitous and the forces of political retrogression and violence are most prosperous, we have begun to see a fresh crystallization of constructive thought. Where war is not blasting the land, we see a new spirit of order emerging here, there, at widely separated points, but always apparently born of the same impulse. The coalescing of intentions that is the necessary first step toward the building of our new world seems to be taking place. We are beginning to agree on certain details and preliminary drafts of our plans of Utopia, and these have not been suggested by preachers or prophets but are being determined by those deep-seated, almost subconscious racial preferences

240

from which all powerful movements derive their strength. We have glimpses of what we want, and these grow clearer and more inclusive, and by a kind of unexpressed agreement we set about bringing them into existence. The tools grow familiar in our hands, and we begin to see what it is we want to do with them. So the new world begins to be built, actually in concrete materials, while the bloody battle of doctrines and panaceas whirls over the heads of the abstracted workers. It will be a beautifully ironic thing, but quite in keeping with the ways of destiny, if we find one day that Utopia has actually been built while the theorists are still in hot argument over the plans. Ideologies may go shrieking off into space and find, one of these days, that they have no longer any resting place in a world of men absorbed in the new experience of living comfortably, graciously, serenely in an environment designed expressly to that end.

There is a large element of hope in this, but not unjustified hope. It is true the forces of destruction may succeed in delaying its realization a few hundred or a few thousand years. But there are evidences that its realization may be much more imminent than the angry clamor in the world would seem to indicate. The builders have this advantage, that they deal in concrete, persisting realities and minister to age-old desires of the human race. These are far stronger than the artificial loyalties and hysterical devotions that have been induced in men from time to time in the course of history as they are being induced today—only to fade out in the face of recovered sanity. There are times in every man's life when he realizes that he wants above all things peace, gaiety, friendliness, the opportunity to work and create in an atmosphere of well-being. The builders have this desire on their side and they work for its realization.

The job is vast and complicated, of course. We begin to attack it tentatively, from this angle and from that. Step by step, still in a spirit of delighted experiment, we are advancing toward the heart of the problem. We know very well that that heart is in men's hearts, and is not in steel and glass: but we know too that things built are both an expression of thought and an influence on thought, and that if a fair and orderly world can get itself built it will be because thought has become fair and orderly; while the building of it will be one of the profound influences inducing clarity and serenity in men's minds.

Thought itself is a function of our bodies, for we are earth-bound creatures. We know and feel only through our physical senses: our mental sustenance like our bodily food comes from the earth. We learn from the world with which we have contact, and as we operate on that world, shaping it nearer to our desire, we in return are shaped by it. So that if here and there a few stones of Utopia are being laid, it is because a first sketchy plan of Utopia is becoming clear to a certain number of men— not as an idea or a theory may take shape, but as the plan of a structure to be built in concrete substance tomorrow. These men see the truth that happiness is not to be induced by talk and wrangling argument, by the winning of wars or framing of governments or the passing of laws or the adoption of this or that economic or political creed. Happiness is a condition of living and will come to be when men have agreed on how they want to live in peace and amity with one another, in a state of mental vigor, social dignity and physical well-being. As this vision becomes clearer to more people, they discover that they have in their hands the means to bring it about; wherever they are allowed to do so they begin tentatively to create an environment in which such a level of living is possible; and as the new frame takes shape, their aims are clarified and their will becomes more imperative.

These first stones of Utopia may seem trivial factors in a harassed world: their significance becomes apparent when we see them as signs of the growing vigor of order and sanity in the midst of confusion and ill will. It may not seem important that we are giving increasing care to the right making of our goods and appliances, so that they give better service and at the same time give us esthetic pleasure while they serve. But I believe that the element of good will and pride in work is stronger than the element of self-seeking in this renaissance of craftsmanship in a new phase. So with the rebuilding of our industrial plants in forms that give pleasure and dignity to work, and the steady shift of emphasis in industry away from routine muscular labor toward skill and intelligence: throughout all industry the amount of mere weight-lifting and burden-bearing is steadily decreasing, the proportion of thought and planning is steadily increasing. Laboratories are growing larger, the range of their research wider, the immediacy of results less urgent. Chemists, physicists, metallurgists, engineers, are daily embarking on enterprises of remote and uncertain outcome—and almost daily they are returning with unexpected benefits for the race. New materials, new processes, new knowledge and controls, are being laid in our hands as contributions toward our new world. All of this enlarged activity can be explained on selfish grounds—and it is true that it justifies itself even on selfish grounds as a better policy than stupid shortsightedness. But it is definitely a shifting of emphasis toward a richer and fuller life both for those who do the work and those who share in its results: it is a recognition of the advancement of human happiness as the soundest—and the most profitable—aim of all activity.

Outside the frame of working, in the phase of daily living, there is a similar shifting of emphasis toward the communal good as the aim of endeavor. There is an appalling amount of work to be done before a gracious life becomes generally possible. But the little that has been done has opened up vistas of order and charm to many who had patiently accepted squalor as the normal condition of life. Our homes, except for a few, are still badly planned and badly built and stifling to spiritual growth. Our towns are still chaotic and exasperating and stultifying. But we are all having contact, in minor ways, with samples of what approaches Utopian perfection: in the carefully thought out and incredibly efficient appliances that come into our homes, in the amazing cars we drive, the planes we ride in, the bridges we cross, the parkways we traverse, even some of the shops we visit to do our buying. There is a growing restlessness with the general scene into which these superior achievements bring a devastating effect of contrast. We look at our homes with disillusioned eyes, we turn a hostile and resentful gaze on our towns. We ask with unconcealed bitterness why we or anyone else should be subjected to the indignity of squalid living in a world where fullness of life awaits only our will to create it.

We are beginning to develop more and more precise ideas of just how we want to rebuild this dilapidated world, we begin to draw blueprints and prepare estimates. Ever so many of us are at work on schemes of communal living where urbanity will be achieved without loss of touch with the earth and things that grow in it. Beauty we see as the constant setting of all life, beauty that is an outward evidence of inward rightness and health. Things that are clearly envisioned have a way of getting themselves realized, and when our concept of what we want to do is sufficiently clear and generally accepted, the work already started in small ways will expand into the proportions of a wholesale reconstruction. We know, without worrying about it, that if we succeed in accomplishing it we will remove as a matter of course the obstacles that now prevent men from living as fully as their capacities permit. The rebuilding of the world implies inevitably the rebuilding of its economic and social organization, and inevitably the operations must all proceed together. Only so can one be corrected against another and all be made to work together: an environmental, economic, social organism that will function as one scheme of life.

This is the job of design. It is big enough, God knows, to enlist any number of men and any degree of ability. We who are making the first tentative and fumbling efforts will no doubt seem exceedingly inconsequential in contrast with the giants who will come after us and co-ordinate all the factors in the vast task of world-building: but we have the excitement of explorers and the satisfaction of pioneers. That should be enough for one generation.

CHAPTER SEVENTEEN: PROGRAM

"To the modern man his physical environment is merely new material, an opportunity for manipulation. It may be that God made the world, but that is no reason why we should not make it over." —BERTRAND RUSSELL

In our times we have had a number of Five Year and Three Year Plans, which were going to make a notable increase in human happiness. But the specified time has passed with misery registering, if anything, a somewhat more painful level than before. Social reorganizations on a stupendous scale have been launched, based on widely different statements of principle but all aimed at achieving a more abundant life for everybody. At this date, the enormous energy generated in these movements by this high aim is, in every instance, being concentrated on keeping a small group of exceedingly unattractive men in control of the lives and fortunes of their fellow citizens. Men feel an overpowering impulse to rebuild their world, and are the dupe of any specious plan. The result to date is a deep and growing skepticism as to the adequacy of any man's brain for the task of planning society, and the adequacy of any man's moral stature for the task of putting a comprehensive plan into effect. All our planners and leaders fit themselves rapidly and neatly to Santayana's definition of a fanatic—one who redoubles his efforts when he has forgotten his aim.

The trouble with our planning is that it is too comprehensive and too detailed, and too exactly programmed. More plans for human betterment have been wrecked on their own principles and programs than on any overt opposition. We see only a little way into the future, and yet we lay out exact inflexible plans of campaigns into this country whose terrain has never been seen or mapped. We assume that we shall reach our objective by seven league strides instead of by the careful step-at-a-time that is the inevitable method of human progress. Our headlong rashness lands us in ditches too wide for leaping and up against walls that bloody our heads. The duces and fuehrers and commissars and social reformers of this kind and that rush noisily on ahead, each with his own banner of salvation and each into his own morass. Men grow increasingly doubtful of the possibility of finding our objective tied up in any compact formula, or of attaining it by any simple social bouleversement.

Yet all the time, while leaders shriek and bombs fall, the builders are at work. The vision of a rebuilt world grows clearer to more men, and the step-by-step progress toward it does not falter. The builders feel into the future, groping carefully, aware of their own ignorance and ready like all good scientists—"knowers"—to adapt their plan instantly, at any moment, to the new truths and the unforeseen conditions that may be revealed as they progress. If they make a plan, it is one of objectives only, and these not too definite. A good scientist says, "In the light of the evidence so far revealed, this appears to be true." The builders say, "So far as we can see from where we stand, this appears to be desirable."

As for programs, these must be limited to today's and tomorrow's work—the tasks we can see immediately before us. It is impossible to say, "We will first do this, and then that, and afterwards that." We can only say, "We will do, as fast and as well as we can, the multitudinous tasks that lie around us, clearly to be seen, and crying to be done; as we accomplish these we will advance to the new tasks then revealed to us." All progress is opportunist, and all plans should be tentative.

So, when we list the objectives that appear to us, today, to be desirable, it is obvious that no definitions can be precise and no sequence of achievements can be exactly forecast. We can see a little way, yes, because we have certain known factors that are still malleable, still waiting to be cast into their ultimate form. And we can see certain needs that are inherent in human nature, certain circumstances that must exist if the gregarious human animal is to live happily together in large numbers on the surface of a subjugated world. But scientists and engineers are at work in the laboratories and shops, ready to surprise us at any moment with ncw resources that may require a recasting of our plans. Our advance must be along a very wide front, slowly, moving up one division here, supporting it with another there.

The rebuilding of our cities will depend on the decentralization of industry, and both on the reorganization of our transportation systems. The recasting of our dwelling places into civilized forms will depend on all these three factors, and all four will depend on the speed with which men can adjust themselves to changing circumstances and broader outlooks.

The political and economic scheme is not the bottle-neck many theoretical world-builders think it. It is a convention and should be a convenience, and it will not be revised successfully according to any *a priori*, absolute dogma: it will be adjusted as we proceed, step by step, to make it work under the circumstances we have definitely decided are desirable. We are a race of individual men and not a race of principles, theories, or causes: we advance not by theoretical agreement but by agreement on concrete, tangible circumstance about which there can be no battle of definitions. The problem of design is the creation of an environment in which men can live with health, interest, good will, urbanity and dignity. It will be accomplished as these attributes of life are clearly envisioned as an aim by more and more men, and as the task advances it in turn will reveal to more and more men a conception of life endowed with these attributes.

The major fields on which design must work can be listed only consecutively, but their order is not an order either of importance or of time. They are interdependent and work on them must proceed simultaneously. Also our view of them now, it must be repeated, is tentative and based only on factors known today. Constant revision of our view must be effected as we advance in the light of new knowledge, added experience, and broader understanding.

1. The increasing interdependence of men is knitting the whole human race into one social and economic organism, so that a strike in Detroit is felt on a rubber plantation of Brazil and a frost in Florida affects the breakfast tables of Chicago and London. Against the weaving of this racial network, a wave of nationalism is at the moment fighting a vicious but a hopeless counter-action. It is doomed to collapse because men can no longer live apart from other men, even in national groups. We shall accept this fact, and plan accordingly, or we shall abandon the whole system of specialized production and general exchange we have been building up for three half-centuries, and relapse into barbarism for lack of an alternative. There is no absolute assurance that we shall make the right choice, but our system is still so young, so vigorous and so expansive that it is hard to conceive of its destruction. Probably we are witnessing the last stand of an isolationist philosophy which served well enough for many centuries and which our conservative race is loath to

relinquish as it is loath to relinquish any old and cherished attitude. We may kick and scream, but in the end we yield to inevitable change.

Our system, if it persists, will continue to be based on the free movement of men and goods. This makes our transportation facilities a critical factor in our civilization, as they have been since the beginning of the Industrial Revolution. The pattern of life in America in the Nineteenth Century was determined by the railroads more than by any other single influence. The reform of the railroads is certainly among the most pressing problems confronting us today, if it doesn't actually top the list. And this reform is no mere matter of building streamlined trains or any kind of lighter and faster equipment. The principles of railroad construction and operation are basically wrong for this year of grace and will have to be supplanted by a fresh approach to the whole problem.

When railroads were first built a century or so ago, the most practical method of constructing a smooth highway for swift traffic was to lay two iron rails on wooden ties, and equip vehicles with flanged iron wheels to fit these rails. This was an expensive and a rigid system, but it worked. The cars could run on nothing but the rails, transfer from one set of rails to another could be accomplished only by a complicated switching system, the radius of curves was very large, the friction between wheels and rails provided little traction for hill-climbing, it was necessary to build enormous weight into the rolling stock. Because of all these facts, railroads sought straight lines and level routes, and the country became crisscrossed with a sparse grillwork of inflexible steel highways.

Along these highways industry was forced to coagulate, towns and cities grew and population became congested. "Off the railroad" became a hinterland in which only agricultural pursuits could be followed with any success. When this system had become finally fixed, a third of a century ago, a far-sighted man in Detroit began building cheap automobiles and the whole pattern lost its reason for being. So did the steel rails and the flanged wheels.

The railroads maintain the roadbeds of a hundred years ago, but all the wide interstices of their stiff gridiron have been filled with a new network of highways of a very different type. Over these new, smooth, concrete ribbons, light cars and trucks carry passengers and freight swiftly from door to door. There is a new flexibility, a new convenience, a new economy in this modern system of transportation. There is a new congestion on the highways, of course, but traffic is no longer stiffly canalized by the steel rails: it flows, in easy freedom, over the land. So long as the railroads are *rail* roads, they cannot hope to compete. They are being bled to death by a competition they cannot meet.

But the railroads have a priceless asset: they own broad rights-of-way that still are usually the shortest lines through what are still the densest concentrations of population. These rights-of-way are almost gradeless as compared with motor-highways, they follow shortest routes, they have no sharp curves, they are almost and can be quite without obstruction by cross traffic. Their breadth is only partially used at present. Suppose these rights-of-way were paved with concrete from edge to edge! Suppose they were divided into traffic lanes for varying services, and all their passengers and freight carried in light, powerful units of relatively small size and low cost, powered by internal combustion engines and borne on rubber tires. These private, specialized highways could then perform a service which the public highways cannot perform and their usefulness and their prosperity would return together.

The center lanes of these reborn "railroads" would be concrete-paved but steel-walled channels (using as much steel as the present system requires, no doubt) for very high speed traffic. Torpedo-like vehicles, automatically controlled, would be shot through these channels at speeds only reached by airplanes now. With necessity for human steering and control eliminated, these speeds could pass two hundred miles an hour with safety. Instead of a Twentieth Century train leaving the Grand Central Station once a day for an overnight trip to Chicago, we should have capsules of a manageable size departing on their breathless four-hour flights at hourly intervals, or oftener.

These very high-speed vehicles would have teardrop forms as perfectly streamlined as airplane bodies. Their motive power probably would be an airplane motor and propeller mounted on the nose. They would be borne on a series of wheels placed in a single line below the body, but as speed accelerated most of the weight would be lifted off these wheels. Fins and automatically operated ailerons at the tail would assist in maintaining equilibrium both in the straightaway and at curves. Short streamlined projections at each side, like very stubby wings, would enclose rubber-tired wheels which would contact with the steel sidewalls of the channel, and thus eliminate the necessity for directional control. Spacing, starting and stopping would all be automatic. Thus we should have most of the advantages of airplane transport, such as speed, largely air-borne weight and operation by instruments, but we should avoid all the present hazard of airplane travel.

Next the central high-speed lanes would be lanes for long-haul, heavy traffic, carried in trailer trains longer than are practicable on public highways but far short of present freight-train lengths. These trailer trains would be broken up at loading point and destination, for convenient transport over public streets and roads. For the traffic on this new system would be door-to-door traffic, except in the case of the high-speed capsules.

252

In spite of many handicaps, medieval craftsmen often succeeded in finding an admirable solution to the problem of living under the difficult conditions of their times. Rothenburg-am-Tauber, in Germany.

113

The pressure of circumstances acting on all alike, with shared ideals and common motives, enforced order and coherence on the medieval town. A street in Rothenburg, Germany.

114

NEW YORK CITY HOUSING AUTHORITY

The confusion of our times and our unmastered crafts have produced a squalid disorder as the too-common setting of modern life. Jerry-built slums—in almost any of our cities.

FAIRCHILD AERIAL SURVEYS

116

Typical of countless speculator-built suburban developments. A total lack of intelligent planning, but a standard of living far above many industrial slums. Below, the dreary monotony characteristic of these projects.

USHA PHOTOGRAPHS BY SEKAER

A rational order begins to appear amid chaos. Cedar-Central Apartments, a low rental housing development, Cleveland. Eighteen acres out of a vast slum—650 dwelling units, 20% coverage. Walter R. McCornack, Architect.

There has been too much patient acceptance of ugliness as
the normal frame of our lives. This picture of familiar slum
conditions is from the film "The City", photographed by
Ralph Steiner and Willard Van Dyke.

A planned environment for childhood, in Jane Addams Houses, Chicago, a low-rental housing development on the site of a former slum. 1,027 dwelling units on 22 acres, coverage 27%. John A. Holabird, Chief Architect.

Project for a partly rebuilt San Francisco. All land, air and water termini concentrated in one great pier system, leaving the waterfront free for parkway development, and eliminating all inter-terminal freight and passenger traffic from the city streets. Widely spaced skyscrapers in business sections, seven hills developed as self-contained residential communities connected by elevated highway.

STOWE MYERS

Model of a possible future metropo-lis, with multi-level traffic system, and multi-story buildings supported by external steel piers or central steel columns and overhead trusses. Author's designs.

ALL THREE PHOTOGRAPHS BY COURTESY OF THE
UNITED STATES STEEL CORPORATION

Already demonstrations of rational city planning are being made, the emergence of order amid confusion. Manhattan approach to Triborough Bridge. O. H. Ammann, Chief Engineer; Allston Dana, Engineer of Design; Aymar Embury, Architect.

Above, traffic distribution system, Randall's Island, Triborough Bridge.

Below, 79th Street Entrance to Hendrick Hudson Parkway, New York City.

124 *Hutchinson River Parkway, Westchester County, New York. Typical of the great parkway system in the vicinity of New York City and prophetic of all future rural highways.*

Hendrick Hudson Parkway passes through a thickly settled section of the Bronx without disturbance to the community or interruption of its own stream of traffic.

Jacob Riis Park, Long Island, one of New York City's superbly planned municipal beaches. Parking lot above, beach with holiday crowd below. Orderly, convenient, beautiful; non-commercial in aspect but self-supporting.

Astoria Park Municipal Swimming Pool, New York, below the Triborough Bridge. New York's Department of Parks plans and builds for human happiness. Robert Moses, Park Commissioner.

At the Astoria Park Swimming Pool—visitors for the
moment in a prophetic sample of a reconstructed
world.

Outer lanes would be for fast, short-haul traffic, both passenger and freight. Here, cruising speeds of a hundred miles an hour or more would be normal. Access to public highways would be provided at convenient but not too frequent intervals, always, of course, by means of over- or under-passes without crossing of lanes.

On these roadways there would be no such thing as one vehicle passing another in the same lane; automatic controls would keep vehicles in the same lane a safe distance apart; there would be no cross traffic of any kind, and the entire system would operate under rigid supervision which would maintain maximum speeds with safety. Thus a method of swift and direct transport, under private ownership but public regulation, would supplement the public highway system, the two complementing each other and integrating their services.

2. The public highway system will inevitably develop along the lines indicated by the more advanced construction of today, and forecast more than ten years ago by such men as Le Corbusier and our own Hugh Ferris. Multiple lanes and elaborate clover-leaf intersections are not uncommon now and will be greatly expanded in the future, the whole aim being to canalize traffic according to speeds and to eliminate interference, friction and cross movements. Multiple level streets in cities have existed on paper for years and tentative beginnings have been made toward their construction. Their final realization, however, depends on a radical revision of city plans, which must go much farther than double or triple decking of our present street systems, since these are definitely impractical in our present city scheme.

The conversion of our present railroad rights-of-way into a system of swift motorized transport would relieve the highways of a great burden of commercial traffic they are now compelled to accommodate. This traffic should and will follow the commercial lanes of the converted railroads and return the public highways to the democratic uses for which they were intended. These highways should recover the charming aspect of the old, pre-automobile country roads. In the parkway system in the environs of New York City we see how successfully this can be done. Park Commissioner Robert Moses will have a monument in any Utopia we succeed in building: he built the first roads that lead to it.

3. Our vehicles of transportation will undergo an orderly process of evolution, of course. It is impossible to predict their development beyond the stages now generally foreseen because any radical advancement depends on discoveries and inventions not yet made. These may be in the nature of new forms of motive power, either in fuel or engine design. The utilization of atomic energy is a well-known dream of the physicists, and it is not improbable that where an objective is so clearly defined it may be attained. Engineers are aware that the reciprocating piston involves an appalling waste of energy, and it is probable that we may discover "cool power" as we are now nearing a realization of "cool light." New metal alloys of greatly increased tensile strength will also have a profound influence on vehicular design.

Automobile design will follow clearly predictable lines until it is diverted by some of the advances mentioned, or by others as fundamental. Automobiles will be more cleanly streamlined, less easily damaged by contact, have higher power-weight ratios. Trains, as we now know them, will cease to exist. Water transport for pleasure has already reached a high stage of development and it will continue along the same line of evolution. Commercial water transport will produce simpler, more perfectly integrated forms, with resultant improvement in speed and reduction of operating cost. It is probable that our present type of luxury liner will be superseded by planes as a means of rapid transport, but will continue to serve for pleasure cruises.

More than any other form of transport, aviation awaits certain basic discoveries or inventions we cannot yet foresee. Already it is amazingly efficient and safe, but there still are fatal crashes too frequently, and airports, uneconomically vast, are growing larger instead of smaller. Undoubtedly there will be improvement along the lines now so far advanced, but one cannot help feeling—and it really is an intuitive feeling—that there are certain huge gaps in our knowledge, which must be filled before aviation can supplant land transport to any great degree. The discoveries we may make perhaps have to do with the nature of the force of gravity, of which we now know only its effects. It is not inconceivable that we may come to understand this force at least well enough to control or counteract it by means of forces analogous to itself. A generation that has seen the science of radio communication develop is not startled by such a prediction. Certainly we need to acquire some basic knowledge which will enable our planes to rise practically vertically, hover motionless at will and descend as gently and safely as a falling leaf. Until we can do these things aviation will remain in a primitive stage. What the design of our planes will be when we can do them, no one can foretell. In the meantime, it is probable that molded plastics will largely supersede metal alloys in the construction of our present-type planes, with the manufacturing process much simplified as a result. These molded planes will be lighter, stronger, cheaper, swifter. And there will be great advancement in the control of flight by radio beams and other automatic agencies.

4. The motorization of our highway system has removed most reasons for industries to cluster close along the railway lines. The motorization of the railroads, and their integration with the public highways as supple-

mentary commercial transport systems, will complete this decentralization of industry. Factories need not be on railways, workers need not live near factories. Already, in the fine country west of Dearborn, Henry Ford has established twenty-five or thirty small water-power plants as a practical demonstration of decentralization. These factories are located in extremely attractive surroundings, and each one employs twenty-five to three hundred and fifty workers in the production of particular parts or in skilled operations. These men and women work under ideal conditions, they can live on the land and cultivate their gardens with Voltairean equanimity. They are the forerunners of great numbers of workers who will escape the city slums and recover the pleasure in work their ancestors, if good craftsmen, may have known.

Light, cleanliness, order, healthful conditions, are already the commonly accepted objective of industrial planning. Aside from Mr. Ford's venture, many factories have been built in recent years in a form worthy of a civilization more advanced than ours. The elimination of smoke and dirt and the utilization of waste products are making these plants acceptable in any setting. They are acquiring the bright, metallic, orderly aspect which thrills us in so many of our modern products, but they are only forerunners of the shining factories of the future. From these factories, drudgery and mere burden-bearing will have disappeared; machines will do all the work of beasts, men will do the work that only rational animals can do. The laboratories, engineering departments and drafting rooms will be proportionately larger than any we can show today: the work of creating, discovering, planning, designing, will have grown to overshadow all other activities in the industrial world. Work will be creative.

5. The flight from the cities has already become something of a mass exodus. The well-to-do first abandoned their urban "mansions" for subur-

ban houses in larger acreage. The wage earners, each in his family car, have discovered that their radius of possible residence is as great as the millionaire's. Many atrocious "subdivisions" have been built to receive him in flight, but great numbers of men are acquiring the habit of passing critical judgment on these efforts. The verdict is viciously adverse. As more people realize what housing can and should be, thousands of these crowded, flimsy breeding-boxes will be mowed down to be replaced by rationally planned residences, more economical of space.

The city will become a place of business, barter, intellectual and artistic exchange, social enjoyment and amusement, rather than a place of residence. Large numbers of people are necessary to support these phases of life, they must exist at focal points of population. But the city will be more sparsely built, a collection of tall towers separated by gardens and greensward, crossed by transport systems moving on different levels. The city air will be clean, for coal will not be burned within its limits and wood will be burned only in fireplaces—for pleasure. Our internal combustion engines will actually complete their combustion internally and the air will be free of their gases and fumes. The city will be a place of wide spaces, sunlight, greenery in summer and clean snow in winter. It will be quiet, urbane, civilized beyond anything the world has ever before accomplished in the line of city-building.

The country as a whole will become urbanized. That is, population will spread more evenly over its surface, but with the amenities of life available for all, and with frequent urban focal points at which the larger group activities can be pursued. This spread of population will not impair the beauty of the country, but will enhance it. And large areas of forest, plain, streams, lakes and ocean front will be preserved in a virgin state, so that wild life may flourish and the pleasures of solitude may be enjoyed. Agri-

257

culture will be integrated with our other industrial activities and become a scientific method of producing foodstuffs and industrial raw materials, instead of the somewhat haphazard, archaic craft it is today. Intensively practised, as a branch of bio-chemistry, it will require less land than at present but will produce more abundant and better results. Our enormously increased consumption will require all its production.

6. The dwellings of people will be of two types: one a development of the present apartment house, the other a type of detached house. The apartment house, or living tower, will be built in areas where there is reason for a congestion of population. This congestion may reach fifteen or twenty families per acre, which is considered sparse settlement today—but not more than ten per cent of the ground area will be occupied by buildings. The space between these widely separated towers will be utilized for playgrounds, gardens and parks. There is nothing new about this idea, but it has never yet been realized in actuality—always the free space is not adequate for the number of residents. The towers themselves will be, of course, much more sane and economical structures, and much pleasanter to live in than the present apartment house. The aspect of these steel and crystal towers, rising at intervals in glistening brilliance above the tree-tops and the rolling lawns, will be amazingly beautiful. People may come to love their homeland with a more passionate devotion than they have any cause to feel today.

Detached houses, semi-detached or row houses will be built in areas where land is less in demand. Well-to-do people—and there will be well-to-do people, never fear—will build houses as they please, of course. These will be progressively less archaic and more creatively planned, and not all will be good but the average will be higher than now. The great improvement will come in the homes of people of moderate or little means.

258

These will be constructed of large-scale, pre-fabricated units, as was outlined in Chapter Five of this book, and they will represent a far greater value for their cost than can be obtained by any sort of building methods practised now. They will not only be better and cheaper, but they will compose into far more desirable communities than ours.

It is probable that these communities will be organized on the "Neighborhood Unit" plan as first outlined by Col. Clarence Perry of the Russell Sage Foundation.[1] That is, large population groups will be formed of a mosaic of mainly self-sufficient, self-contained units, each including forty-five hundred to ten thousand people. Such a group is adequate to support schools, shops, amusements and recreational facilities, but small enough for mutual acquaintance and a more or less coherent social life. Anyone who has grown up in a small town knows how much he gained from intimate acquaintance with the cross-section of humanity such a community contains. This knowledge of our fellows, this schooling from childhood in group living, is essential to successful citizenship in the world, and these are advantages which cities as we know them have largely failed to provide. The "Neighborhood Unit" plan would restore to our communal life this helpful intimacy and mutual dependence, and yet a number of such units would be able to support the urban advantages which depend on larger population groups. The plan also facilitates the design of gracious, spacious and delightful towns, as everyone who has studied it will agree.

7. The better world of the future will require an enormously increased production of goods, and their more general and equitable distribution. There is a psuedo-philosophic attitude which maintains that possessions

---

[1] *Housing for the Machine Age*, Russell Sage Foundation, 1939, is Col. Perry's fullest statement of this plan.

are a burden and a handicap, and this may frequently be true, although one often suspects that the disdain of property is partly compensatory. But there is a sense in which possessions are a liberating force, essential to any real freedom of thought and action. For instance, our modern civilization is predicated on the assumption of a varied diet, refrigerated foodstuffs, adequate heating in winter, copious hot and cold water, and ubiquitous bath tubs and water closets. These things recede into our background, and we give them no thought. But they have freed us from appalling discomfort and disease, and from futile preoccupation with our bodily functions. One must live in a society which does not enjoy these facilities to appreciate how largely they enable us to ignore our bodies except as a source of pleasure.

Some of the advanced thinkers point out, derisively, that America is no happier because modern kitchens and bathrooms are so general. But the point is, they are *not* general. In some circles and levels, yes, but a majority of our people still make shift without them. They will not fulfill their mission until they are the normal equipment of all our living. A great many other things, still rarer, must also become universal possessions before our life can proceed on the plane it should occupy. Interesting, stimulating, creative work, for instance; emancipation from drudgery and a gracious setting for daily life; freedom of movement, free exchange of thought; bodily well-being and mental equanimity. A few people enjoy these advantages now: they should be equally available for everybody.

They all depend to some extent on our physical equipment for living. To make them general requires a great expansion and improvement of this equipment, in the fields of production, transportation, exchange, communication, housing, education, recreation. They demand the removal of staggering quantities of debris; the wreckage of past abortive efforts now cluttering the landscape, hampering our activities and rasping our nerves. They depend on the substitution of a rational order, convenience and rightness, so that the physical background of life becomes a facile aid to freedom and a source of pleasure instead of an irritation and a defeat. They demand in short that reconstruction of our environment we have been talking about since Chapter One.

If this reconstruction could be accomplished only through the loss of individual freedom of action it would not be worth attempting. Anti-social activities will be eliminated, but the field of constructive opportunity will be enlarged by this general polarization of endeavor. Greater freedom of action, broader scope for individual initiative, are among the major objectives of any rational effort, and to sacrific them at the outset is to admit that our task is impossible before we start. Utopia by fiat is a contradiction in terms. Our better world will be built because men envision it, will it, unite without organization or compulsion to create it. Individual initiative will not be sacrificed: it will be focused on a common end through individual acceptance of a common standard of rightness.

We have the means for the task, already in our hands. We have attempted here a tentative outline of the technique that must be applied to one important phase of the work—the phase of physical design. This would have been a too ambitious undertaking except for our deep conviction of the unity of all design—that we may learn from minor efforts how to accomplish major ones. The major efforts await our will. We believe we see this will clarifying, focusing, gathering up its mighty strength.

APPENDIX A: THE PROPORTIONAL SCHEME
OF THE PARTHENON

In analyzing the mathematical system of proportions used by the designer of the Parthenon, we should be careful to adopt the designer's approach, and not the mathematician's. If this system is really determined by the principles of dynamic symmetry, it contains innumerable relationships which make it a fascinating exercise in analysis; but these may be mere consequences of the method and not necessarily consciously planned by the designer. This designer had his mind not on mathematics but on a building. The form of this building, in its essential elements and even in its details, was predetermined for him. He was not required or allowed to invent a new scheme: his problem was to adjust the relationships and refine the composition of given elements. He desired to create recurring ratios within his scheme: that is, a system of constant proportions which would bind the whole structure together in one rhythmic whole. For this purpose he had only the simplest instruments of precision—cords and levels—and no easy method of handling arithmetical fractions. His building was not built, but existed only in his mind and in such plans as he prepared. He needed a simple geometrical method of determining his proportional harmony, a usable method that could easily be applied as the building progressed.

He found this method in a scheme consisting of golden-section rectangles, root-five rectangles, squares, and their diagonals. (It will be recalled from Figure 7, Chapter Ten, that a root-five rectangle is equivalent to two golden-section rectangles overlapped to the extent of their squares. Its length is the diagonal of two squares.) All these are easily delineated by means of a cord and two points, and with such simple tools he was able to develop an amazing scheme of recurring proportions, in which the golden section is the controlling factor.

The facts cited here are extracted from the late Jay Hambidge's analysis in his interesting book, *The Parthenon and Other Greek Temples, Their Dynamic Symmetry* (Yale University Press, 1925). His work is ingenious and convincing, but he does not elucidate the scheme as a process of creative design, and he uses his habitual arithmetical rather than geometrical technique. I have tried to present the scheme here as a practical designer might have worked it out in advance of construction, not as an *ex post facto* analysis. I have dealt only with an end elevation, and even this is by no means completely presented. Only enough has been cited to demonstrate the designer's method of creating rhythmic relationships between his areas, and the reader should bear in mind that the system has been carried down through all the details of the façade, and throughout the plan and lateral elevations.

The façade of any Greek temple of this period had four principal subdivisions:

The stylobate, or platform and steps,
The columns,
The entablature, consisting of the horizontal epistyle, frieze and cornice, supported by the columns,
The pediment, or gable.

In this design there are three principal horizontal lines:

The top line of the stylobate, on which the columns stand,
The dark shadow-line where the entablature rests on the columns, and
The top line of the entablature.

Of these the most important line, visually—most important in the whole façade—is the second, because of the deeply accented shadow beneath it.

264

The designer evidently started with a simple rectangle into which his whole façade scheme could be fitted. This rectangle has the maximum dimensions of the whole—the width of the ennustyle, or leveling course which

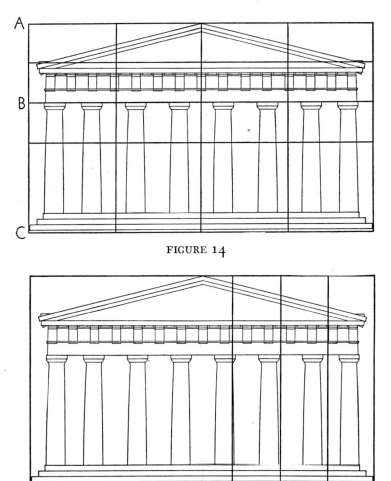

FIGURE 14

FIGURE 15

was the base of the structure, the height from ground to peak of gable. This rectangle he composed of four squares and twelve root-five rectangles, arranged as shown in Figure 14.

265

This same space can be subdivided as in Figure 15, where it is seen to consist of a square and three of the spaces left when two squares are subtracted from a root-five rectangle, as in Figure 10, Chapter Ten.

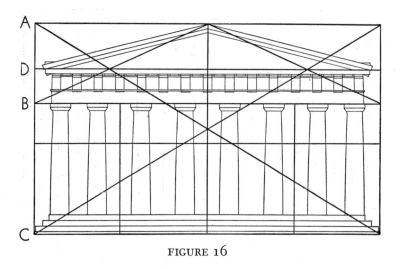

FIGURE 16

It might have been supposed that the designer would begin with a simple golden-section rectangle or root-five rectangle, but neither of these areas would have had the amazing versatility of the area he chose. His freedom would have been confined within a more rigid frame, and the range of possible relationships would have been far less wide and subtle. The area chosen enables him to preserve the golden section principle, and to apply it with easy fluency.

As a starter, the line B in Figure 14 divides the total height exactly at the golden section. Thus, AB : BC :: BC : AC. This line became the baseline of the entablature, that most important horizontal line of the whole façade.

The eight root-five rectangles above the line B may be considered as two larger root-five rectangles, as in Figure 16. Thus the entire entablature and pediment are contained exactly within two root-five rectangles. The diagonals of these larger root-five rectangles, and the diagonals of the whole area, cross at points which locate the top line of the entablature, D of Figure 16.

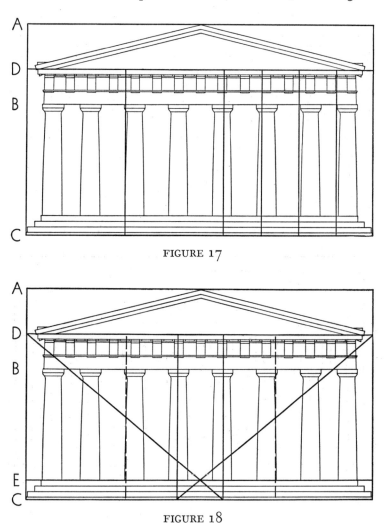

FIGURE 17

FIGURE 18

The space below the line D is composed of two golden-section rectangles and four of the spaces left over when two squares are subtracted from a root-five rectangle, as in Figure 17.

267

APPENDIX A

If we draw a pair of golden-section rectangles at each end of the area below line D, they will overlap as in Figure 18. If then we draw the diagonals of these double golden-section areas, the diagonals will intersect at a point which locates the top of the stylobate, line E of Figure 18.

We now have located those three principal horizontal lines of the façade, at E, B and D of Figure 18. The space between E and D may be divided exactly into four golden-section rectangles, placed vertically, in which are contained the two central elements of the façade, the columns and the entablature. The columns are the most important *vertical* elements of the façade, extending from line E to line B, and must be spaced within this area.

The diagonals of Figure 18 are repeated in Figure 19, and it is seen that they intersect line B at F, F'. The area contained between lines E and B,

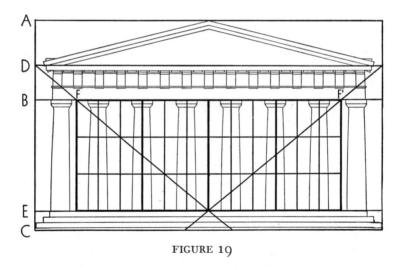

FIGURE 19

and lines F and F', also can be divided exactly into four golden-section rectangles. Each of these four can be divided into nine smaller rectangles of the same proportion, known as reciprocals. This subdivision is shown in Figure 19. If we consider this trellis as consisting of six vertical groups of

268

six golden-section rectangles each, we see that each group exactly locates one of the six interior columns of the façade.

For optical reasons it was necessary to reduce slightly the space between the outer pairs of columns, but this was not done in any haphazard manner.

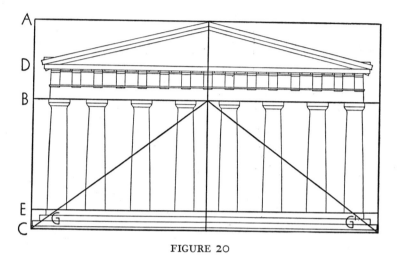

FIGURE 20

Diagonals drawn from the center of line B to the lower corners of the major rectangle intersect the line E at G and G′ (Figure 20) and thus locate the center lines of the end columns exactly.

The principal elements of the façade have thus been located, and their proportions fixed. It should be obvious that the designer applied, consciously and consistently, a geometrical method of creating rhythmical proportional relationships within his scheme. The relations cited could not possibly be mere coincidences—they could only be the result of intention. Any reader who is not convinced of this is something more than skeptical. But if he wants further proof he can follow Mr. Hambidge's analysis through its intricate details to the point of absolute conviction. All the areas of all the elements and all the details of the scheme can be measured in rectangles similar to those already cited; not only all the areas of the façade itself, but also the voids left within the major rectangle, after the façade is delineated.

For instance, the entablature itself, between lines B and D of Figure 16, consists of six golden-section rectangles, laid horizontally, while the voids left at either end of the entablature, between B and D, consist of two golden-section rectangles, placed vertically. These six golden-section rectangles of the entablature are also equivalent to four of the column-spacing rectangles, which in turn each consists of six golden-section rectangles.

That portion of the entablature known as the epistyle consists of forty golden-section rectangles. Each triglyph is a golden-section rectangle. The metopes are wider, and also vary in width, being expanded toward the center to harmonize with the greater weight of the pediment above; but the average dimensions of these metopes show them to consist of two squares and a column-spacing rectangle.

The standard column dimensions appear to be those of the eastern angle columns, and others vary slightly from this standard for purposes of optical correction. These standard dimensions show the column to occupy the space of five squares, centered vertically within the column-spacing rectangle.

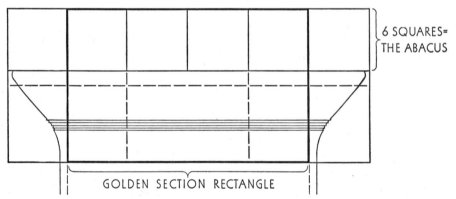

FIGURE 21. *The whole rectangle of the column head is equivalent to a column-spacing rectangle.*

The head of the column occupies a space similar to a column-spacing rectangle, placed across the top of this row of squares. If a golden-section rectangle is placed within this space, occupying its full height, it will exactly define the diameter of the column within its flutes, at the point where it meets the capital. In other words, the top diameter of the column and the height of the capital are in extreme and mean proportion.

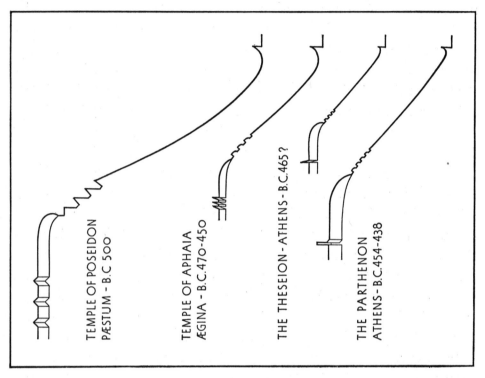

TEMPLE OF POSEIDON
PÆSTUM - B.C 500

TEMPLE OF APHAIA
ÆGINA - B.C.470-450

THE THESEION - ATHENS - B.C.465?

THE PARTHENON
ATHENS - B.C.454-438

FIGURE 22

Mr. Hambidge shows diagrammatically (op. cit., p. 30 to 36) how the curves of the echinus (molded portion of the capital) could be accurately drawn by the cord-and-point method. By this means a workman could prepare a template for a capital of any scale, maintaining always exactly the same proportions and relationships. Thus we see how the extraordinarily dynamic line of the Parthenon capital was achieved, as an evolution from the less firm and virile lines of previous efforts. It is a line which, vividly re-

271

called by many of our forms in airplanes, cars and machines of various kinds, has a peculiarly modern significance.

The convenience of such a system in preparing plans without the aid of arithmetical fractions, scales or blueprints is obvious. It completely eliminated any need, such as we now are under, to draw plans "to scale." The modern practice is to draw plans to a scale of one-eighth inch, or one-quarter inch, say, to the foot. The Greek architect could not do this, but so long as he constructed his design of these geometrical rectangles of constant proportions, he had no need for any complicated system of arithmetical enlargement. He could draw his plan any size he chose; it could be enlarged to any size, and enlarged again if need be: the proportions of all details would always be the same, and every detail would take its proper place in the total scheme. The slightest error would instantly be evident, because it simply would not fit.

The ratios of the entire design scheme, when checked arithmetically, are accurate to thousandths or at most hundredths of a foot. The only variations are for the purpose of optical correction, and, as everyone knows, a most subtle and elaborate scheme of correction was applied to the lines and masses of the structure. However, where these corrections occur they are only slight, invisible variations from a norm which itself is completely accurate in its conformity to the proportional scheme.

As an example of this accuracy, it might be supposed that the principal rectangle of the façade—that bounded by the length of the entablature, and by the height of the columns and entablature—would be significant. As a matter of fact, it is very nearly a root-five rectangle. But the error, though small, is still too great—three or four inches in more than a hundred feet! We are forced to reject this root-five proportion as not intentional, since no such error occurs in any of the internal proportions we have cited. The designer evidently considered these internal relationships of first importance, and adhered to the scheme which gave him the amazing system of integration of which we have examined only a few details.

There is no doubt but that this perfection of rhythmic relationship is the quality that has made the Parthenon the delight and despair of centuries of designers. We can console ourselves with the fact that such ultimate achievement is possible only in a predetermined, completely evolved design scheme, where the designer's problem is one of adjustment only and not of invention. We have few if any problems presented to us today in this final stage of development: our age is too young and changeful. But they may be encountered if our swift advance should slow down, and our procedures crystallize to routine. This would signal the end of our age. After a Parthenon is accomplished there is nothing better to be done along that line.

APPENDIX B: AMERICA'S CAPACITY TO PRODUCE AND TO CONSUME

The Brookings Institution in Washington is probably our most reliable and unbiased source of information on American economics. Its findings are completely impartial, factual, and devoid of any trace of propaganda; as a result they prove their value by infuriating both the most radical and the most conservative elements of the population. Two of the Brookings Institution's publications—*America's Capacity to Produce* and *America's Capacity to Consume*—should be made required reading for all citizens and especially for all having a part in government.

The first of these volumes, issued in 1934, presents ample statistics leading to a conclusion (pp. 415-430) that in the peak year 1929 this country was utilizing 81% of its existing capacity to produce, in plant, equipment and man power. The possibility of taking up the slack of 19%, in its entirety, is extremely doubtful, as this slack represents such factors as obsolete plant and equipment, overexpansion in certain industries such as explosives where capacity far exceeds any normal demand, inevitable hitches and delays in the chain of related operations, etc. Therefore the estimate that our capacity might be utilized up to 95% seems, to a novice, highly optimistic.

However, such an increase in the normal rate of production was approximated for a short time at the peak of our wartime effort, in the mid-months of 1918. This increase, estimated at 15% above normal, was the result of such strain and such regimentation as would not be tolerated as a constant condition. The conclusion is reached (p. 428) that while some increase in productivity is possible even in prosperous times, any major stepping-up

274

would require a basic technological revolution. It "could not be achieved by the mere reform of our distributive institutions."

America's Capacity to Consume, on the other hand, presents appalling facts about the state of our population in this same prosperity year of 1929. We may be startled to learn that 42.3% of our total population existed in a state of "Subsistence and Poverty"; that is, this proportion of our people consisted of families having an income under $1,500 and unattached individuals having an income under $750. Another 35.7% existed in a state of "Minimum Comfort"—family incomes $1,500 to $3,000, individual incomes $750 to $1,500. (P. 87.) Thus, a total of 78% of our whole population had incomes providing for none of the luxuries of life and only the minimum comforts, if any! Unquestionably people in this class went to the movies and had permanent waves, but these indulgences necessarily represented a sacrifice somewhere else in the scale—in essential vitamins or decent domestic surroundings.

Now, the Bureau of Home Economics of the Department of Agriculture has made four classifications of diets, for a family of two adults and three children: they can be kept alive for a time at a cost of $350 per annum; they can exist on $500, if extreme care is exercised in the choice of foods and they don't hanker after variety; "adequate" variety and balance can be had for $800; while a "liberal diet"—greater variety and better quality—costs $950 (1931-32 prices). Among non-farm families, it appears that only those with an income of $3,000 spent enough on food to obtain the "adequate diet" at $800; while only those which had passed the $5,000 line spent enough to enjoy the "liberal diet." In percentages, 16% (of non-farm families) had enough income to provide an "adequate diet," and only 10% were able to dine "liberally." (P. 123.)

After ten years of depression, conditions both as to production and consumption are unquestionably far worse in 1939 than in 1929. An increase in productive efficiency has been made in the interval in many plants and processes, without doubt; but this may have been entirely offset by the

275

abandonment of plants, the loss of morale in unemployed labor, and the failure to train new generations of labor. As to consumption, the millions unemployed and the millions on relief are tragic evidence of the reduction of purchasing power far below the too low levels of 1929 "prosperity."

As our friends of the Brookings Institution mildly remark in summing up, "it would seem a reasonable minimum aim of our national economy to provide the entire population with a 'liberal diet' "—at only $950 per family of five, mind you!—together with an equivalent standard of shelter, clothing and other consumer goods. But to do this, allowing for no increase for families in the $5,000 class or above, would require an increase in food production, *above 1929 levels,* of around 40%; shelter and home maintenance would be nearly doubled, attire and adornment and other consumer goods and services would be more than doubled. (P. 124.) Taking the population as a whole, "the unfulfilled consumptive desires of the American people are large enough to absorb a productive output many times that achieved in the peak year 1929." (P. 127.)

"Such an increase in productive output is far beyond the capacity of our economic system today." It would still be just as impossible if a Hitler, a Mussolini or a Stalin ordered it to be brought about according to his own special brand of economics. "Whether we live under a wage, price and profit system or under a completely communistic method of government, it will always be true that the level of consumption or the standard of living can be raised only through the production of food, clothing, shelter, comforts, and luxuries." (P. 132.)

An increase on the scale required can be accomplished only by the technological revolution mentioned above; and this would mean a wholesale replacement of plants and equipment, the development of countless new automatic processes, the employment of every glimmer of ingenuity and every ounce of man power in the country; and all this in turn would require time.

In the years of great technological advance from 1900 to 1929, the output of each unit of man power in the United States was increased by less than

40%. (P. 131.) This process could be speeded up by concerted effort; and the increases required to raise our population above the subsistence level, to a level of decent comfort, are not beyond the range of technological possibility. It would seem that this problem should be engaging our undivided attention. And it is obvious that what we are now suffering from is not overproduction but underconsumption; and that "technological unemployment" is a specter of the distant future, when environmental reconstruction and the provision of decent living conditions for all will have taught us how to use the leisure that may come as a reward of our efforts.

APPENDIX C: COLLATERAL READING

This is not intended as even a limited bibliography. Any adequate bibliography of the subjects glanced at in this book would exceed the size of the book itself, and I have neither the time nor the qualifications to compile it. My intention here is merely to list some of the books I have found useful or enjoyable or both, with the thought that there may be a few readers who are not already familiar with them.

In the field of esthetics there is a large and mainly futile literature. Many very long and very dull books have been written to explain the nature of beauty, and often they have been written by men who never created a beautiful thing in their lives, not even a beautiful sentence. I have not found the classical treatises on the subject helpful, and many of the more modern efforts have the musty smell of doctorial theses. They exist on a plane of dialectics, and never make contact with reality. A notable exception is George Santayana's *The Sense of Beauty* (Scribners, 1896), itself a work of art. After more than a generation it is still fresh and sensitive, and achieves the most satisfactory definition of beauty I have yet discovered. Our concept of art has changed and expanded in forty years, but Santayana's lucid thought can still clarify and enrich our current experience. His volume on *Reason in Art*, in the *Life of Reason* group (reprinted by Scribners, 1922), is a less crystalline but still illuminating book. A more modern treatment of esthetics, brilliant, sane, realistic and diverting—and much more than the primer its title suggests—is Leo Stein's *The A.B.C. of Aesthetics* (Boni & Liveright, 1927).

John Dewey's *Art as Experience* (Minton, Balch & Co., 1934) is one of

278

the most profound and completely satisfying of all works on the philosophy of art. In spite of Dr. Dewey's habitually turgid style, he keeps his nose to the trail of reality like a bloodhound and occasionally gives tongue in a surprisingly vivid and epigrammatic flushing of an elusive truth. His chapter on "Nature, Experience and Art" in *Experience and Nature* (Norton, 1929) is also full of wisdom, and in fact his works are invariably useful handbooks to anyone conscious of the problems of the modern world. Dr. Dewey's philosophy deals with life in the "tough-minded" fashion he frankly admires. In a more limited field, the volume on *Beauty and Ugliness*, by Vernon Lee and C. Anstruther Thompson (John Lane, 1912) is an interesting exposition of the empathic theory of esthetic responses. Prof. Langfeld's *The Aesthetic Attitude* (Harcourt, Brace and Howe, 1920) is a summary of current thinking on esthetics, and relates some interesting laboratory experiments.

On the mathematics of design, Jay Hambidge's work is the most important ever done, probably, although it needs to be interpreted by the designer in terms of his own activities. *Elements of Dynamic Symmetry* (Brentano's, 1926) and *The Parthenon and Other Greek Temples, Their Dynamic Symmetry* (Yale University Press, 1925) contain the fundamental principles of Mr. Hambidge's system of proportional geometry. His analyses of Greek vases have seemed to me, generally, too complex to have been constructed by a practical designer. I cannot see how these schemes could have been applied, simply and easily, to the shaping of a whirling mass of clay on a potter's wheel. Major proportions, of course, may have been so applied. The highly scientific works on phyllotaxis and the works of Colman and Cohn, cited in the note on Page 144, expand this subject in opposite directions. Claude Bragdon's *The Beautiful Necessity* (Knopf, 1922) is a brief explanation of "regulating lines" by a gifted architect who deserted to mysticism.

I know of no satisfactory history of design. There are histories of ornament, and innumerable treatises on special phases of design, specific epochs, or individual designers. But there is no history of design as the evolutionary adaptation of form to functions, materials and techniques. The histories of architecture are the best guides to the subject, although they deal only with building. Banister Fletcher's (Scribner's, in perennial editions) is the standard textbook, voluminous, detailed, explicit, but it is somewhat pedestrian reading and needs the discipline of a classroom to hold one's attention to it. *A Short Critical History of Architecture* by H. Heathcote Statham (Scribner's, 1927) is easier going for the lay reader, although the author's understandable reverence for all things British needs to be discounted. *From Rameses to Rockefeller*, by C. H. Whitaker (Random House, 1934), is a well written and interesting history from a somewhat leftist viewpoint, and one is dazed to discover that architecture is really an ancient plot of the rich and powerful to enslave the poor and weak. Any comprehensive history should be supplemented by monographs on special phases.

Unfortunately we have no good exposition of Greek design, but Greek design can best be studied in the tragedies of Aeschylus, Sophocles and Euripides, the comedies of Aristophanes, the dialogues of Plato and the lovely fragments of the Greek Anthology; these to be supplemented by some of the admirable volumes of photographs now available, particularly *The Acropolis*, by Walter Hege (Weyhe, 1930). The writings and the buildings are all products of the same creative spirit and express the same pellucid thinking, and so illuminate each other. Of modern works, *The Greek View of Life*, by G. Lowes Dickinson (Doubleday, Page, 1911), is worthwhile.

In the field of Gothic art, the most satisfying and sensitive interpretation is Henry Adams' *Mont St. Michel and Chartres* (Houghton, Mifflin, 1913). Its peculiarly lyric quality is never cloying to this reader at least, and I have put it to the test in the Archbishop's Garden at Chartres and in Madame Poularde's excursion center on St. Michael's rock. It re-creates the mood of a period that was not at all rational but possessed of a mighty lyric frenzy and at the same time a canny practical genius in the field of engineering. *Mediaeval Art*, by W. R. Lethaby (Scribner's, 1904), is a readable and comprehensive history, and the same author's essay on "Mediaeval Architecture" in *The Legacy of the Middle Ages* (Oxford, Clarendon Press, 1926) is a fine interpretation. In French, the standard works of Mâle, de Lasteyrie and of course Viollet-le-Duc are scholarly and well illustrated. The unbelievable buildings themselves, still dreamily waiting to welcome visitors to France, are by far the most eloquent exposition of the Gothic spirit.

The fiery and often phrenetic spirit of the Renaissance can be caught in the well-known works of J. A. Symonds and Burckhardt, than which nothing better has yet been done, and in the many volumes of photographs that are available. There are several good biographies of Michelangelo and da Vinci, and the latter's *Notebooks*, edited by J. A. McCurdy (Reynal and Hitchcock, 1938), are fascinating. Geoffrey Scott's *Architecture of Humanism* (Scribner's, 1924) is a brilliant exposition and defense of the Baroque movement which, as I have said, proves it to be indefensible, except as light entertainment—which, of course, is not of negligible value.

The phase of art technically known as "Modern" has already inspired a formidable literature. Perhaps the best introduction to the subject is Louis Sullivan's *Autobiography of An Idea* (American Institute of Architects, 1922), one of the finest memoirs ever written in America. It paints the background of the movement and traces its genesis in the mind and work of its First Master. Le Corbusier's *Toward a New Architecture* (Payson & Clarke) states the developed creed of Modernism, in the style of a major prophet. I do not find Frank Lloyd Wright's books as interesting as his buildings. He too speaks with the voice of a prophet, but a somewhat garrulous prophet given to rambling. However, I highly recommend the chapter entitled "The Passing of the Cornice," in Wright's *Modern Architecture* (Princeton University Press, 1931). It relates a poignant experience that may very well have advanced the modern movement, via Wright, many years in time. Hugh Morrison's *Louis Sullivan* (Norton, 1935) is an adequate supplement to the priceless *Autobiography*, and H. H. Hitchcock's *Architecture of H. H. Richardson* (Museum of Modern Art, 1936), overdocumented and overreverential toward every crumb that fell from the master's drawing table, still is an interesting account of how the spirit of sound workmanship was struggling to new life in the welter of the Industrial Revolution, even before Sullivan and Wright gave it definition and direction.

H. H. Hitchcock's *Modern Architecture* (Payson & Clarke, 1929) is a satisfactory history of the movement to the date of publication, and Bruno Taut's *Modern Architecture* (Studio, Ltd., 1929) is a continental review of the same subject. *Modern Architecture* (Museum of Modern Art, 1932), cataloging and illustrating an admirable exhibit organized by the Museum of Modern Art, New York, collects the principal masters and their principal works in a review of this new academicism. Sheldon Cheney's *The New World Architecture* (Longmans, Green and Co., 1930) is comprehensive and readable, none the less interesting because it is not quite so precious and aseptic as some other treatises. *Modern Building* by W. C. Behrendt (Harcourt, Brace, 1937) is the most recent of worth-while histories of the movement. There are many monographs on individual designers and special classes of buildings. The development of modern architecture is now so rapid, so much a matter of daily advance and accretion, that only the architectural magazines can keep us in touch, from month to month. These fine publications, such as the *Architectural Forum*, the *Architectural Record*, and *Pencil Points*, are brilliantly edited and invaluable.

In the field of housing there is a growing literature. Catherine Bauer's *Modern Housing* (Houghton, Mifflin, 1934) is a world-wide survey, intelligent and conscientious, quite the best in its field. *Recent Trends in American Housing*, by Edith Elmer Wood (Macmillan, 1931), gives us the background for the American movement that has since been cutting its eyeteeth (little more) under governmental stimulus. *Rehousing Urban America*, by Henry Wright (Columbia University Press, 1935), is our very ablest treatise on the practical, rather than the historical, phase of city planning and housing. *City Planning*, by Werner Hegemann (Architectural Book Publishing Co., Inc., 1936, 1937, 1938), in two volumes of text and a folio of pictures, I find discursive and garrulous, too time-consuming for the somewhat meager rewards it offers. Le Corbusier's *Urbanisme* has been published in English as *The City of Tomorrow* (J. Rodker, 1929) but his *La Ville Radieuse* (Editions de L'Architecture d'Aujourd'hui, 1935) still awaits translation. Both are characteristically brilliant, imaginative, somewhat perverse, and delightful. Again the architectural magazines are our best liaison with a movement that is too vital at present for the slow pace of historical narrative to keep abreast of it.

Our swift scientific and technological progress is reported in *The Advancing Front of Science*, by George W. Gray (Whittlesey House, 1937), and *Tools of Tomorrow*, by J. N. Leonard (Viking Press, 1935), both fascinating to the layman. *Men and Machines*, by Stuart Chase (Macmillan, 1929), is a swift and interesting account of the Industrial Revolution up to its date, and while a deal of water has run under many bridges since that epochal year of 1929, the history is still authentic. Bertrand Russell's *Scientific Outlook* (Norton, 1931) treats with not too heavy a hand of the sociological adjustments that are entailed by our increasing power over our environment. Lewis Mumford's two massive works, *Technics and Civilization* and *The Culture of Cities* (Harcourt, Brace & Co., 1934 and 1938), deal with aspects of the same subject, are enormously documented, ponderous, pedantic, but interesting if one can stand the voice of God in which Mr. Mumford habitually speaks. A dash of humility would make him a more engaging and even more convincing writer.

In the field of industrial design, Sheldon Cheney's *Art of the Machine* (Whittlesey House, 1937) reports journalistically on this predominantly American phenomenon, while Herbert Read's *Art and Industry* (Harcourt, Brace & Co., 1935) and Geoffrey Holme's *Industrial Design* (Studio, Ltd., 1934) survey it from the British viewpoint. There are any number of interesting monographs on modern design in furniture and interiors, shops, glass, lighting, textiles, etc.

The evolution of design today is so swift that even a sketchy bibliography such as this is outdated before it appears. A book five years old must necessarily deal with ancient history, if it deals with history at all and not with unchanging principles. That is why Santayana's *Sense of Beauty*, Adams' *Mont St. Michel and Chartres*, Sullivan's *Autobiography*, and Le Corbusier's *Toward a New Architecture* are still fresh while so many reportorial efforts have staled.

INDEX

Acropolis, Athens, 67, 199

Adams, Henry, 121

Aesthetic Attitude, The, Langfeld, 103

Agricultural Revolution, 21

Airplanes, 56, 109, 164, 165, 178, 255

America, 22, 24, 52, 70, 189, 206, 209, 213, 233, 239, 240, 250, 260, 274, 276

America's Capacity to Consume, Leven, Moulton, Warburton, 274, 275

America's Capacity to Produce, Nourse and Associates, 274

Amiens Cathedral, 200, 224

Antoinette, Marie, 206, 207

Arch of Titus, Rome, 160

Architecture of Humanism, Scott, 55

Aristotle, 109

Art as Experience, Dewey, 128, 178, 195

Art of Glass, The, Neri, 22

Arts of Expression (see Painting, Sculpture, etc.)

Athens, 150

Automobiles, 57, 58, 63, 106, 178, 179, 184, 254

Bach, Johann Sebastian, 129

Baroque style, 55, 186, 208

Barry, Mme. du, 182

Bathroom equipment, 61, 62, 260

Bauhaus, the, 215, 224

Bay Bridge, San Francisco, 167

Bayreuth, Germany, 129

Beauce, France, 121

Beaux-Arts, Ecole de, 56, 188, 203, 209, 214, 215

Beethoven, Ludwig van, 129

Behaviorism, 135

Behrendt, W. C., 214

Bernhardt, Sarah, 212

Blois, Château de, 200, 201, 208, 209

Boas, Franz, 10, 116

Boulder Dam, 14, 110

Bragdon, Claude, 118, 139

Braille System, 103

Brancusi, Constantin, 16, 65

Bridges, 76, 167, 168, 178

Brookings Institution, 95, 274-277

Brooklyn Bridge, 167

INDEX

Brunelleschi, Filippo, 164, 167, 171, 179

Bureau of Home Economics, U. S. Dept. of Agriculture, 275

Caen (see St. Stephen)

Carcassonne, France, 12, 36

Carothers, Dr. Wallace Hume, 31

Ceres, Temple of, Paestum, 123, 160

Cézanne, Paul, 27, 117

Chartres Cathedral, 119-121, 185, 200, 208

Chicago, 188, 201, 203, 210, 249, 252

Church, A. H., 143

Circle-and-square system, 158-160

Clothing, simplification of, 212

Cohn, C. Arthur, 144

Colman, Samuel, 144

Cologne Cathedral, 200

Colonial Revival, 209-211

Columbian Exposition, Chicago, 1893, 209, 210

Community planning—past, present disorder, future, 12, 36, 61, 189, 237-240, 256-259

Corbusier (see Le Corbusier)

Corinthian style, 72, 183, 229

Corning, N. Y., 22

Cuba, 84

Daily News Building, New York, 172, 180, 188

da Vinci, Leonardo (see Vinci)

Dearborn, Mich., 256

Decentralization of industry, population, 23, 61, 255-257

Detroit, 42, 249, 251

Dewey, John, 47, 121, 125, 128, 134, 138, 178, 195, 219

Directoire style, 206, 208

Doric capital, 165

Douglas planes, 109, 164, 165

Dreyfus, Henry, 215

Du Pont Building, New York World's Fair, 171

du Pont de Nemours and Co., E. I., 31

Dynamic Symmetry, 144-147, 157, 159, 264

Eastman Kodak Co., 31

Egyptian builders geometricians, 68, 146, 147, 184, 202

Eiffel Tower, 170

Elements of Dynamic Symmetry, Hambidge, 144, 145

Empathy, 191-195

Emperor Jones, The, O'Neill, 134

Empire State Building, New York, 188

Empire style, 209, 210

Engineering, partnership with design, 92-94

England, 12, 112, 240

Erectheion, Athens, 199

Euclid, 91, 141

Europe, 24, 34, 53, 207, 213, 233, 238

Exposition architecture, 170-173

Eye, structure of (see Vision)

Factory design, 63, 256

Fair architecture (see Exposition)

Ferris, Hugh, 253

Fibonacci series (see Summation)

Florence Cathedral (see Brunelleschi)

Florentine style, 208

Ford, Henry, 33, 251, 256

Ford car, 29, 33, 73, 104, 182

Ford Exposition, New York World's Fair, 173

Fouilhoux, J. André, 173

France, 21, 39, 68, 70, 114, 120, 181, 182, 186, 200, 208, 210

French craftsmanship, style, 208, 210

Freud, Sigmund, 128

Furniture, 62, 77, 78, 87, 212

Galileo, 222

Geddes, Norman Bel, 173, 215

General Motors Building, New York World's Fair, 173

George Washington Bridge, 167

Georgian style, 45, 206

Giotto, 139

Glassblowing, 22

Glessner house, Chicago, 201

Godowsky, Leopold, Jr., 31

Golden Gate Bridge, 167

Golden Section, 151-160, 263, 266-271 (*also see* Dynamic Symmetry)

Gothic art, architecture, design, 39, 42, 68, 115, 120, 138, 165, 166, 169, 173, 186, 188, 199, 208, 229, 230

Gothic builders, designers, 68, 114, 136, 137, 169, 179, 185, 199, 200, 203

Gothic Revival, 209

Grand Central Building, New York, 180

Grant, Gen., period of, 22, 210, 211

Greece, 39, 114

Greek architects, artists, builders, geometricians, 67, 68, 89, 91, 108, 114, 121, 143-154, 160, 198, 199, 202, 272

Greek architecture, art, design, 39, 42, 46, 67, 108, 114, 115, 119, 136, 144, 145, 165, 199, 264

Greek Revival, 209, 210

Gropius, Walter, 202, 213, 215

Hambidge, Jay, 144-146, 153, 154, 157, 158, 264, 269, 271

Hammersmith, England, 50

Harrison, Wallace K., 173

Hearing, mechanics of, 126 (*also see* Music)

Highways, 23, 189, 251, 253, 254

Hogarth, William, 166

INDEX

Housing—design, low-cost, prefabrication, 58-60, 73-75, 258, 259

Housing for the Machine Age, Perry, 259

Howell, William H., 125, 126, 129, 130

Human body, 53

Ictinus, 47, 136, 139

Indians, American, 10

Industrial Design, 33, 225, 227, 228

Industrial Revolution, 6, 7, 20-22, 24-28, 32, 69, 103, 207, 217, 236, 237, 239, 250

International School, 75, 171, 213, 214, 229

Invalides, Paris, 166, 167

Italy, 55, 208

Japanese art, 209

Japanese module system, 74

Jeans, Sir James, 131

Johansson Gauges, 29

Kaufmann house, Bear Run, Pa., 172

Kitchen equipment, 61, 62, 184, 260

Kodak Park, Rochester, 31

Lakehurst dirigible hangar, 185

Langfeld, Herbert Sidney, 101, 103

La Scala, Milan, 129

Le Corbusier, 158, 172, 186, 202, 213-215, 229, 253

Lee, Vernon, 5

Lethaby, W. R., 67, 206

Light, as factor in design, 82

Lincoln-Zephyr car, 182

"Line of Beauty," Hogarth's, 166

London, 22, 249

Louis XII (see Blois)

Louis XV—period, style, 21, 45, 87, 182, 209

Louis XVI style, 206, 208

Louis Philippe—period, style, 209, 211

Low-cost housing (see Housing)

Lucite, 81

Machine Age, 28, 34, 41, 49, 51, 52, 70, 94, 104, 106, 109

Manhattan Bridge, 167

Mannes, Leopold, 31

Mansard, J. H., 166

McGraw-Hill Building, New York, 188

Medici tombs, 225

Mees, Dr. Kenneth, 31

Michelangelo, 47, 186, 187, 189, 225

Middle Ages, 202, 209, 238

Mimeograph, 179

Modern Building, Behrendt, 214

Modern Style, 215

Moderna, 187

Morris, William, 50, 51, 209

Moses, Robert, 254

Mount Hymettus, 67

Mount Pentelicus, 67

Müller, Sophus, 10

Mumford, Lewis, 22

Music—structure, rhythm, 43, 44, 129-131, 175, 176

Music, A Science and an Art, Redfield, 131

Natural forms—design, structure, unity, 53, 54, 98, 143, 144, 151

Nature's Harmonic Unity, Colman, Cohn, 144

Needham, Joseph, 219-222

"Neighborhood Unit" plan, 259

Neo-classic style, 208

Neolithic tools, 10

Neri, Antonio, 22

Neuschwanstein, 209

New England, 12, 237

New York City, 167, 172, 203, 254

New York World's Fair, 170-173

Newton, Sir Isaac, 222

Nile River, 146

Nîmes, France, 55

Norman architecture, 120

Nuremberg, Germany, 36

"Occam's Razor," 112

On Growth and Form, Thompson, 143

On the Relationship of Phyllotaxis to Mechanical Laws, Church, 143

Oud, J. J. P., 214

Owatonna, Minn., 118

Paestum (see Ceres)

Painting, 16, 27, 116, 117

Paris, 166, 240

Parthenon, 67, 89, 108, 119-121, 136, 144, 153, 160, 196, 199, 263-273

Parthenon and Other Greek Temples, The, Hambidge, 264

Perisphere, New York World's Fair, 170, 172

Perry, Col. Clarence, 259

Petit Trianon, Versailles, 182, 183, 188, 196

Phidias, 47, 120, 136, 139

Philadelphia Savings Fund Society Building, 204

Photography, 31, 127, 132

Picasso, Pablo, 16, 117, 214

Plastics, 80, 81

Plato, 151

Pont du Gard, Nîmes, 55

Poore, H. R., 175

Prefabricated housing (see Housing)

Primitive art—our status as primitives, 113-116

Primitive Art, Boas, 116

Proportional Form, Colman, Cohn, 144

INDEX

Queensborough Bridge, 167, 178

Railroads, 23, 250-253
Raphael, 139
RCA Building, New York, 180, 188
Redfield, John, 131
Renaissance, 46, 55, 116, 118, 136, 158, 188, 200, 219, 225
Rheims Cathedral, 160, 180-183, 185, 196
Richardson, H. H., 201, 211
Rockefeller Center, New York, 181, 183, 188, 189
Rococo style, 166, 208
Rohde, Gilbert, 215
Rohe, Mies van der, 172, 202, 213, 214
Roman architects, builders, designers, engineers, 55, 67, 68, 158, 184, 198
Roman architecture, 55, 118, 188
Romanesque style, 208
Rome, 22, 70, 161, 186
Rothenburg-am-Tauber, Germany, 12, 238, 239
Rouen (see St. Maclou)
Russell, Bertrand, 246
Russell Sage Foundation, 259
Russia, 51

St. Maclou, Rouen, 139, 200
St. Maria del Fiore (see Brunelleschi)
St. Martin de Boscherville, Church of, 121, 123, 163
St. Peter's, Rome, 186, 187, 196, 225

St. Stephen, Church of, Caen, 120, 121, 139, 182, 208
Sainte Chappelle, Paris, 224
San Francisco, 167
Santayana, George, 15, 35, 67, 246
Schools of design, etc. (see Teaching)
Science and Music, Jeans, 131
Scientific method—intuitive factor, 219, 220
Scott, Geoffrey, 55
Sculpture, 16, 27, 65, 185, 199
Senses, the (see Hearing, Smell, Taste, Vision)
Sight, sense of (see Vision)
Sistine Chapel, 225
Skeptical Biologist, The, Needham, 219
Skyscraper, function of, 75, 76
Smell, mechanics of, 125, 127
Spencer, Herbert, 56
Spengler, Oswald, 9
Square-and-circle system, 158-160
Steel, per capita use of, 70
Steel construction—revealed structure, 68, 76, 168-170, 188, 189, 203 (also see Bridges)
Stein, Leo, 135, 138, 162, 191
Sterne, Laurence, 112
Sullivan, Louis, 50, 52, 53, 118, 170, 171, 188, 206, 210
Summation series, 144, 152, 153, 160, 182, 184

Taj Mahal, 164, 179

Taste, mechanics of, 125-127

Teaching of architecture, design, etc., 223-231

Technics and Civilization, Mumford, 22

Temple of Ceres (see Ceres)

Textbook of Physiology for Medical Students and Physicians, Howell, 125, 126, 130

Thales, 147, 148

Thompson, D'Arcy W., 143

Thompson, Dorothy, 232

Toward a New Architecture, Le Corbusier, 158

Trianon (see Petit Trianon)

Triborough Bridge, 167, 178

Trylon, New York World's Fair, 173

Twentieth Century train, 252

United States (see America)

United States Steel Building, New York World's Fair, 170

van der Rohe, Mies (see Rohe)

Van Gogh, Vincent, 27, 117

Versailles, 206, 209

Victorian era, style, 51, 204, 206

Vignola, 187

Vinci, Leonardo da, 21, 47, 98, 141, 225

Vision, mechanics of, 126, 127, 132, 133, 175, 176, 180

Voillet-le-Duc, E. E., 120

Washington, D. C., 22, 274

Watt, James, 23, 24

Wells, H. G., 51, 229

Whitman, Walt, 84

Williamsburg, Va., 12

Wood, as a material, 77

Woolworth Building, New York, 180

World War, first, 24, 212

World's Fairs (see Exposition)

Wright, Frank Lloyd, 50, 52, 53, 118, 172, 202, 210, 213, 215, 224, 229